Aristotle for Novelists

Aristotle for Novelists

14 Timeless Principles on the Art of Story

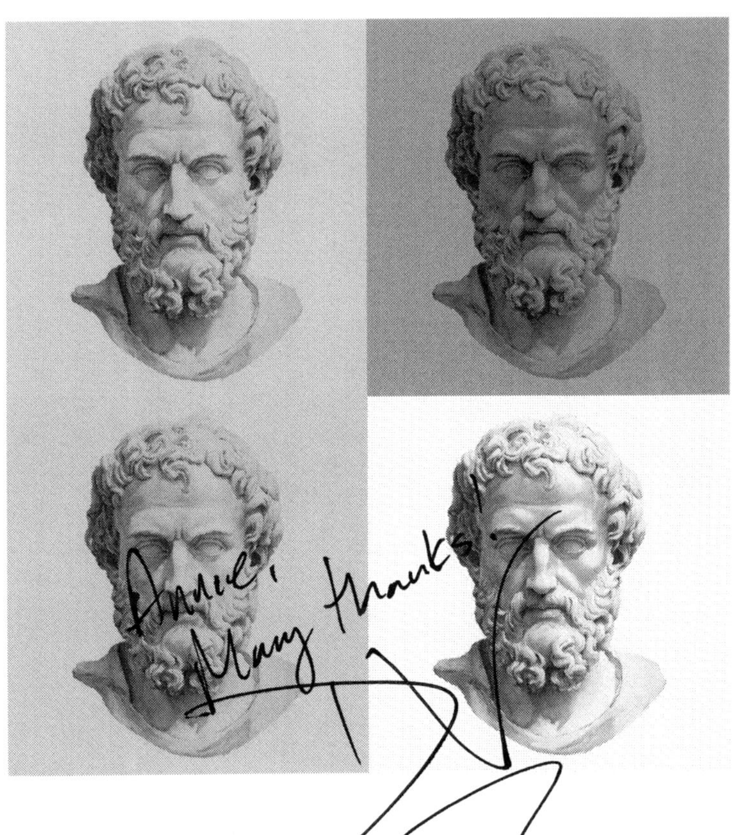

Douglas Vigliotti

Aristotle for Novelists: 14 Timeless Principles on the Art of Story by Douglas Vigliotti

Published by Slightly Crooked

www.slightlycrooked.pub

ISBNs: 978-1-7375482-3-2 (paperback), 978-1-7375482-4-9 (ebook)

Printed in U.S.A.

First Edition: November 2024

Cover design and art by Allan Nygren

For more about the author, visit DouglasVigliotti.com.

Contents

For you, whoever you are, wherever you are,
fate has brought us together. I hope this
book helps you write a story that
you can believe in.

A Little More Than an Introduction

> *Write the story, take out all the good lines, and see if it still works."*
>
> — Ernest Hemingway

Aristotle was history's greatest novelist. The problem? He never wrote a novel. Sure, he would've had to invent the form, since it didn't exist yet, but I wouldn't have put it past him.

Aristotle was one of the most influential thinkers the world has ever known. He spent twenty years studying at the Academy in Athens under Plato (who studied under Socrates before him). It's said that he often disagreed with his teacher.[1] I like to think it was that type of divergent thinking that led him to be so impactful and prolific. What can I say? I'm a sucker for freethinkers.

During his short life, 384 BC to 322 BC, Aristotle wrote over 200 works—although only thirty-one survived —and almost none were designed for public consumption.[2] The actual numbers are still debated, but I'm not sure it matters. Consider these treatises more like notes, the remnants of his thinking on a plethora of topics. This is why today we have so many interpretations and translations of his work. What did he mean? What didn't he mean? In many cases, that's up to the reader to decide.

The fact that Aristotle's concepts and philosophies are still relevant over 2,300 years after the fact is a testament to the power of his ideas. His work is said to have shaped—and, in some instances, been the foundational material for—many disciplines still currently studied around the world. Sciences, arts, economics, philosophy, psychology, politics—the list is long. He was a polymath before we even had a term for it.

Fortunately, one of those surviving works is *Poetics*. It was never meant to be a guide but rather his notes on the nature of tragedies (and epics). The work ends with the introduction of a second book on comedies, but that part has never been recovered. *Poetics* has been translated many times, each translation providing the reader with something a little different. Personally, I've read three different translations—Samuel Butcher's (1922), Malcolm Heath's (1997), and Philip Freeman's (2022). They all circle around the same core ideas, only tweaking on the margins. For continuity, most of the quotes I use in this book will come from the Freeman translation. All are noted for you. In some respects, reading that version was the final nudge I needed to write this book.

There are many writers across multiple disciplines who have concluded that *Poetics* is the definitive source for storytellers. Aaron Sorkin, for one, has been Aristotle's most strident supporter, stating in his MasterClass, "You should be evangelical about Aristotle's *Poetics* . . . All the rules are there."[3] Of course, Sorkin is not a novelist, he's a screenwriter—a great one, I might add. In drama, Aristotle's principles have been used forever. But I don't know of anything designed solely for the novelist. So here we are. I've taken the ideas and adapted them for writers of fiction.

Although I try to stay faithful to Aristotle's intention and the text, or at least the translations I've read, this book is not a word-for-word retelling of *Poetics*. I only use Aristotle's thoughts as a foundation, combining them with ideas from other masters of storytelling, many of which I've included at the end of this book in a long list of resources for additional reading.

Naturally, with each principle, I share my own thoughts, which are rooted in my experience as a reader and writer. This should never be mistaken as absolutism, even when I say "absolutely." Language is fun like that. I am not a translator, nor am I claiming expertise in ancient Greek or anything of that nature. Like you, I'm a writer. If you want to read *Poetics*, check out one of the three translations I mentioned above or a handful of others that are in print. It's the first thing I'd recommend after reading this book—if for nothing else than to check my bullshit.

Smile. You didn't think this was all going to be stone-cold serious, did you?

Alright, tell me more.

Aristotle for Novelists deals mostly in structure, technique, and theory. I can't and won't tell you how to style your prose and stories, although this book will offer some thoughts on style since Aristotle had his own on the matter.

Most style suggestions require personal taste. Nothing is objective when it comes to art. Don't let any pipe-smoker tell you different. If anyone tries to steal your artistry, run the other way, fast. Stay far from the soul suckers who tell you they "know" how it should be done. As if art is produced on a conveyor belt. These people serve the God of Duplication. The God of Commerce. Nobody knows what the reader wants, they only know what they've read before. Or in the words of the great filmmaker William Goldman, "Nobody knows anything."[4] Of course, he was talking about Hollywood, publishing's slutty cousin. Same bloodline, though.

Don't get me wrong. If your goal is to get paid for your work, then I support you and want you to. This book will likely help. Just not directly. Not with marketing, or a snappy title, or a shiny cover. It has little to do with commercial success (an uncontrollable outcome), but honestly, I don't know of any self-respecting writer who would tell you they *know* how you can get rich from writing fiction. The best artists, authors or otherwise, know there is too much luck involved.

Writing novels is a lot like being dropped in the middle of an ocean. The only thing you can do is swim. If you don't start swimming, you'll drown. So you just start swimming, knowing there's land out there somewhere. Stay afloat and move forward—that's your goal.

Where you wind up is less up to you than you think. All you know is that if you tread long enough, you'll hit something hard eventually. *Fuck, it's only a buoy,* you think. *Or a piece of shrapnel floating at sea. Gotta keep paddling.* Maybe you're lucky enough to have a boat come up and offer to save you. Of course, you get in—you're tired and worn down.

After you dry off and get a little food in you, it won't take long for you to realize that you're in *their* boat. Your fate is subject to their skills, knowledge, and wisdom. Are you really sure you want to be in that boat? Or were you just drowning, and you had no choice? Hey, you can always jump out and start swimming again. Like I said, there *is* land out there—some of it posh and luxurious, some desolate and deserted. But it's out there. So here you are, floating in the middle of the ocean again. Or perhaps for the first time.

This book will help you swim.

Writing is *not* story.

As a novelist, writing is the method you have chosen to tell your story.

Craft is an overused buzzword that means a lot of different things to a lot of different people. Haruki Murakami wrote it best in his book *Novelist as a Vocation,* "It goes without saying, but if you take a hundred novelists you'll find a hundred different ways of writing novels."[5] To my understanding, the sentiment couldn't be truer. For our purposes, craft means storytelling and writing.

My dad often reminds me, "Doug, all a book has to be is a good story, well told." The best ideas are simple, but profound, and Dad's is both. So that's how I read everything. How's the story? How's the writing? Believe it or not, they are two independent qualities. You can definitely have one without the other, and when you look for it specifically, it happens way more than you think. It's also why you can learn from all types of stories, not just novels.

It's hard to pinpoint what makes someone's writing work. Sure, I have my theories, but it's hard to tell how much of that is based on taste and preference, and I imagine that's similar for most reasonable people. That's not to say I don't believe in my opinions—trust me, you'll hear them—it just means it's much more difficult to pinpoint what makes writing work than what makes a story work.

Across mediums and genres, there are things that good stories do, repeatedly. You'll learn those things in this book. Consider it big picture, wide lens, and top-down. That said, this book will show you *a* way, not *the* way. Only you can decide what ultimately works for you.

However, when it comes to writing, none of my opinions are more important than this: you should embrace *you* on the page. In the 15th Principle, I will share more about this—it's the 15th because it's mine, not Aristotle's. Good or bad, you are your only differentiator. Your voice is the only thing you have in this world. This is why self-censorship is the worst kind of censorship. And sadly, today we see it in droves. Don't allow external pressures to dictate what winds up on the page. Write the story that needs to be written in the style it needs to be written.

But remember, writing is *not* story.

Style aside, working stories are more similar than you might think. And to me, that's the forever objective: to work. As in, does the story work? Does the story not work? It's the only thing I try to do with my novels, and consequently, the only thing I will advocate to you.

One of my notes to myself reads: *story is why they come, writing is why they stay.*

I find the note helpful both as a writer and reader. Steal it if you'd like. For you, that means opt out of this book at any point. I mean that with all sincerity. I dump books all the time at fifty or a hundred pages. I either enjoy an author's sensibilities or I don't. What *is* "good" writing? I don't know. You either like how a writer sees the world, or you don't. (Lucky for me, this is a short book.)

Lastly, before we get started . . .

As a novel lover, you've probably found yourself saying more than a handful of times, "The movie ruined the novel!" Most of the time, this is true, but it's also inevitable.

Screenwriting is more rigid than novel writing. At its best, a movie is the leanest, most potent version of a novel. *Mystic River* is a great example. *Fight Club*, too. *No Country for Old Men* another. At its worst, a movie is the sparsest, most watered-down version. Pick one. There are plenty.

But watching films can be a useful way to identify these principles; because the stories are dramatized, they are much leaner. Therefore, the principles are more pronounced. Which is why I use film examples interchangeably with novel examples throughout *Aristotle for Novelists*.

Consider these 14 principles a foundation for any story. They are universal—you'll see them in your favorite movies and TV shows, and yes, although a tad more disguised, you'll see them in your favorite novels, too. Yes, I swear.

It doesn't matter if you're a plotter or pantser. It doesn't matter if you write genre or literary fiction. And it doesn't even matter if you're a rookie or seasoned vet. Regardless of your style, taste, or genre, these principles will help you, as well.

In *Poetics*, Aristotle notes that an unreflective writer may produce the same *tekhne*, a Greek term for skill, art, or craft, as a reflective writer. Malcolm Heath, the translator of the Penguin Classics edition of *Poetics*, mirrors the idea: "A joiner taught to make a piece of furniture in a particular way may do it perfectly, even if he does not understand the reasons why that is the best way to do it; he may even do it better than a colleague who has more understanding but less manual dexterity."[6]

In either scenario, the principles are baked into the work. This is powerful. Even the naive can appear to know what they are doing—that's how natural these principles are to a working story. This is the magic you now possess at your fingertips.

My hope is that this book won't keep you from the keyboard for too long. It is short for a reason. So read it, then enjoy your favorite novels and films. I bet you'll find many of the principles. All I am doing is pointing out what's already there. I only write with conviction because I believe what I am writing. I wish the same for you.

I can hear the echo of Aristotle now. Courage is a dance between fear and confidence.[7] Fear is expected. Confidence is required. Blunt, but apropos. Do you hear him, too?

Swim, my friend, swim.

Principle #1

Novels can be tragedy or comedy.

Writing a novel is hard work. Writing one that works is even more difficult. We want to stack the odds in our favor. So, for our purposes, there are only tragedies and comedies.

Maybe you're thinking, *This isn't a play, or a film, it's a freaking novel.* I know, I hear you. I felt the same way, but hear me out. In *Poetics*, Aristotle wrote only about tragedies (and epics, but for our purposes, just think of those as tragedies with a larger and longer scope). Part Two on comedies was one of the lost works I mentioned in the Introduction. But again, we can rely on other masters of craft to pull us through here. *Poetics* has been traditionally used as a reference in drama more than literature, but that's just semantics—story principles are universal. In Aristotle's day, the term *poetics* (or poetry) implied something much grander. If he were alive, I believe he would say novels could be included under the scope of the work.

I've heard people simplify tragedy and comedy with

the following definitions: a tragedy is a serious story with a sad ending, and a comedy is a humorous story with a happy ending. Now, as much as I like heuristics and shortcuts, these are not good ones. The definitions imply things that aren't necessarily true. Trust me, I like simple, but these definitions are too reductive.

I've always found it useful to think of stories as shapes, as in, how they move. Kurt Vonnegut agreed, except his theory had eight shapes.[8] If you look at them more closely, you can deduce his eight (via how they move) to tragedy or comedy. What is moving, you ask? Your protagonist. Everything is based around the protagonist. Even in a multi-story plot, starting as constrained and narrow as possible is the best way to go. Then from that point building, adding, or creating what is necessary.

You might be thinking, "But my story has a zillion characters and they're all important." Yes, this is true, but the shape of your story revolves around a single character. You can mask him or her. You can have a double protagonist (like in one of my favorite movies, *Heat*). You can do many different things, but to create your story shape, you'll need a protagonist.

All accouterments can be added later, but even then, I'd urge you to be cautious. The further you move from the essence of a story, the less powerful the source. Just like the sun, the closer to it, the hotter it is. Same goes for your central storyline. Don't dilute its essence. Add something when it adds to (or extracts more of) the essence of the story. If it just adds another layer, think twice. Start by designing your story shape with a single protagonist.

Great, so you have a protagonist, right?

Everyone has one. It's the reason why they start the story in the first place. That protagonist should have wants and desires and someone or something standing in the way of getting what they want.

These obstacles come in the form of internal flaws and external opposition, which is how most stories play out, over, and over, and over again. Conflict is the basis of stories. At least, good ones. Internal conflict. External conflict. Stories need tension. Someone wants something, someone or something stands in their way. Scene after scene after scene. In its most reductive form, that is your story. It's the basis for every story from *The Sun Also Rises* to *Gone Girl*. Conflict. Are there stories that don't do this? Sure, but they are boring as hell.

A tragedy should be defined by a protagonist who starts off good (or ambivalent), then things get bad temporarily before things get better, good, great, and then their downfall begins, in which, they end up worse off than they started.

Now, when I say *good*, I don't mean morally. I mean situationally or in correlation to their wants and desires versus their flaws. When your protagonist starts off, they probably haven't reckoned with their flaws yet, which makes them ambivalent. Aristotle thinks the best stories are about good people who make mistakes.[9] Antiheroes and morally corrupt people also make great protagonists. They're not good people, but they're good enough *relative* to the world they're living in.

Personally, I love antiheroes, as I find them to be a

truer representation of humans. They are more relatable. Perhaps this is one of the big reasons why the antihero has become so popular in modern storytelling. (I blame—and love—Tony Soprano.)

In your mind, if you picture the tragedy story shape, it's a line that moves straight out from left to right (Act 1), then begins to squiggle up and down a bunch of times (all those obstacles) while moving upward until it reaches a peak (Act 2), then moves straight down to an ultimate low (Act 3). This is an early glimpse of how three-act structure works, something I will touch on in Principle #3.

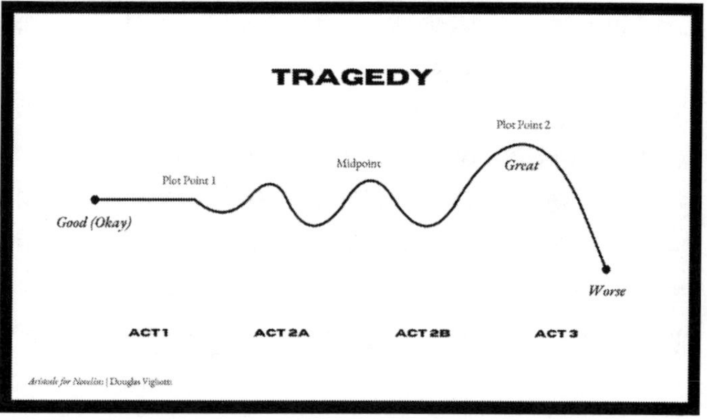

In a tragedy, your protagonist falls from good to bad fortune and is not able to overcome their character flaw(s) and/or opposition. As a result, they are worse off than they started, hence a sad ending. Although not as heartwarming as a comedy, it still works.

Traditionally, tragedy is about "characters of the higher type"[10] who have the ability to fall, as in those who are noble, admirable, et cetera. In a modern sense, we can have variations on this idea, like Bud Fox in *Wall Street*, an everyday man who rises, then falls. Or Richard Papen in *The Secret History*, who lies and longs to become a member of an elite class only to wind up complicit in a murder. David Mamet has said it best: "Tragedy is a celebration not of our eventual triumph but of the truth."[11] Or, as Aristotle writes in *Poetics*, the best tragedies will "evoke pity and fear,"[12] and by doing so, bring a type of catharsis for the audience, a purging of emotions.

Just like a headache that throbs and then subsides, tragedies feel good when they end. You know something is off, people are getting away with it, and you want to see those truths, flaws, and injustices exposed for what they are. Like *The Road*, the hardest truth about life is revealed—all humans die. Now the boy must brave the world without his father. The more pity and fear, the more cathartic the resolution. As Mamet suggested, the truth comes out, and we like it.

A comedy should be defined by a protagonist who starts off good (or ambivalent), then things get better temporarily before things get worse, bad, horrible, and then their rise begins, in which, they end up better off than they started.

Again, heroes, antiheroes, everything is in play here. Remember: when we talk about comedy (or tragedy) we are talking about the story shape of our protagonist's journey. Not genres. Not humor. Not characteristics of the protagonist. Just their journey. That's it.

In your mind, if you picture the comedy story shape, it's a line that moves straight out from left to right (Act 1), the begins to squiggle up and down a bunch of times (all those obstacles) while moving downward until bottoming out (Act 2), then shoots straight up to an ultimate high (Act 3). Again, we will touch on three-act structure in Principle #3.

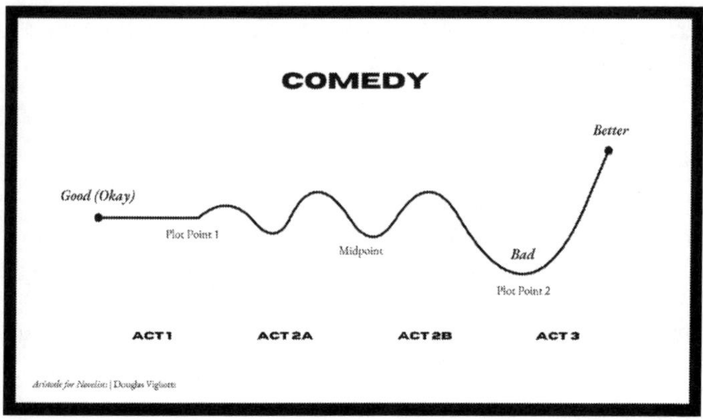

In a comedy, your protagonist rises from bad to good fortune and is able to overcome his or her character flaw(s) and/or opposition. As a result, they are better off than how they started, hence a happy ending. Traditionally, this is about "characters of a lower type"[13] who have the ability to rise, as in, peasants, middle class, et cetera.

Although we see this a lot in a modern sense, we see variations all the time with people of a higher type who are lower relative to their environment and rise to overcome their challenges. Queen Elizabeth II in *The Crown* comes to mind, but there are many others. Comedy is what most people want, most of the time. The Hollywood ending, right? It works because of an overcoming of those obstacles (internal and/or external) and ultimately the defeating of evil, even if only temporarily. After all, that's why the Gods of Commerce invented sequels. Oh, right, you're a novelist. I meant, series. The story marches on! (Which sort of proves its own point. In genre fiction, there are comedic novels galore.)

If you really want to simplify, and need something extremely shorthand, you can think of a tragedy shape as: **good → great → worse**, and a comedy shape as: **good → bad → better**.

Great, so you have a story shape?

You might be surprised at how simple this is, even in the most complex novels. The more clarity you have, the better off you'll be when it comes time to write the story. It's not *exactly* what's going to happen, just the shape of the story.

As a novelist, I know this type of planning can be really daunting because you're like, *I just want to write my damn story*. I feel your pain. I just want to write the damn story, too. Among novelists' biggest fears is that planning will stifle creativity or kill spontaneity. This couldn't be further from the truth. The fear is rooted in the romantic notion of the wild, free-flowing artist that has been mythologized over time. Even the Henry Millers of the world are way more intentional than they appear to be. The shape of story is your friend. Invite her in.

There will always be three novels, anyway—the novel you want to write, the one you did write, and the final novel. The idea, the first draft, and the rewritten and well-edited version. Simply put: unexpected things happen once you start writing. Each version will be different, no matter how much planning you do. So, then why do a base-level of planning at all?

First, it ensures your story will work and move properly over time.

Second, restraints breed creativity. They make you *more* creative, not less.

Third, it helps you get down that "shitty first draft"[14] —the most important part. Going back to what I just said above, you can't get to the final novel without the first draft. Something is always better than nothing. Or as Jodi Picoult has said, "You can't edit a blank page."[15]

A little planning helps when the writing gets tough. Artistry will come down to *how* you connect the dots. And your first dot is simply to answer this question: are you writing a comedy or tragedy? Does your protagonist overcome their internal and external obstacles and end up better off or does your protagonist succumb to those obstacles and end up worse off?

Principle #2

Novels should be consistent.

In all fairness, Aristotle doesn't say this directly about story, but he does imply it and outright say it about characters, which you will read more about later. I think it's more than reasonable to assume he would extrapolate the idea out to a novel, as well.

Although most novels are stylistically consistent from beginning to end, the whole novel does not *have* to be the same. The story might dictate a necessary style change from chapter to chapter, part to part, et cetera. In *A Visit from the Goon Squad,* Jennifer Egan does this mood and style shift chapter to chapter so well to portray thirteen different characters. Episodic? Maybe, but I will touch on that in Principle #9. Another great example is *Trust* by Hernan Diaz, a novel told in four parts, each with a unique writing style and voice to match the puzzle-like story. The key is consistency in each chapter or part. That's what matters. That's what they do.

So, tragedy or comedy, you'll have to make a few key decisions on how you're going to tell your story. In

Poetics, Aristotle insists that authors need to answer three questions. He calls them *medium*, *object*, and *mode*.[16] I've slightly altered them for you without altering their meaning.

1. Medium: How is your story told? What is the style and structure of your story?
2. Object: What characters are essential to tell the story other than your protagonist? Are they of higher or lower type?
3. Mode: Who is telling your story? Will you use present or past tense? Will you use a first-, second-, or third-person point of view?

Since the first two questions will be discussed in Principles #12 and #13, I want to focus on the final question. Consistency is important for each, but technically speaking, question three is most critical.

Now, you can always mix tenses and POVs, but it's important to understand when and why you are doing it. I am of the belief that tense and point of view should be in service of the story itself. I think Aristotle would agree. But this is a question only you can answer. I don't know the story you're telling. There are pluses and minuses to everything, including tenses and POVs.

In a basic sense, tense means, is the scene, chapter, or story happening now? Or did it happen "back then"? Present and past are the two tenses you will use 99.9% of the time. In a novel, a quick way to identify this is through verb usage: a matter of "say" versus "said."

As for POV, first person can be limiting, but there's

an intimacy with it that doesn't exist in other points of view. It also answers the "who is telling the story" pretty squarely. Most times that is your protagonist, but not always. Think: *The Great Gatsby*—Nick Carraway (narrator) and Jay Gatsby (protagonist). First person places limitations on the narration, but that's not necessarily a bad thing. For one, they keep you tighter to the central storyline, but they also create a natural built-in suspense. I wrote my book *Tom Collins* using first person, present tense with straight linear plot sequencing (as in, no flashbacks or anything) for that reason. The limitations helped me. I traded layers for urgency. Wide for narrow. It's what I felt best served the story.

Second person is super rare, but there are plenty of examples like *Bright Lights, Big City*, and one part of *Tomorrow, and Tomorrow, and Tomorrow*. In the latter, Gabrielle Zevin's usage was super clever, but then again, so was Jay McInerney's entire story. Second person places you, the reader, in the protagonist's seat—*you* do this, *you* do that. It has a very distinctive quality that can be hard to pull off, but if done well, like those examples, it can be quite memorable.

Third person is the most expansive. It gives you the most flexibility. But it doesn't answer the question of "who is telling your story" as squarely. Again, limitations aren't always a bad thing. Too many options can be a noose in your mind and on the page. It's more like, what type of story are you trying to tell? Or maybe there's a genre norm that you're trying to conform to, or perhaps one you're trying to break.

If you go with writing in third person, there are variations you'll have to familiarize yourself with. Are you going with limited third person? This is almost like first person but through a third person lens. Or are you omniscient? This is like an all-knowing God, a technique often used in Sci-Fi and Fantasy. Although, for a crime novel, *The Godfather* is very effective with omniscience.

All of these choices start to tie into style, so it's important to hash these questions out early. Your goal is to never lose tense or POV. It's hard to catch everything, of course. Editors exist for this reason, but writers should strive to be technically sound from a narration standpoint. One, it's how you get better. Two, it's how to write a coherent story. Just like a musician missing a note, not every listener may be able to tell, but it's still poor technique. And too many mistakes make for a sloppy, inconsistent novel. That's something a reader will notice. Even for the unorthodox writer, consistency *is* the thing that makes their writing work. Nothing absolves consistency.

Principle #3

Novels have a beginning, middle, and end.

If you want a working story, this is a critical concept. Three parts, each connected through consequence (as in, one causing the other), closed on the ends. The beginning is the starting point, the middle the consequence of the beginning, and the end is the consequence of the middle (and the beginning), which provides closure (something I will discuss in Principle #9).

Now, before every novelist jumps down my throat, and says, "Bullshit! I always start my novels in the middle," I hear you. I know this is a common technique, especially in my preferred genre of crime fiction: show the crime, then backtrack or build up to it. But that's not quite what it appears to be.

A writer must have a strong grasp on their beginning, middle, and end. Why? One word: pacing. (Actually, there's another big reason, but I'll save that for Principle #4.)

If you don't know what part of your novel is the beginning, middle, or end, then how do you know your novel is paced well? As in, *am I spending too much time in the beginning*? Put me to sleep, why don't you. *What about the middle?* Okay, we got it—get to the point already. *Or the end?* Wait, that's it—*that's* how it ends?

You see what I mean. You can really screw up your novel if you don't have a grip on the beginning, middle, and end.

Here's the deal. You don't have to use three-act structure to build your novel, but you must have a beginning, middle, and end. No, it will not stifle your creativity. Yes, I promise. In fact, it will most likely enhance it. As evidenced by every movie ever made—almost all follow strict form, most composed via three-act structure. Why? Because that's how plays are written, and that's where screenplays are derived. But, you might be thinking, this is a novel! I know, and none will set up a beginning, middle, and end like three-act structure.

Going back to Principle #1, three-act structure will help you design the shape of your story. It sets up the story perfectly to tell a tragedy or comedy, ensuring your protagonist's journey will be full and realized. Malcom Heath writes it best in his introduction to his translation of *Poetics*: "It is not enough to juxtapose prosperity and misery; the change from one to another must be the result of a sequence of necessarily connected events."[17] This means it's not enough to show your protagonist's journey —do they change or not—but it also has to be a result of the sequence of events. This interconnectivity of the protagonist's journey/change with the sequence of events is the basis of what makes an Aristotelian plot. Something I will cover in Principle #7, but *The Nutshell Technique* by Jill Chamberlain[18] is a great technical resource for this, as well. If your protagonist's journey is disjointed with your sequence of events, your story will not convey the emotional impact you're hoping for. Enter: three-act structure (combined with Principle #1).

Here's an example of interconnectivity.

Take *Rocky*. I know, it's a movie, but it's a fucking great one (to learn from), and it's also one most people know and one of my favorites. Sure, Sylvester Stallone is the perfect match, as an actor, for Rocky Balboa. But in this case, Sly is even better with his pen. He's a writer first, and we see that in the story he tells on the screen.

Rocky is not your typical underdog story. It's not about winning and losing. The reason why the movie is so emotional, and why I want to cry every time I watch it, is the masterful storytelling. *Rocky* is about love. Love for himself. Love for Adrian. In that order.

Rocky Balboa's character flaw is that he's dumb (sad, but true) and doesn't believe in himself. By the end, even though he loses, which is a smart storytelling choice that makes the movie even better because it's more logical and believable (both things I will talk about in later principles), he overcomes his flaws and proves to himself and Adrian that he *can* do it. Now, that change alone is powerful—we all have been there in some capacity—but there's so much more that makes the movie cohesive (another aspect I will talk about later), hence more powerful.

Everything that happens in the movie's sequence of

events is connected to that change from Rocky not believing in himself to believing in himself. The movie is about Rocky overcoming his fragile self-esteem which juxtaposes perfectly against the fact that he is a hulking, tireless fighter. How could *he* have low self-esteem?

The B Story, the secondary storyline, with Adrian, which could just as easily be the A Story, the primary storyline, is the love story, which aids the emotional impact of Rocky's change. He wants to prove his worth to her. The side characters, like Paulie, in their own ways remind Rocky that he can't do it. These are obstacles. Mickey doubts Rocky, challenging him to overcome his flaws. Another obstacle. Despite losing, he overcomes the obstacles, winning each of them to his side along the way, and his change is realized. From lack of belief to belief. What can be more powerful than that?

Well, I'll tell you what. Apollo Creed is the exact opposite of Rocky. He goes from arrogance to (probably) doubting himself. Knowing for sure is part of why *Rocky II* is a great sequel. We want to know just as much about what happens to Apollo as we do Rocky. Why? For a guy like Apollo, what can be worse than losing face, being embarrassed in front of the whole world? Nothing. His journey is the epitome of what happens when things become too external. It's actually Apollo's inability to change that causes his demise—a common case for antagonists. More importantly, Apollo only adds and aids the emotional impact of Rocky's journey.

Rocky is way more than an underdog story. The fact that Rocky proves himself to everyone else is just a kicker for him proving to himself and Adrian that he can do it.

That he can go fifteen rounds with the champ. Winning and losing doesn't matter. Love is what matters.

Wait, but I don't write novels like that.

I'm happy you brought this up. Or I brought it up. Whatever. If you haven't gauged by now, I talk to myself. You do, too. You're a writer. Anyway, genre fiction, literary fiction, whatever sub-genre you're in, it doesn't matter—you can still use three-act structure.

Here's why.

For novelists, three-act structure informs the internal structure of your novel, the structural spine, or whatever you want to call something the reader won't see. The only thing readers care about is being entertained. They want to feel something. Three-act structure helps with that by ensuring the story works, flowing naturally over time, providing the emotional impact you are hoping for and keeping the reader from snoring.

I call this next part the "external layout." It's what the reader reads.

Think of a three-act structure as the framing of a house. You need the framing. And most of the time, it's bland and uninteresting. But it has high utility, and it's supportive—without framing, you have no house.

Everything else is what the buyer sees. Two or ten bedrooms. Brazilian hardwood. Quartz countertops. White shutters. Whatever. It's as unique as you want it to be. *That's* your external layout. This is more or less the "structure" part of Question One from the previous principle.

There are endless examples of external layouts in novels. I already mentioned *Trust*, but *The Son* by Philip Meyer is another. It offers three distinct POVs from three different generations of a Texas oil family that rotate (one, two, three, one, two, three, one, two, three) over the course of the narrative to provide an expansive look at the past 160 years. But the examples are endless. Every novel I've written has used three-act structure, but all have different external layouts.

I love *different*. Odd. Weird. Unique. Risky. You can set up your novel using a three-act structure and get as wacky (or not-so-wacky) as you want with the layout of your story. The beauty of this is that it gives you more flexibility (as an artist) while still knowing your story will work. (Note: each genre has norms, something I will discuss in Principle #14. But if you're diverging from those standards, you do so at your own risk—critically or commercially.)

What is three-act structure?

In traditional three-act structure, there are five main points: inciting incident, plot point 1, midpoint, plot point 2, and climax. For a novelist, I think you can get away with three points: plot point 1, midpoint, and plot point 2. Here's why.

If your chain of causality is strong, then the inciting incidents should take care of themselves. For a novelist, the case can be made that the chain of causality is the most important thing, rendering everything else moot. But I still think having a solid three-act structure (and story shape) is smart. Do I dare repeat myself? Why not? It's my book. You'll be in a better spot to ensure your story works. Then, all you need to do is connect the dots using the rest of what you'll learn in this book.

Act 1: This is where you're setting up the world—the characters, their wants/desires, flaws, backstories, etc. You've got to establish this so your reader knows the stakes. Again, you're a novelist, there is art in how you achieve this.

It's typically the easiest act to write, because it's what drew you to the story in the first place. Similar to your protagonist, it's likely the reason you sat down to write the story. The set-up should be roughly 25 percent of your story. Plot point 1 is the marker, scene, chapter, or whatever that will kick off Act 2. It's usually when your protagonist gets the thing he wants, but he's got to overcome or achieve something to obtain it. Another way of looking at it is: they're about to enter a whole new world —sometimes literally, but most times figuratively. They know something they didn't before, and this opens up their world.

Welcome to Act 2.

Act 2: This is where your protagonist is met with confrontation—it's the antithesis of Act 1. It's a brand-new world with new stakes. There's some want/desire that has been fulfilled, but only if your protagonist can overcome the obstacle(s). It's also where you would deepen your story with subplots and—depending on how complex your novel is—your B, C, or D story.

Of course, the A story is your protagonist's journey. For two reasons, this is the hardest act to write. One, you're now in a new world and no matter how subtle, you've got to keep creating stops and starts, reversals and recognitions (more on this in Principle #11), otherwise you risk losing your reader. Two, because it's the longest act. It should take up about 50 percent of your manuscript. You can really get lost and off-track here, but lucky for you, you know your story shape and have a midpoint you're working toward.

I typically break Act 2 up into 2A and 2B, separated by the midpoint. In a traditional sense, the midpoint might be referred to as the midpoint twist: something happens that amps up the tension and keeps the reader not only guessing but moving along in your story. It reverses reader expectations in a large way. Now, this tension continues to rise until you reach Plot Point 2: the ultimate high, the peak in a tragedy; or the ultimate low, the bottom in a comedy. Plot Point 2 is the marker, scene, or chapter that kicks off Act 3. Your protagonist is ready to dig down and overcome (comedy) or fall down and tumble (tragedy).

Act 3: This is where you bring resolution to the story. At this point, you have enough momentum to bring the story home, so it's a bit easier to write than Act 2. But just because you bring it home doesn't mean it's good. There will be a lot more on endings (and resolutions) later.

The real challenge lies in the decisions you make to bring your story home. It's the lasting impression for your reader. Some have said—scratch that; *many* have said—that the only two important aspects of a story are how it starts and how it ends. The shitty part is that only equates to maybe 10 percent of your novel.

I know, it's like *what the fuck*, but that's what "they" say. It took me a long time to come around to "them" on this one, but ultimately, I do agree. It makes sense. We always remember the beginning and end, while the middle is murky. Just think about your favorite novel. It shouldn't take much convincing. I should note that the climax happens in Act 3, which is the point you've been building to throughout your novel. The tension you've been creating has been brought to its most intense point. Will your protagonist rise or fall? Will he or she overcome her flaws? *Dun, dun, dun.*

Quite simply, Act 3 provides a resolution to the question you set up in Act 1. It's the payoff. Will the boy get the girl? Will the detective solve the mystery? On a podcast interview, I heard Ken Follett speak about endings, and I'm paraphrasing, but he said an ending should answer the question while raising another question.[19] I really liked this idea. It's the basis of providing resolution without restoring order, an idea that squares well in my mind. It just feels real to me.

When I said I don't write like that, what I meant was I don't outline.

Ohhhh, you're a pantser, right? I should have known. Well, for you, I'd suggest a bare minimum outline. Five to ten lines. You can do it. Something small, miniscule even, then just label it—*beginning*, *middle*, and *end*. And make sure they're all connected through consequence.

But don't take my word for it. Aristotle thinks you should outline, too, then fill in the episodes and details.

Yes, really. In *Poetics*, he even outlines the *Odyssey* in seven short lines. Did you hear me? The *Odyssey,* it's like 135,000 words or something.[20]

Any story can be outlined into a basic plot outline. Not detailed. Not elaborate. Not even with a hook. It should just be bare bones. Steven Spielberg said, "If a person can tell me the idea in 25 words or less, it's going to make a pretty good movie."[21]

Most call this type of story "high-concept," even in novels, but I think every story, novel, or otherwise should be reduced to the bare bones. The point isn't that Spielberg is talking about movies and you're writing a novel. The point is to consider his films—*Schindler's List*, *Saving Private Ryan*, etc. They're intricate, detailed, winding stories. If he can still reduce them to the bare bones, you can, too.

Here's my first novel: *Tom Collins* is a story about a sales guy who wants recognition at work. He gets it via an award from his new boss but also learns that days earlier he slept with that new boss's wife (beginning). Worse, the award comes with a getaway to his boss's beach house so they all find themselves together on a weekend trip. But even *worse*, he realizes that he might have feelings for the wife, all while his boss offers him a promotion (middle), forcing him to decide what matters most in life (end).

Maybe your novel isn't as high-concept. That's okay. All stories can be reduced to their bare bones. In his book *Bambi vs. Godzilla*, David Mamet shares this simple story outline structure.[22]

1. Once upon a time ... (Beginning)

2. Then one day ... (Beginning/Middle)
3. And just when everything was going well ... (Middle)
4. But at the last minute ... (Middle/End)
5. ... and they lived happily ever after. (End)

I added the signifiers for the beginning, middle, and end. Many use this simple outline technique. Why? Almost every story fits it. Or at least every comedy. But, maybe more importantly, you'll be able to explain your story to other people.

People want to know what your story is about. What people? Everyone—agents, editors, readers, friends, family, you name it. But, they won't follow you past a few sentences. Their eyes will get big then narrow, and they'll shake their head once or twice, up and down, looking as if they're listening. But what they're really thinking about is lunch.

How do I know? Because after you finish, they'll say, "Interesting, so, do you know what they're serving for lunch?" If you attend any writers' conference, you'll realize that a surprisingly low number of authors can explain their stories concisely. I don't blame them. Why should they know? They're writers, not infomercial salespeople. You'll probably even realize it about yourself. Why? Because people are going to ask you, and you're going to stumble and mumble something or drone on detail after detail. I've seen it. I've done it.

You won't. Because you'll have a bare-bones outline ready to go.

But I know. You don't write like that, you're a

pantser. The whole point of *pantsing* is writing to figure shit out. Okay, fine. I didn't sell you on any kind of pre-work or planning, but maybe you should listen to our pal Sly Stallone, who said in a 2023 documentary: "I'm a big believer of when I write to not worry about the flawed aspect of it. I know that maybe ninety percent is worthless. But the idea that I have a beginning, middle, and end is very important to me."[23]

So maybe, after you write your story, it's a good idea to retrofit a mini-outline or three-act structure. Are you telling a tragedy or comedy? Does the story work?

Is the protagonist's journey a direct consequence of the sequence of events?

Is there a beginning, middle, and end? How long is each section? Is the story well-paced?

Of course, pacing implies speed over length. Every story needs a start and finish, which raises a whole other question about total novel length. How long should it be? Funny you should ask.

Principle #4

Novels have an appropriate length.

I suspect this principle will raise a few eyebrows. What is "appropriate," anyway?

How long is "long"?

How short is "short"?

Per Aristotle, the lower limit should be considered long enough to allow a change from good fortune to bad or bad fortune to good in accordance with what's probable and necessary. And the upper limit should be considered the amount someone can reasonably hold in their mind's eye.[24] You might already see how this ties into Principle #1, seeing that your story shape—tragedy or comedy—signifies the change in fortune associated with the "appropriate" length. Yeah, yeah, but what about that mind's eye thing?

Let's get practical.

Over the years, length norms have morphed, and every form has a standard. As a general rule, for a novel, you're safe anywhere between 75,000 and 100,000 words. Mysteries definitely fall into that range, although they could be lower, but you're out of the safety zone.

YAs are shorter—maybe 60,000 to 75,000 words. Thrillers are similar to science fiction or fantasy at usually 90,000 to 100,000 words.

Most memoirs and literary fiction fall into that 80,000- to 90,000-word sweet spot. Novellas are typically under 40,000 words. Technically, any fiction over 40,000 words is a novel, but as I've mentioned, genres have norms.[25] Write outside them at your own peril.

As Aristotle suggests in *Poetics*, you want to be able to keep the entire story in your mind's eye. This is important not only for the writer, as Principles #9 and #11 will prove, but it's also good for the reader. They'll be more engaged. I'm not completely for mindless reads, but writers shouldn't pander to their readers, either. Entertain, yes. Pander, no.

A reasonable goal for any writer is to keep the reader dreaming, immersed in the story. If you go outside the norms, it gets increasingly harder to keep the entire story in your mind's eye. It's already difficult enough within normal novel length ranges.

Here's why proper length is so important.

Let me be clear: you can write your novel at whatever length you want. However, you should be aware there are industry standards. If you want to be traditionally published—as in, someone pays you for the rights to publish your novel—then writing outside of those norms is a bad idea (let's call this scenario one). If you're indie or self-published, then writing outside of those norms could be a bad idea (let's call this scenario two). Okay, now let me expound.

In scenario one, being traditionally published is the apple of your eye. Let's say you've written a 130,000-word mystery novel; well, you'd better chop that sucker down to somewhere between 75,000 and 100,000 words, or else your chance of finding an agent (to represent it) or an editor (to consider it) is slim to none. They're too inundated. They don't care. Well, not like you think they do. They might be looking for a novel like yours, but they won't look at *your* novel unless it's within standard range—there are too many other projects that are. Too long is a non-starter.

So is too short. All they see is more work. "Come back to me when it's finished," is what they'll say. There might be some fringe cases here, but why dance with the devil? Not to mention—okay, I will mention, because this whole book is me mentioning things—I'd bet my left foot you have a pacing problem when there's at least 40,000 words of fat in that novel. I could be wrong, but I assure you that I don't want to lose my left foot.

In scenario two, you've got the same 130,000-word mystery novel locked and loaded, but now you're self-publishing, so screw the machine, right? I'm a cowboy—woohoo! Who cares what the industry thinks? I get it, I get it. I love the bravado and confidence. Believe me, I do. But you should still chop that sucker down to about 75,000 to 100,000 words.

Why? Because unless your mystery novel is radically

different from every other mystery novel, you still probably have a pacing problem. This is bad for readers. And it's (probably) the worst kind of pacing problem—too slow. Why don't you just bore me to death? If you're going outside the bounds of proper length, go with too short over too long. Like the adage goes, "Always leave 'em wanting more." Or as David Mamet has said, "Get into the scene late, get out of the scene early."[26]

Let's move on to another important reason—it's going to make writing your novel easier. I'm talking about the actual construction of your novel. Let's say you're writing an 80,000-word novel—a perfect length. Then we know our Act 1 should be around 20,000 words, Act 2 should be around 40,000, and Act 3 should be around 20,000. If you're reaching each of the plot points at those benchmarks, then I will bet my left foot (again) that your novel is well-paced. Start connecting those dots. I'm not suggesting that it has adequate tension, well-written characters, a strong plot, or anything else, for that matter. But I am saying you probably do not have a pacing problem.

Then why do my favorite novelists write longer novels?

Great question, but an easy one to answer: they have established audiences and readers. And it's quite possible they've built up the skill or street cred to pull it off. As a newbie, you likely have neither. It's unfair, but that's life. Like Lenny Bruce writes in his memoir, the truth is "what is," not "what should be."[27] This also happens to be a core idea in so much ancient thought, Eastern philosophy knows it as radical acceptance[28] while Stoics later called it "the art of acquiescence."[29] The rest is just an illusion of the mind. Save all those fictions for your novels.

Wait, what about epics? Right, right—the epic. Of course. "Remember this," Hemingway wrote in *Death in the Afternoon*. "All bad writers are in love with the epic." [30] Grand is not better. Often, it is much worse. Or at minimum, much harder to pull off.

At the end of *Poetics*, even Aristotle concludes that tragedies are superior to epics.[31] They are less concise and more difficult to hold in the mind's eye, hence they are less likely to provide the emotional impact you're hoping for. I think for every great work of significant length, there are at least nine that aren't good.

Even for the well-established author, writing outside length norms is risky business. I read novels by great writers all the time that I think are too long. As a reader, I think most novels are self-indulgent, my own included. *Cut. Cut. Cut.* I almost always think they would be better if they were shorter.

Your story could be much shorter, most of the time. And trust me, I know that's hard to hear. I empathize—all those small details, off-shoot chapters and scenes, and flashbacks add up to something big. It's a novel, after all. If you can't indulge here, where can you? Good point. Still, though, cut the fat. You can achieve it in fewer words. Pacing is king.

Not to mention, the theory of 1+1=½ applies here. If you say the same thing twice, it reduces the impact to half of what the better of the two would do alone. Less is more. Two is not always better than one. In fact, it's often worse. Sure, repetition does have a purpose from time to time. But for me, just like Stephen King's now-legendary (but not original) advice suggests, you must "kill your darlings."[32] Trim the fat and keep it moving.

Principle #5

Novels have a complication and resolution.

On a one-pager containing all my most important craft-related notes, atop the page sits this one Aristotle quote:

> *"Many poets tie the knot well, but unravel it ill."*[33]

If three-act structure is the basis for internal structure, then this two-part theory is the basis for the external layout. No matter how you structure or write the novel—POV, tense, linear versus nonlinear, et cetera—there is always a complication and resolution. But as the quote above suggests: a great complication does not indicate a great resolution, which is why I say treat them as two different skills.

A strong complication will gradually ratchet tension, primarily using the core technique of creating conflict, big and small. Someone wants something, and someone or something stands in the way of getting it. A strong resolution will maintain tension while solving tiny problems, answering minor questions, introducing essential information, and subtly revealing how things will be settled.

It's sort of like *pressure, pressure, pressure, pressure, midpoint, pressure, pressure, release, hold your breath, then relief.*

When I read novels, I always look for when the knot begins to unravel. When does that writer start their resolution? Genre writers have less flexibility than literary ones. But eyeing for this will help you with your work.

Right, right, I know, you want something more solid. So, when *should* you begin to unravel the knot?

Just like most of these principles, there is a good deal of subjectivity, which is why consuming stories with the knot question in mind will help you. Some believe you should keep it tight for as long as possible. Aristotle thinks you can delineate the complication and resolution from the moment the change in fortune occurs for your protagonist.[34] That would probably put the marker right around Plot Point 2 or the beginning of Act 3. I say, if you're using three-act structure, then the midpoint serves as a good place to start the transition. Give the reader a little something. That doesn't mean you reveal everything, not even close, but you begin to loosen that knot, just a bit. Never answer the *big* question, just start answering smaller ones. You'll probably create a few more anyway.

In my eyes, this principle and/or that quote above is key to a novel that works. Maybe I've taken it for granted that you have an adequate knot, or better said, you've built a strong and interesting complication for your protagonist. There is a technique to incrementally create tension, i.e., building up that knot stack, but I will get to it in Principle #8 (and #12).

If you've written a great complication, then your reader will be dying to devour the rest of your story. If only just to find out what happens to this poor protagonist and their band of buddies. Kudos, my friend.

Contrary to current industry standards, I don't believe a novel *needs* to be shot out of a cannon to work. One, it's hard to maintain that pace. Two, many of my favorite novels don't do that—they take their time. They don't put me to sleep, but they build gradually. The latter is not the norm anymore. This mostly has to do with our waning attention spans and the evolution of technology and culture, and perhaps at this point, even our biology. *Speed, speed, speed. Now, now, now.* Sadly, yes, even in our novels. (More on this in Principle #7.)

However, for many reasons, it's a bit easier to write a complication than a resolution. Again, your protagonist and first act are likely to be the reasons you wrote the novel in the first place, so you have a ton of momentum. Plus, you haven't *really* had to solve any problems yet. In that case, don't worry, they're coming.

The complication comprises Act 1 and, at minimum, the first half of Act 2. That's precisely when you might realize you're rowing a boat upstream, one of the paddles fell in the water, there's a hole in the keel, and you're sinking fast. It's hard to transition into the resolution, which is why I recommend a baseline level of plotting, then connecting the dots. Like David Mamet writes in *On Directing Film*, "If you don't know what you want, how do you know when you're done?"[35]

I know many writers don't start this way, but I do, so I'll recommend it—begin with the end in mind. How do you want your novel to end? This is the final dot you're building toward. Personally, I'm always trying to say something with my work. I know there's debate here, and this might even go against classical theory on story structure. Even some storytelling masters that I love and listen to, like Aaron Sorkin, don't believe you should try to say something with the work.[36] Instead, he thinks you should do only what's necessary and let the subtext reveal itself. But if I told you I did that, I'd be lying. What can I say? I always start with the end in mind, with something I'd like to say through the work.

Time for me to get myself in trouble.

As a reader, I see shitty resolutions more than I'd like to. The only way I can make sense of this is by starting with the top of the funnel. As in, how the publishing industry (for fiction) evaluates and takes on projects.

The publishing industry favors writing over storytelling. If you buy that, which I don't think will be that big of a stretch for most people, then it's easy to see how you can have so many shitty resolutions. When you pitch a project, they just want the writing. Sure, they ask about the story, but as I mentioned earlier most writers can't even speak about their own work well. So "they" just say,

"Send me a sample. It's all going to come down to the writing."

Of course, we both know writing is entirely subjective, which is why you get so much duplication and not a lot of risky (more fun) art, but that's not the point. What matters is that the story becomes second fiddle.

The industry tends to hide behind great writing and/or legacy authors. Makes total sense. It's a business. But neither guarantees an excellent resolution (or great story, for that matter). The former should be obvious. A great writer can blind you with their prose. The latter is earned. From a commercial perspective, they have a large enough readership where great resolutions might not matter as much anymore. As long as they write in their voice, hook you in the first fifty pages, and end it strongly, that's all that matters. Here's the reality: everyone in publishing is too busy (and almost everyone is underpaid). The agents. The editors. The publishers. It takes too long to worry about anything other than the most "important" aspects of a book: voice, hook, ending. *Hurry, hurry. Get it off the conveyor belt. We got mouths to feed and jobs to keep.*

So, ultimately, who does the responsibility fall on to write a great resolution?

You and me. So, let's get to work.

Of course, good and bad resolutions are subjective.

A resolution is not just the ending, it's how we get there. Just the other day, I read a *mega* bestseller by a *mega* author I like and respect, and I was left saying, "C'mon, really?" As in, *this is how you're going to unwind this plot?* Of all the places this story can go, *this* is where it's going?

Ultimately, does it matter? Probably not. Not for him. Not according to the thousands of five-star reviews on Amazon. This is what makes art great, though. It's a conversation. I'm just one person. (Note: I will share a lot more on why resolutions or plots falter in Principles #9, #10, and #11.)

I should mention, I have so much respect for anyone who has ever written a novel. Let alone multiple. The boundlessness of the entire process can be strangling. It's *incredibly* hard work to produce novels again and again. But this isn't about judgment or indictment. It's about craft. Resolutions, to be specific.

Charles Bukowski said it best, "Once a man has leaped 18 feet straight up in the air and then comes back and only leaps 13 feet, it's just not enough for us."[37] At the same time, it does make you appreciate the brilliance of an author like Stephen King, whose consistency is astonishing.

I love writers, so I'm always rooting for them. I won't betray my own people. I want every novel to unravel the knot perfectly every time, including my own. But just wanting it doesn't make it so. You and I actually have to do it. So yeah, it's all subjective, but as a reader we should strive for radical objectivity, as in, nobody gets the benefit of the doubt. A shitty resolution is a shitty resolution. It's the best way to evaluate stories. Mostly for selfish reasons, you're a writer—why else? It will refine your taste and help you write your own novels.

We've all been there, witnessing a plot unfold in an impossible, irrational, or contradictory way. How frustrating is that? Try to avoid those same mistakes that make you shake your head. It is the best guide I know. Tie your knot well, but untie it even better.

Principle #6

Novels are told through imitation of action.

This principle is sort of a hybrid of two Aristotle theories. It's important to grasp what is meant by imitation, or *mimesis* as he calls it. Since we were kids, imitation has come naturally to us. It's how we learn to live. This is one of the main reasons Aristotle believes we are drawn to stories in general.[38]

Storytelling is an imitation of life.

The principle does not mean you must write realist fiction, but it does mean your story should reflect the vastness of life. Aristotle insists the best stories are about family and friends, as opposed to enemies and neutrals.[39] Not just for the built-in tension, but for how they represent life more vibrantly for most people.

The second important aspect of this principle lies in the word *action*. Don't get this confused with blowing shit up, setting off fireworks, or anything like that—it refers to the literal meaning of the word, as in, to act, or to do a thing. Perhaps my favorite Aristotle quote regarding this matter is:

"A storyteller should say as little as possible as the narrator, since this isn't imitation."[40]

It means your characters are not you, the writer, so stay the eff out of the story. Even more so, your story is about what your characters do (over what they think or say), hence the imitation of action. In *Poetics*, Aristotle compliments Homer on being good at this—I guess we should all strive to be more like Homer.

Crime great Elmore Leonard felt similarly about writers. He believed one should try to remove themselves from the narrative.[41] As in, do not interfere with the story, just keep that plot moving. Or in short, leave your characters alone. It's funny, though, because Leonard has a very distinct style that is unmistakably him, so it's easy to think he's being contradictory, or to at least confuse his intent. But voice is style, not personality. You might already have a problem with this, thinking, *Well there goes that, my entire novel is narrated, and by me no less!* Oh, don't be so dramatic. This principle is more related to the golden rule of writing: *show, don't tell.* Sentence by sentence, scene by scene—that is imitation of action.

Show, don't tell—right?

There is a difference between these two sentences.

1. He was shocked.
2. His jaw dropped.

It's not that you can't write the first sentence, I have

before, it's just a lot more telling than the second sentence. Of course, this doesn't speak anything of context or what surrounds the two short sentences. You're a writer, though. I know you've heard "show, don't tell" before, so I won't beat you over the head with it. With that said, I do have some thoughts.

For starters, it should be noted that most people recognize showing as (technically) better writing than telling. At least in fiction. However, you can find *many* novels that tell a lot. I'm talking about massively successful novels. Think of this like any other art—the most technically gifted aren't always the bestsellers. Some people generalize this over-telling to genre novels more than literary novels. But honestly, I've seen it in both. The difference between genre and literary (for me) has less to do with style and more to do with form. Literary fiction is more of a slice-of-life story, while genre isn't. Instead, genre has genres. It's a matter of form, not style. There is one slight wrinkle. As some stories age, they enter the "literary" canon even when they weren't billed as such when they were first published. This mostly has to do with cultural evolution, artistic influence, et cetera. All things outside our control.

If you think about it, you've been "telling" stories your entire life. This makes telling more intuitive for the writer and reader. Verbally, or in practice, nobody takes a sentence (or two) to describe how the vase looked in the corner of the room, they just get on with the story. On the page, that vase might be necessary to set the scene (or it might not).

In my opinion, the best use of telling is for perspective on the narrator. Maybe reasoning, intentions, or worldview. Most often, how a first-person narrator thinks about life. Or even better, how they think about what is happening in the story. Maybe the shape of the vase in the corner triggers a thought about their body or the time a vase broke on the heels of an argument with someone. It's always a fine line any writer must walk with diatribes, rants, etc. They can get exhausting. Unless, of course, that *is* your narrator. Not you, the writer. Your narrator or character. There is a big difference. I know you're writing the story and ultimately, this comes from your mind, but if you listen to your characters, they will do what's necessary.

There is a line between "saying something" with your story and forcing your characters to act in ways you would. Leave morals out of this. Let your characters be characters. Don't judge them. In regards to "telling," if your narrator is a ranting maniac, so be it. Truth is more important to your characters. More on this later, though. Just know you're in good company. Many great authors have adopted a narrator like that—*Portnoy's Complaint* by Philip Roth comes to mind.

Showing demands more of the writer and reader. Perhaps this is why it is considered "better." There are many ways to show—zoomed-out or zoomed-in. This zoom concept is about proportion related to everything else in your novel. Some novelists shrink the scope, zooming in on conversation-to-conversation action. Others widen it, zooming out on every restaurant the protagonist stopped by that day. What you choose to zoom in or out on is your decision as a writer.

Of course, style choices could vary story to story. Voice included, but not as much. Sensibilities even less so. I find sensibilities are most consistent, which is why liking a writer's sensibilities is the most important thing. Like any artist, writers go through periods.

But back to this zoom concept for a moment. Some writers pack a lot into one chapter, and by that I mean, just a lot of action, doing shit, moving around place to place, street to street, or whatever. This style seems to be more traditional. Other writers focus on one small scene, then cut. As a matter of taste, I prefer zoomed-in. So, to date, this is how I tend to write my stories. It's just how I see the stories in my mind. Scene, cut. Scene, cut. I don't know why, and I don't really care. This is where the style, voice, and sensibilities of a writer come in. How do *you* see the story?

Depending on your motivations, the type of story, and your readers (what they expect and whether you care or not), showing versus telling might not matter to you. But let me remind you of imitation. Does your story mirror life? Does it contain the vast array of qualities, emotions, situations, problems, and challenges that humanity has to offer? The actions (and decisions) of your characters in those predicaments are what will define them, so showing just makes the most sense to me. Perhaps a best life practice, too—to be who you say you are. Actions over words, right?

Principle #7

Novels consist of plot, character, reasoning, speech, music, and spectacle.

Plot is the most important aspect of your story. *Wait, what did you just say? What about character?* Relax, relax. Don't kill the messenger. This is just what Aristotle believes.[42] Hey, I warned you in Principle #3 that I would be coming back to plot. I suspect the importance of it will offend fifty percent of readers. Let me remind you that most times, the greatest rewards are found encountering and battling the greatest resistances. Friction is necessary for growth.

In Principle #5, I claimed the publishing industry favors writing over storytelling. The question I have is, what's more important: writing or plot? It's true that favoring writing over storytelling is a lot different than saying plot is the most important aspect to your story, *but* the former does imply that a great writer can tell you a shitty story (with a bad plot) and you, the reader, would still be satisfied. There are many who would agree. I am not one of those people. Here's why.

I've never read a writer, not one, not even the best of the best whose writing didn't take me five, ten, or twenty pages to get used to. For me, writing is that subjective and that different from person to person. Sometimes, I never get used to the writing, but still, if the story has great promise, I'll keep reading.

Not to mention, the only people who remember "great writing" are other writers—again, subjective at best. Everyone else remembers the story. I've never read a better stylist, word for word, than Vladimir Nabokov. Yet, still the thing Nabokov is most known for is *Lolita*. Why? The story. Even Nabokov admits, "*Lolita* is famous, not I. I am an obscure, doubly obscure, novelist with an unpronounceable name."[43]

The emotions of the reader depend on the success or failure of the characters in action, which are your plot events. Even in a character study, or literary work of fiction, you do not observe characters in isolation. They are doing something, as bland or exciting as it might be. A story cannot exist without plot, but it can exist without character. Humbert Humbert needs to pursue Dolores to make *Lolita* work. He must act and decide. This tells us what we need to know about him. Plot makes the story.

If characters suck, the story might not be good, but as long as the sequence of events works, then you have a working story. Most novelists recognize this as a chain of causality—it's why "pantsing" works for some writers. Maybe the reader loves your protagonist (I hope so), but practically speaking, most readers just want to go, *oooh* and *ahhh*. They want something to share with a friend.

And that something is almost always the plot. As in, "You're never going to believe what happens. " Or, "I won't ruin it for you, but . . ."

Here's a brief overview of the six components.

Plot: Aristotle states, multiple times, that plot is more important than character(s). "Character instead is a by-product of action," he concludes. "Actions and plot are what a tragedy is about. This is what matters."[44] He even calls plot the "soul of tragedy."

I know this is a tough pill to swallow for most writers. They love their characters. I love my characters, sometimes. It also might mean the pre-work planning you don't want to do might actually be beneficial. *Rut-roh.* Don't worry, as I've mentioned above, pantsing could work for you.

A working *simple* plot has three conditions: one, a protagonist's change in fortune (story shape), two, a self-contained series of continuous and connected events (three-act structure), and three, *one* has to result *from* two. That's it. Of course, the parentheses indicate my preferences. A *complex* plot is a simple plot with at least one reversal or recognition[45]—something I will address in Principle #8.

Character: Character is the basis for your characters. The "s" is important. Characters are different from character. The former is physical, as well as emotional, mental, and relational. The latter character (no "s") is the moral disposition of the character, which is revealed through their actions.

Decisions and choices are what this foundational component is all about. Your character is who your characters are, and that is solely defined through their actions, decisions, and choices (which reaffirms the importance of plot).

Reasoning: This is *why* your characters are doing what they are doing. It is the moral reasoning a character uses to make their choices and take their actions, which in turn defines their character. So, this all may start to sound too analytical, making it lofty in technique, but it's not. Reasoning could be demonstrated to the reader through dialogue or thought. Never forget, though, just as in life: what the characters do is what matters most.

I've already said it, but I will reiterate it: characters are defined by their actions. If their purpose is good, *they* are good. That is why the antihero works, and the villain is still a villain. Reasoning is the element of story that characters use to make their choices.

Speech: This is your dialogue. More importantly, *how* your characters speak, not just what they say. Speech has a rhythm, which is why it's always recommended to read out loud. Many people will argue strongly against using patois in your dialogue, but I say, if your character dictates it, which is different than you dictating it, then you have an obligation to distinguish their speech.

Dialogue is my favorite aspect to write. But it should be noted that there are many people who favor description (or straight prose) over dialogue. They might suggest that if you love dialogue, go write a screenplay. To me, that's bullshit. There are no formal rules in storytelling that say how much dialogue you can or can't use. With that being said, if you're attempting to go a traditional path with publishing, you might meet some resistance. It's worth noting that, when done well, dialogue is easier to read than description, but that same quality also makes poor execution easily recognizable.

Music: This doesn't have as much relevance for the novelist. In movies or plays, you might consider this the original scoring and/or the music that is selected to carry different aspects of the narrative. Just think about *Jaws*. You never see the shark, but all the impending doom is built on that one bit of music. Something the novel couldn't do. If you've seen the movie, you can probably hear it now. All it is, is an E and F or F and F Sharp, played over and over again, but it sets the basis of suspense for the entire movie.

Sadly, as a novelist, we don't have this dynamic feature. You can still insert music into your novel, though. What your characters listen to might deepen them—the era they were born, subcultures they're involved with, moods, et cetera. Music can also set the stage for any scene. If Frank Sinatra is playing in the background, it's a lot different than if Eminem is playing in the background. What does that say about the environment of your scene? I use music a lot, because I love music. But there is another way to think about the musicality of your novel—the sound of your novel. Dialogue and prose has cadence, tone, and rhythm. Sound is something I will touch on in Principle #13.

Spectacle: Is your story subtle? Is it loud? Is it ornate?

According to Aristotle, this is the least important aspect of story.[46] I agree with him. It doesn't pertain to the change of the protagonist or sequence of events at all, which may or may not work.

"Over the top" is almost the entire focal point of modern film and a large segment of the fiction writing world. All of this could be a societal movement based on technological evolution. It has unquestionably affected the way we consume art. We are living through an era of entertainment that puts spectacle before story. To me, this is its own tragedy. The technology boom has turned us all into a bunch of impatient consumers. Children are entertained in the same way—speed, noises, lights, and colors. I find the similarity disturbing. It's all about the boom, crackle, pop. The razzmatazz. We should remember another Bukowski musing: "Bad taste creates many more millionaires than good taste."[47]

A great story will work in the absence of spectacle. Case in point: I recently attended a high school musical, *Legally Blonde*, that was totally underfunded—almost nothing for stage sets. But it didn't need it. The story carried the performance, and the actors played their parts well. Consequently, I left even more impressed than if it had excessive spectacle. If you like crime, read Fuminori Nakamura (*The Thief*) or Chris Offutt (*The Killing Hills*)—totally naked, unpretentious writing where spectacle takes the back seat. Or perhaps one of my favorite literary novels *Miles from Nowhere* by Nami Mun.

Certain genres demand higher degrees of spectacle. And spectacle can enhance the right story at the right time, no question. With that said, consider whether you're pandering with excessive spectacle. Or worse, covering up a real story problem. To paraphrase Hemingway: Write the story, take out all the *spectacle*, and see if it still works.

Principle #8

Novels should contain reversals and recognitions.

In the previous principle, I raised your attention to the notion of *simple* versus *complex* plots. For emphasis, a simple plot has three conditions: one, a protagonist's change in fortune (story shape), two, a self-contained series of continuous and connected events (three-act structure), and lastly, one has to result *from* two. A complex plot is a simple plot with a reversal or recognition linking one and two. You're probably best served infusing your plot with at least one reversal or recognition, turning your work from simple to complex.

Here are straightforward definitions.

A *reversal* is a change of any situation into its opposite—let's say from good to bad fortune, or vice versa. A *recognition* is a change from ignorance to knowledge.[48] The latter can happen through signs, memory, inventions, or reasoning—all fine, but Aristotle thinks the best recognition arises from the plot itself.[49] Meaning your characters learn something new based on the sequence of events in your plot. It's a realization of something based on the actions taken or decisions made by that character or another character. It stems from the plot. This type of recognition provides the most emotional impact. (That is great writing in action.)

For me, this has always been a very helpful distinction: characters are always acting either knowingly or unknowingly. The difference is crucial to how they're viewed by the reader. It will distinguish their character. One of the most powerful mechanisms in storytelling is a last-minute reversal, as in the character takes an action in ignorance, only to learn the truth moments after that action is taken.

Spoiler alert: this is what makes the ending of *Mystic River* so damn powerful. It's painful yet satisfying because the main character pays for his crimes by having to live with the fact that he killed an innocent man, a childhood friend no less, one he felt a responsibility to protect since they were kids. It drives a stake in your heart and delivers justice. A masterful ending. It also hits on Aristotle's theory that the best stories are about conflict between friends and family (rather than enemies or neutrals.) When executed well, stories about friends and family pierce the heart like no other. The built-in emotion, history, and drama are unmatched.

How do you write reversals and recognitions?

The easiest way to think about this is via two words: "but" and "therefore." *But* this happens—reversal. Or *therefore* that happens—recognition. The goal is to try to never use the word "and." As in, *and* this happens. It's not just less dramatic, but it's also less probable, which means it could weaken or break the chain of causality.

Scene by scene, in TV shows, "but" and "therefore" are the basis of drama.[50] It happens so much and so often that all you have to do is watch your favorite TV show tonight and you'll see it. With that said, novels do it all the time, as well, but it'll be quicker and easier to notice by flicking on the tube. I am confident you will recognize it instantly, then pick up your favorite novel and view it through that lens with more ease.

On that note, let's look at this mock novel scene. After a one-night stand, a man wants to get back home, so he creeps out of bed, quietly puts his pants and shoes on, then tip-toes out of the room, and he opens the front door. Finally, he can breathe, so he lets out a sigh of relief, *but* he feels his pockets and remembers the keys to his car are still on the nightstand. Shit, now he has to go back inside, Or does he? He could just walk home. Or call an Uber? Or a friend? But that's not believable, his car is there, of course our guy goes back inside. What happens next?

In my head, he goes back, *she wants* to go to breakfast, and *he wants* to go home. Two people want different things. He tries to weasel his way out of breakfast with her, but on the heels of last night, he feels bad for leaving.

Next up: the breakfast scene.

A litany of things *could* happen but one of the things that Aristotle thinks (and I agree) is that your job is to depict what *would* happen. In our mini example above, you can be sure that whatever happens next, it's going to lead to another "but" or "therefore." Why? Because that's how scene-to-scene stories increase tension. Everything appears to be going well, *but* something interrupts, and it sets off another chain of events. In novels, this could be much more drawn out, because the form allows it, but in genres like thriller or rom-com, you'll see this technique frequently—be it intentional or intuitive.

How subtle or overblown do you make a reversal of fortune? Well, that's up to you. It's a style choice. As a reader, unless you're a craft junkie looking for it, you're not even aware that this tried-and-true technique is working its magic. Readers just want to be entertained, myself included. As a writer, though, you need to know that this is how to entertain. You want your reader dying to find out what will happen next.

On a macro level, this reversal or recognition technique should play itself out over the course of an entire novel, as well. In a way, this is where you've been heading the entire time. More or less, this is what Aristotle was talking about when he compared simple versus complex plots. There's always something standing in the way of a resolution.

So, what stands in the way? This is your choice. When will you interject that reversal or recognition? The goal is to increase pressure little by little, like turning a screw, until eventually you're able to release the pressure in a satisfying way. It's a gradual game of push and pull with the reader, or maybe even better, a game of "there, not there," like a magic trick. All great pantsers have figured this out intuitively, which is one of the reasons they can pants it so well. Why? Because remember, we are imitators, and tension works the same way in real life —through conflict—so why wouldn't we instinctively write stories this way?

Even still, many times on a chapter or scene-by-scene level, checking after you've written them for "but" and "therefore" will help you. Otherwise, you risk the dreaded "and." But don't worry, for that, there is an entire principle.

Principle #9

Novels should be logical.

In this book, I noted somewhere that the case could be made that all you need to write a novel is a working chain of causality—don't make me go and check, it's somewhere I promise. (Fine, I checked, and it was in Principles #3, #7, and #8.) The more important thing is why. And for *that*, let's turn to Aristotle.

> *"There is an important difference between an event happening* because *of another event or simply* after *it."*[51]

The distinction above is critical to the readability of your novel. It means your novel must be logical. This is at least fifty percent of what adds up to a working plot, a self-contained series of connected events. In your novel, there's a massive difference in one event causing another versus random shit happening at the same time. You might be thinking, *Alright, alright, I get it.* Do you, though? Because it's way easier to write "ands" than you think.

And this happens.

And this happens.

And this happens.

Coincidence is much worse than cause and effect, which is why we try to avoid it. The key to a novel rests on the fact that everything is causal. As in, the story can't happen unless *that* happens. Plotter, panster, doesn't matter, all great writers know that sound logic rests at the center of their story.

Of course, this does not mean the sequence in which you release information or structure of your scenes have to reflect straight linear storytelling. External layout was something I discussed in Principle #3. It could be as creative and unique as you want it to be.

Timing of when the reader knows something is important to suspense, and not just cliff-hanging thriller suspense, but more subtle levels of suspense, as well. As in, *why do I need to know that? What's going to happen next?* Readers assume you are writing a novel with a strong chain of causality. They don't actually think it, but it's been ingrained in them story after story. There is one type of storytelling that doesn't rely on it, the episodic. As in, each episode (or chapter or essay or whatever) is individual. Aside from maybe characters or themes, they are not necessarily connected to each other in a meaningful way. But the reader knows this already, so it's not jarring. As I mentioned earlier, *A Visit from the Goon Squad* might fit the bill, but it depends on who you ask. Most essay or novella collections do. (Think: *Reasons to Live* by Amy Hempel or *Owning Up* by George Pelecanos . . . or, every sitcom ever made.)

If your novel feels lifeless, it's quite likely there are one of two problems: you don't have enough reversals or recognitions, or your chain of causality is broken. In other words, it's not logical. As it pertains to this idea, here's another one of my favorite excerpts from *Poetics*:

> *"A plot should be structured so that if any of its episodes were rearranged or removed, the whole story would be disturbed and dislocated. If this isn't the case, then that episode is not an essential part of the whole."*[52]

It raises the question of essentialness. I know you're writing a novel, so standards are a bit different. You can be extraneous in certain ways that you cannot with other forms. However, it's still best to know when and how much you're including that is not necessary to the plot itself. Any deterring too far from your chain of causality (and/or central storyline) could hinder the reading experience. Or it could deepen it. It's sort of like the difference between *The Great Gatsby* and *Moby Dick*. Two iconic novels from the literary canon, each with a wildly different approach: one is super lean, and the other rants about whales for pages and pages and pages. Both fulfill Aristotle's promise about essentialness. *Gatsby*, obviously. *Moby Dick*, not as clearly, but it would be less of a story without the whale chapters.[53]

The best piece of writing advice I've ever heard.

Write what is logically supposed to happen next.

That's it?

That's it.

Let me slightly alter that statement and say, it's the best piece of drafting advice for writers. And it didn't come from any novelist—it came from two screenwriters, David Mamet[54] and Sidney Lumet.[55] Scene by scene, action by action, your North Star should be writing what is *surprising but inevitable.* Inevitable based on what? Inevitable based on who the characters are and how *they* would respond in that situation. Another one of my Aristotle favorites:

> *"In characterization as in plot, we should always aim at what is necessary or at least probable, so the character says and does what is needed or likely."*[56]

If you remember back in Principle #6, on imitation of action, I suggested you stay the eff out of your story. Or maybe that was Aristotle, too. Whatever. It's as true now as it was then. It's not what *you* think is inevitable, it's what your character thinks is inevitable.

Don't mistake this with being predictable, though. Just like life, what is inevitable is only predictable in hindsight. But that's the goal. It means your chain of causality is probably strong. Your job as the crafter of chaos, the wizard of words, the master of metaphor, is quite simple: write what is logically supposed to happen next. And, the reader will think, *Of course, I should have known!*

Principle #10

Novels should be believable.

When I read any writer, I typically ask myself two questions:

1. Do they leave me wanting more?
2. Do I believe them?

If yes to both, then I'm a fan.

I don't want to focus on the first question, because too much or too little is an aesthetic choice. Generally, I prefer minimalism, but that may or may not be your taste. With that said, perhaps my favorite experience is when a writer proves me wrong (and I believe them). It's not that more-ness can't lead me to want more, it's just harder. Richard Price is a good example, an author of socioeconomic door-stopper crime novels that I love. But me? I always err on the side of less: fewer words, fewer metaphors, less description, less of everything. I shared earlier the 1+1= ½ theory: two of something reduces the power of one thing by itself. Cut the second, improve the first, and now you've got something. So often, we're prone to be self-indulgent, droning, on and on and on. It's too much. Give me less. I want the two-hour concert, not the three-hour one. The movie, not the TV show. The 250-page novel, not the 500-pager. In either case, question number two awaits.

Aristotle wrote: "As far as possible, stories shouldn't contain any unbelievable parts."[57] But I prefer to draw your attention to this excerpt from the first translation of *Poetics* I ever read:

"Probable impossibilities are preferable to implausible possibilities."[58]

Since we know that we need to have a working chain of causality, let's place the focus on believability. As in, do you really want to pull this thing off? It's not about what *could* happen, it's about what *would* happen. The former is okay, but the latter is almost always more entertaining.

It's like "they" say: truth is stranger than fiction. Or what Tom Clancy said: "The difference between fiction and reality? Fiction has to make sense."[59]

The point is that readers have a bullshit radar—believability is critical.

So, what needs to be believable?

In a word? *Everything.*

Storyline. Characters. Dialogue. Actions.

Prose. Thoughts. Metaphors.

Of course, the beauty with this principle is that *you* dictate the rules, the world, and what the reader should expect. This is all part of the job of Act 1.

What are the rules of the game? The stakes? The norms?

What is the style of your story? Tone? How does it feel?

How will your characters act? Or speak? Or think?

What is acceptable? What isn't?

The list is endless.

In the Philip Freeman translation of *Poetics*, Aristotle repeatedly uses the phrase "based on what is probable and necessary." And in the Samuel Butcher translation, the role of the writer is to depict what may happen based on the law of possibility and necessity.[60]

So let that be our shorthand question. Based on the characters or standards in the world that I created or am depicting, is *this* probable, possible, or necessary?

Please don't confuse this with writing true to real life. Realism is a choice, just like surrealism, magical realism, et cetera. The principle just means that you should follow the unwritten rules you've laid forth early in your novel. And most of all, don't pull something out of your petunia later, breaking the chain of causality or raising a believability question.

It's about consistency, really. Not being dry or lifeless. It's about continuity and unity. Of course, the question for you is, do you believe me?

Principle #11

Novels should be cohesive.

One might suggest that a shitty resolution stems from either of the two previous principles. Either it's not logical, as in, your chain of causality is broken; or it's not believable, as in, *I don't buy what you're selling me*. It's possible. But most shitty resolutions are rooted in a lack of cohesion. They don't tie together well with everything that has come before it. That's why I love this Aristotle idea:

"The solution to a plot problem should come from the story itself."[61]

I cannot stand when I'm reading a book and something comes out of nowhere to solve a plot problem. It's like, "What the . . . ?"

That doesn't mean you can't introduce new characters (objects, challenges, et cetera) as the story goes on, but they must fit inside the bounds of what is inevitable and believable. Or what Aristotle calls "probable and necessary." He urges writers to avoid "*deus ex machina*," [62] a plot device that comes from outside the story to unexpectedly and unlikely solve a plot problem. Your solutions must have relevance to the plot and world you've already depicted in the first half of your story. The best novels have a feeling of wholeness and unity. (*City of Thieves* by David Benioff is a terrific example, but geez, there are so many.)

Classic examples of cohesion in action.

There are quite a few literary techniques that all hinge on cohesion. Take Chekhov's gun: if you're going to show me a gun in Act 1, then the gun must go off by Act 3—otherwise, it is not needed.[63] Everything should have a purpose. Readers take mental account of this stuff.

Maybe you're thinking, *What about a misdirection, like we show the gun, but it's only there to trick the reader?* Great. You've just keyed on something important. Trickery is entertaining, but it doesn't pack the same kind of emotion as a self-contained plot that doesn't rely on trickery. It's fleeting. For a moment, the reader will be impressed, but soon they will realize they were a victim of sleight of hand, and the story becomes disposable. Most times, trickery is less in the form I just described it (because it's shoddy) and more observed in the form of hiding something the reader should or could know from the outset (because it's debatable.) Either way, a self-contained novel without trickery can be read over and over again; one that relies on trickery can be read only once.

Case in point: I never get sick of the ending of *The Sun Also Rises*, "Isn't it pretty to think so?" My all-time favorite line to end a novel. I can read the book over and over. But once I knew what Amazing Amy was up to in *Gone Girl*, which is still a fun and cohesive novel, my interest waned to read it again. It's the trickery, not the cohesion.

Cohesion is hard to pull off. It's rarer in novels than movies, mostly because of their length. As proven by many published novels, if your chain of causality is strong enough, then that could be enough to get you to the finish line. But this book is about how to make your novel better, and cohesion will almost certainly do that every time.

Let's posit that you manage to trick or misdirect the reader with that gun that doesn't go off. I'd still recommend incorporating it into the plot somehow. It's like a MacGuffin, a rather meaningless object that serves as a way to move a plot forward.[64] At first sight, this appears to be trickery, but it's not. Same with a red herring, which is a clue or character that is a distraction from the important question at hand.[65] These are not instances of trickery, because by the end of the novel, the reader knows the purpose of them as it pertains to the plot. The story is still cohesive. If questions that are proposed earlier in the novel are answered by the end, then the story works. Even if, as Ken Follett suggested, they raise another question.

What about endings?

Cohesion is never more important than with an ending. Are you writing a tragedy or comedy? If a tragedy, the ending might not be the problem, it might be how you got there.

Nobody whines about the ending of *Chinatown*, *Romeo and Juliet*, or *The Stranger*. If you do, then you completely missed the point. In my mind, a novel can end when your protagonist's journey is fully realized from good to bad fortune, or vice versa.

If you've written a comedy or tragedy using three-act structure, then your story shape has already been decided and you know how the story will end. Good or bad fortune? Better or worse off? Do they overcome or tumble? You just don't know how you're going to depict it. Endings, like any plot problem, are best when they come from the plot itself.

Again, the goal is self-containment. Aristotle makes an important distinction, though:

> *"Unity of plot does not, as some persons think, consist in the unity of the hero."*[66]

Just because a plot is unified, and self-contained, doesn't guarantee your protagonist's journey has been completed. A good reminder to check your character arc. Did they change or not?

Remember: plots include your sequence of events *and* character journey. But everything, including your ending, should be cohesive. Avoid tricks. Embrace unity. These are the best plots. Not only do they stick together, but they will stick in the mind of your reader, as well.

Principle #12

Novels should be clear but not ordinary.

Every writer dances between clarity and ambiguity. In all aspects of your novel, the clarity-ambiguity spectrum is something you'll slide along.

This is *very* subjective. There are novels that are great because of their ambiguity and novels that are great because of their clarity. Just like a song. Is your novel "Mr. Tambourine Man" or "I Won't Back Down"? Both are great but for very different reasons. Bob Dylan is ambiguous, relying on metaphor. Tom Petty is clear, relying on earnestness. Knowing what makes your writing strong is most important.

The clarity-ambiguity spectrum is something I always have top of mind when I write, rewrite, and edit. It's never not there. How clear is this sentence? Bit of dialogue? Paragraph? Sequencing? Once I've addressed that, I ask: How clear do I want it to be?

Aristotle claims there are two reasons why storytelling began. The first we already covered: imitation. The second reason is why I bring this up now: rhythm.[67]

Like imitation, rhythm was another natural element for humans, something innate, but the people who had a talent for this type of improvisation gravitated toward storytelling. For the novelist, what this implies is the importance of sound, as in cadence, tone, pacing, flow. Or as Aristotle might call it, your "meter." Understanding grammar is not necessary to write. You might be really bad at it, at least at first, but if you do enough reading and writing, eventually you'll know what it's supposed to look and sound like. Many musicians know this concept well. Neither Bruce Springsteen[68] or Billy Joel[69] could read music, but things turned out pretty well for them. Rhythm makes this possible.

This raises another question, though. As a writer, which do you favor: sound or clarity? Elmore Leonard once wrote, "It doesn't have to make sense, it just has to sound like it does."[70]

Again, many musicians know the power of this principle when applied to writing lyrics. Bob Dylan definitely did. Jeff Tweedy wrote about this also.[71] So why not with prose? Well, obviously you can't write gobbledygook because most readers will not continue—they won't know what you mean—but there might be a small number who will. Who knows? Weirder shit has been seen in the arts, no? Consider that one extreme end of the clarity-ambiguity spectrum. On the other end, the writing is crystal clear.

At times, nothing sounds worse than proper grammar. Style is a constant teetering on the clarity-ambiguity spectrum. Just be aware that if you favor sound over clarity, you are going against the grain. This doesn't mean you can't. It just means that if you do, you might get some pushback.

But as one of my favorite Aristotle theories suggests, "The nature of the story itself teaches us what is appropriate."[72]

When in doubt, let the story tell you how much clarity is necessary (or isn't).

Quick detour to discuss dialogue.

Balancing ambiguity and clarity is just as critical for dialogue as it is for description and narration. Maybe more. In my experience, it's easier to be too clear than too ambiguous. Either will not sound right, but too clear is a graveyard. Ultimately, if you're doing a good job with the scene, ambiguity won't hurt you. As a reader, I've been in those shoes, thinking, *What the fuck is going on right now?* A lot of times, I just keep reading and finally pick it up, then actually appreciate the writer for not pandering. Great dialogue has its own rhythm. Sound is everything. There is music in how people speak. I'd rather not know what the hell is going on than read stilted, hit-me-over-the-head-with-it-why-don't-you dialogue. Smooth is good. Disjointed is bad.

There are three aspects to good dialogue.

One, truth in proportion to the character.

Two, further explanation is not necessary.

And three, good usage of tiny actions.

What is a tiny action? It's a tiny little something done by a character to assist the dialogue, something that breaks up speech. For example: "John glanced over Jane's shoulder." Why is John looking over the shoulder? I don't know, depends what is back there, but John knows. It could mean a lot of things. Maybe he's paranoid. Or sees someone he knows. Or he's looking at the clock. Like salt and pepper, tiny actions season your dialogue. Be careful, though, as you can over-season, making the dialogue worse. (Note: the best teacher is your own eyes and ears combined with courage—watch and listen to people, then write what needs to be written.)

Lastly, I have one technical recommendation for dialogue. Only use the verbs "said" or "say." They are the only words you can repeat over and over that won't get tiring. Consider them (almost) invisible. This is something I picked up from the great dialogist Elmore Leonard.[73] If only we could be more like Elmore.

I read many novels that don't follow this suggestion. There's a zillion verbs. Some writers and readers think it's so clever to use "she insisted," " he urged," "she reported," or whatever. Others, like myself, think it's redundant. Just write better dialogue. If you need to nudge with a verb, then you're teetering into the land of explaining. Same goes for adverbs like, "he said bluntly" or, "she said shyly." Just rewrite it. I'm reading a novel right now by a well-known author who seems infatuated with the verb *murmur*. Everyone is murmuring. I'm like, "For the love of God, just write *said!*"

Of course, there is always the option of no verb tag at all, which provides a back-and-forth pitter-patter effect, but it places a higher demand on your skills and on the reader. Again, clarity versus ambiguity. Who is your reader? What do they expect? Do you care? All great questions. Ultimately, how your dialogue *sounds* is going to be the most important factor. Did you pull it off? Is it believable? Is it logical? Everything we talked about earlier applies to dialogue, too.

In all elements of style, moderation is key.

In your work, you'll be tempted to use figures of speech like metaphors, analogies, similes, and such. Listen to Aristotle here, too—moderation is key.[74] Not sure when to cut? Ask yourself: do I really need this? As in, does it strengthen or weaken what I'm describing?

Many times, a better approach is to state what it is instead of providing a similarity. The amazing lead guitar doesn't always *slash*, right? Control isn't as sexy, but confidence is. Patience, control, and subtlety are all signs of confidence.

Another question to consider: is the metaphor accurate, or does it just sound good? Do you care? That's a whole other topic. We sort of touched on it above with sound versus clarity.

Then there is the question every writer knows: is the metaphor commonplace or cliche? This is perhaps the worst violation. However, in dialogue, sometimes, cliche or commonplace works. Think about it, that's how people talk, or better said, that is how *that* character might *really* say it. With that being said, metaphors can showcase your sensibilities. Aristotle was a big fan, as well:

> *"Metaphors are the most important thing for a writer. It's the one thing you can't learn from someone else."*[75]

Do you remember that vase in the corner? The one from Principle #6? Probably not. Doesn't matter. Either way, no two human beings have the same compounded experiences. This means no two people perceive similarities in the same way, and at its core, that's all a metaphor is. It means nobody will see that vase in the corner the same way you see it. We all have our own unique worldview. Describe that vase *your* way.

To me, the vase is shaped like a bell pepper. I don't know why. It just is.

Like Aristotle says above, you cannot learn metaphors, you can only listen to yourself. The same could be said for metaphor on a story level. Many stories are symbolic of a grander theme or scope—something totally orthogonal to the actual story itself. Perhaps that was the thing that made Shakespeare *Shakespeare*. Not the plays themselves, but their metaphors.

Just a few more notes on style.

I feel somewhat obligated to address the use of adverbs. One might consider it a forever-debated topic in the literary community. I don't like them, but many do.

Some say only use adverbs when modifying the verb "said," but I already mentioned that above with dialogue. Others, like Stephen King, don't like them. He wrote, "The road to hell is paved with adverbs."[76] He didn't really say *don't use them*; he just meant that if you use one, you're likely to use more, which can become a problem, so it's best to never start.

Here's another question, though: do you use adjectives at all? If so, how often? They can be quite annoying. What about exclamation points? Or any punctuation for that matter? The mother of all, *italicization*. I've used quite a bit in this book. Did I need it? Did it add or distract? When I read prose, often too much italicization irks me. But on the page, choices are limited on how to stylize words. A writer must make a decision somewhere on how *they* want to. What do you think? Annoying? In my fiction, I try to avoid italicization as much as possible, even with internal thoughts. I prefer it only for emphasis.

Since I mentioned internal thoughts above, how do you feel about thinking attributes? *An interesting question*, I thought. See, like that. What about the length of interior monologues? Or word repetition or alliteration? How long and short are your sentences? Mixing is always a good idea. Same goes for the lengths of paragraphs and chapters.

Are things repetitive? Necessary? Too detailed? Mundane? How lean is the prose overall? Is it too embellished? Be careful, as Aristotle warns us, "overly brilliant language overshadows character and thought."[77] I'm biased, I like minimalism, so I cut, cut, cut. But you decide. You are the writer.

And don't worry, proofreaders keep you in line with grammar (hopefully). Grammar is not style, but a lack of adherence to it could be. Go read *A Million Little Pieces*. (Yes, the controversial memoir by James Frey.) It's a wonderful example of not adhering to grammatical norms.

. . . and about those grammatical norms.

Contrary to popular belief, how much you edit is an aesthetic choice. Editing slowly morphs the original thought and rounds edges—it might make the work better or worse. Think "stage" versus "screen." Live versus not live. Can the reader tell the difference with prose? Maybe not, but I think so.

Energy dissipates the further you remove it from the source. Charles Bukowski hated editing[78], knowing the farther he got from the first expression, the farther he got from the truth. In that regard, Hunter S. Thompson was similar. That could be something you're shooting for.

Every editor will tell you they only want to bring out the best in your work. I believe them, but the real question is, do they know what is best for your work? For that, the jury is still out. It takes true strength to hold a hammer and not hit a nail. It's best to find the essence of what makes something powerful and double down on that rather than conform to a standard.

I once heard record producer Rick Rubin say, "Sometimes you hear mistakes. You fix the mistakes and it's not as good."[79] If you caught a mistake, it's likely you would correct it, but it's worth considering that you may not *have* to. Your writing style is only your writing style because you wrote it.

Remember: most readers don't care about anything technical. They only want to feel something. Happy. Sad. Inspired. So let us return to Bob Dylan, who wrote about music: "The argument can be made that the more you study music, the less you understand it. Take two people—one studies contrapuntal music theory, the other cries when they hear a sad song. Which of the two really understands music better?"[80] The same can be said for fiction. So behind contractions, punctuation, or whatever else you're learning, there is *feeling something*—and without that, you're dead.

Principle #13

Novels should contain true characters.

Here's where I diverge a bit from Aristotle: a character doesn't have to *only* serve the plot. Characters can also represent themes, aesthetic elements, et cetera. The novel form allows for it.

But as a minimalist storyteller, I do feel that every character should serve a purpose for the story. The love interest is a reason for your protagonist to make it back home. The best friend depicts character differences. The gas station attendant is a lens on the small town. These are simple ideas, but you see what I mean. When a reader meets someone, they want to know how they play into the story. On that, I think Aristotle would agree.

People want truth. This is why Hollywood and publishers are dead set on leveraging "based on a true story" or "based on real events" as much as possible. Think: *The Zone of Interest*, *In Cold Blood*, and many, many more. In fact, the genres of historical fiction and true crime rest on this idea. Even when the story on the page or screen is a distant (or inaccurate) depiction of the facts. *Oh, this really happened?* we think. *I've got to see it.* We want to think characters are real (even though they are not). To make stories dramatic, this happens more often than not. An interesting example is *The Iron Claw*, which leaves out an *entire* dead brother because it was perceived to be too much tragedy for audiences to handle.[81] Yes, seriously.

So, what is true?

Aristotle's idea of truth is a bit different, but not much. It's not truth like you think, as in, fact versus fiction. A true character isn't true to real life, it's true to the character.

Who is your character? What motivates them? What hinders them? Once you know who your characters are, all you have to do is listen to them—they will guide you. Characters can be better than us, worse than us, or similar to us, but none of that matters, as long as they are true. On critiquing an otherwise well-written screenplay, Sidney Lumet said it best: "The characters had nothing specific to do with the storyline. That particular story could've happened to many different kinds of people."[82]

In short, the story, and your next novel, should feel like only your characters can live it. Not any character. True characters are essential to the plot of your novel because they will do what is "needed or likely." For our purposes, ultimately, a true character can be defined as one who does what is "probable and necessary" based on who they are and what story you're telling.

How to write a true character?

In *Poetics*, Aristotle says, "Writers and artists in telling their stories are not bound to the same moral standards as others are in their public and private lives."[83] In Principle #6, I said it and will remind you again here: leave morality out of it (unless you're telling a morality story like "The Three Little Pigs," "The Boy Who Cried Wolf," et cetera). Novels are art, not politics. Never let what should be said get in the way of what needs to be said. Your characters are not a statement of you, they are a statement of themselves. If you are writing a character truly, they will act on their own accord, making their own decisions to succeed or fail. As an imitator of action, our only job is to depict characters who convey the story that needs to be told.

Right, but how?

Joseph Campbell wrote it best: "The only way you can describe a human being truly is by describing their imperfections."[84] Showcasing a character's flaws and imperfections is the most essential aspect in the depiction of any character. It makes them human and relatable. Yes, even for the most raunchy, gruesome, grotesque, disturbing characters.

The transgressive author Chuck Palahniuk wrote in his writing-memoir *Consider This* that writing, more than any other medium, is self-censoring. As in, readers don't have to keep reading. They decide with every sentence whether they want to read the next sentence.[85] I love this theory. It's that type of intimacy with the reader that makes things that might not be okay feel okay.

In short, write the damn character as you see fit. Just write them truly, and let the cards fall as they may.

Even more importantly, as it pertains to your plot, if you don't establish a character's essential flaw, how can you depict change? Will they overcome or succumb to the flaw?

In tragedy, most traditionalists call this the "fatal flaw," as in the flaw that buries your protagonist. It's often disguised as a strength—love turns to obsession, ambition turns to greed, et cetera. They move deeper into that flaw, and it's their demise.

In comedy, your protagonist overcomes the flaw—selfish to selfless, hubris to humility. The flaw moves from weakness to strength, hence why they save the day, win the guy, or climb the mountain.

Either way, tragedy or comedy, your protagonist needs flaws and imperfections.

What about bad guys?

I love a little danger. Everyone is tinged with a bit of sin. Some more than others—that's the point.

It's important to remember a Robert McKee theory on story: "The audience will seek the center of good."[86] What does this mean? It means you can write super dark stories, as long as your protagonist is a tad lighter. Not light, but lighter. It's all about relativity.

Relativity is a storytelling technique that has been used forever to make characters more sympathetic or likable—even otherwise shitty people. The ever-popular antihero capitalizes on this idea all the time. Who cares if the protagonist kills people. Did you meet the bad guy? He's a murdering rapist! In a reader's mind, everything is relative.

For your protagonist, nothing represents opposition more than your antagonist—the person, place, or thing that provides the biggest challenge to your protagonist and consequently drives the plot forward. The most interesting thing about antagonists, just like all people (including your protagonist), is that they *think* they're doing the "right thing." It might be evil, but to them, based on who they are, how they lived, and what experiences they've been through, their intentions make sense. I mean, don't we all *think* we're doing the right thing?

In Principle #8, I brought up the idea that characters always act either knowingly or unknowingly. This says a lot about a character and their actions, even if they are incredibly violent. For me, *intention is everything*. If the character's purpose is good, they are good. If it is bad, they are bad. So yes, your protagonist and antagonist may have similar wants and desires (or even flaws). But like any character, your antagonist's actions and choices will define them. Never fail to account for an antagonist's motivations. I've brought up Elmore Leonard quite a few times, and I will again here, he was so good at that.

As I stated above, it's important that the reader understands why a character does something. Purpose is what separates good from evil. If you think about your favorite antagonists, from Ken Kesey's Nurse Ratched to Sly's Apollo Creed, we know a lot about why they're doing what they're doing, even if we don't agree with them. Or maybe you do. You're not one of those people who roots for bad guys, *are* you?

Okay, imperfections. But *how*?

Believability is essential to your story. Right? Well, nothing screams "believable" more than imperfections.

Perfect is a lie that has been co-opted and sold to us. Consider this: it takes someone thirty photos to get the one you see on their Instagram page. I know, because I've watched those people take thirty photos to get the right one. It's as if this person walks around all day, thinking the world only sees them at the same angle as photo number thirty. Come to think of it, delusion would make a pretty good character flaw—do they go deeper into it, or overcome it? And as a result, what happens? Tragedy versus comedy.

The sad part is that we've known for a long time—since the advent of storytelling (a.k.a. imitation of action)—that flaws are what make us relatable, not perfections. So, these flaws must be reflected in your characters. Not just through words and thoughts, but in the actions and decisions of the characters. *Not again,* you think, as the lonely detective orders another whiskey at the bar. Or the distraught housewife pops another Xanax. These flaws and imperfections intersect with a character's wants and desires, with their choices and actions, making your story work (or not). Do they succeed or fail? Do they overcome or succumb? Again, tragedy versus comedy.

For characters, no Aristotle idea rings more true than this one:

"It is for the sake of action that characters play their parts." 87

Actions dictate your characters. What your characters say matters far less than what they do. And this is coming from someone who loves dialogue.

Let's revisit our social media starlet: what do thirty photos and all that filtering say about the character? They can say whatever they want, but it is the action that tells me what I need to know about whether they succumb or overcome, succeed or fail. Haven't you learned from all those unreliable narrators that listening to words can get you into trouble? Eventually, their actions don't line up with their thoughts. Just like in life. Aristotle writes, "People possess qualities based on their nature, but they find happiness and unhappiness depending on what they actually do."[88]

So, in the writing of your characters, it's what they do that matters most. Actions prove purpose. Wouldn't you love to know the agenda of all those social media starlets who seem so perfect? At that point, you might realize the good guy is actually the bad guy. (See: Patrick Bateman in *American Psycho*.)

Some closing thoughts.

Aristotle's four main character qualities are: goodness, appropriateness, relatability, and consistency.[89]

Goodness means the character is good if their choices are good. (Note: a choice is a combination of action and current knowledge.) Purpose is still the root of "good" choices.

Appropriateness relates directly to the trueness of the character. It is the cornerstone of this entire principle. Is your character acting appropriately based on who they are?

Relatability is about imitating life. Are you showcasing flaws and making them human? It is best viewed independently of goodness or appropriateness.

Consistency is Principle #2, right? So you already know how I feel about its importance. And, as Principle #8 reminded us, there is nothing more frustrating than the illogical. Or as Aristotle says, "even if we were to imagine a character who is by nature inconsistent, they should be consistently inconsistent."[90] That's our oh-so-popular unreliable narrator, no?

When writing any character, try to embody the character. Think as they would think. Act as they would act. What would *they* feel in this situation? Not you. The character. Energy transfers through the page, so does emotion. Don't kid yourself, though. Readers can feel what is real. Would your character really say *that,* in *that* way? Would they do *that* in *that* situation? Always look for truth. There is no other way to tell a believable story.

Principle #14

Novels can be criticized for impossibility, irrationality, contradiction, harmfulness, and artistic standards.

Using criticism solely as a basis for whether you should consume something is a dangerous idea. I mean, what if they're wrong? Can the consensus be wrong? I think we both know the answer to that.

What about the individual? Another question too obvious to answer.

Well, what about context? Isn't it better to understand the context of what you're consuming? Maybe, but probably not. Not if that context is packed with an opinion attached to it. I get there is always a bare minimum of influence. But, just listen to your friend. Take the recommendation. Let the back cover convince you. Stop reading after fifty pages, if needed.

Whatever the case, read the novel before you consume any criticism of it.

Form your own opinion. Who doesn't love finding diamonds in the rough? I bet you'd love an underdog novel (or film) about an overlooked novelist who is discovered to be a literary sensation.

Of course, then there's your own art. Many novelists recommend never reading reviews of your work, and you're not going to hear me squabble with those people. I don't think there's much value in reading reviews, but you probably still will. Sadly, we all want to know what others think of us, myself included. But we can try not to care, and for your own sanity, you should at least do that.

Here's why.

What is a review?

A critique says more about the reviewer than it does the work being reviewed. Yes, you heard me correctly. Art is subjective. Reviews are about taste. What one person finds enthralling, another might find snooze-worthy. A stoic woman might be passive. A contemplative man might be brooding. What eyes are looking at those characters? Every reviewer or critic brings their own life experiences, reading preferences, and social pressures to the table.

We all have positive and negative experiences, people we hate, places we love, and those books that will soothe the sorest of sores. However, anything done publicly packs a different kind of pressure. Pressure to fit in. Be liked. Just as you are scared to put your work out in the world, the reviewer may be scared to agree or disagree. Just like actions speak volumes about our characters, recommending any piece of art—book, movie, or music—says something about the reviewer.

Sometimes, I read a book in a genre that I don't normally read, and if I like it, then I'm forced to ask myself a rather silly but true question. Am I the kind of person who likes *this*? I can't be *that* person. Can I? It's difficult to go out on a limb and say: I like *this*. Especially when it's not the consensus. It's more risky, socially and emotionally. Again, I can't be *that* person. Can I? What will *they* think?

A literary agent I respect once told me every book is packed with a pillow message. He meant that every book contains a tiny value statement that says, *if I buy this book, this is what it says about me*—life is good, institutions suck, family is everything, equality for all, et cetera. Books can fall in line with what's in vogue or what isn't. Does your book convey a popular message? I'm not saying it has to. I'm asking if it does. Is a book bad because it challenges societal or industry norms? No, but it might be less shareable.

Almost all reviewing nowadays happens online, which may include anonymity. In one respect, I can see how this promotes more honesty. It's hard to tell someone they suck to their face. It's much easier to be truthful online, or just plain nasty, which can be its own problem. It's easy to shout "this sucks" into a black hole—an Amazon or Goodreads review. It's much harder to do so in person. The distance from humanity is what makes that possible.

In my book *The Gap,* I wrote about this problem of dissonance. The farther away you are from human-to-human interaction, the easier it is to lie.[91] It's why people can have an online persona that differs from real life. I don't recommend it, but distance allows for that. Face to face, what you see is what you get. Sure, there's always been deception, and to a degree (societally) we've normalized lying, but you can sniff that out after a handful of actions. Online, it can go on forever. Not everyone lies online, but it's easier to do so. It's also easier to partake in herd mentality, get your oxytocin spike, and move on to the next victim.

As Tyler Cowen, an ultra-reader, once told me during a podcast interview about how he chooses what to read, "You have to look for markers of quality."[92] That is very true for reviews, as well.

Criticism is good (and bad).

Criticism is good. Still, you should probably only listen to a handful of people who understand what you're attempting to pull off and what your tastes actually are. Everything else is meaningless. Ignore it.

If you want to write a novel, you'll need to get better at refining your taste. All writing is a never-ending string of tiny decisions to radically apply your taste. Which means you've got to read a lot, and critique those books (privately).

You'll need to read like an editor. Someone who can articulate what they think is important and why it matters. In my experience, the best editors don't force themselves on the material, they read it with their (perceived) strengths in mind. How *they feel* your work can be amplified. This is why it's important to find good collaborators. It's a search for strengths, as much as it is weaknesses.

This is more noticeable in the music industry. Any

attuned ear can hear a musician's differences producer to producer. It's not as easy in books, simply because editors are more hidden than producers, but their contributions can be drastic. Not with grammar and all the basic stuff a trained robot can do—I mean with taste, style, and story decisions. Some editors are better because they *are* better. It's a skill. Finding a good fit is ideal.

These principles are a good rubric for reviewing. Over the last five years, along with writing a few novels, these principles have been the basis for how I read books and watch films and TV shows. Crazy? Not really, it sort of gets ingrained in you. It's not like I sit there and force myself to engage with stories in this manner. It's just that as soon as the opening of the story commences, I think, what does this protagonist want? What's standing in their way? Internally? Externally? And if it's a book, technically, I'm looking at POV and tense, then prose style, which takes five to ten pages at minimum.

That's how I know what I (currently) prefer, always hoping something will come along that will disrupt those preferences. It's also why I can write this book with some conviction. I truly believe what I'm saying. A lifetime in sales has taught me the power of unequivocal belief. If you believe you have the best solution, then you have a moral obligation to serve that customer. I don't know if this is the best solution for writing a novel, but I do think you'll be off for having read it. That doesn't mean my word is infallible, it just means I believe it. If you believe it, too, then use these principles as guidelines to review novels, movies, and TV shows. And most importantly, your own work.

And what does Aristotle think?

Below is a quick overview of the five ways he thinks you can be a fair critic.[93] "Fair" being the operative word. It's an attempt at objectivity. Everyone gets the same treatment. You. Your workshop pals. Even the career author on their fifteenth book. (This is something I shared in Principle #5.) I've bucketed the criteria into three categories because things are easier in threes, and three of the five all circle around the same idea.

So, let's start with those.

Impossibility, Irrationality, and Contradictory: This is fiction, everything is possible, right? Yes, but not so fast. I urge you to go back and read the principles on logic, believability, and cohesion. Based on what you've depicted in your story, is what you've depicted *next* actually possible? Or are you reaching? Similar to that, the irrational is believable in humans or characters, but not in your plot. (Remember Tom Clancy: "The only difference between fiction and nonfiction? Fiction has to make sense.") And this leads me to contradiction: are things happening that are not in congruence with earlier parts of your novel? With all these critiques, it could be summed up that the puzzle doesn't fit together. Something is broken. Or perhaps, missing altogether.

Harmful: This quote from *Poetics* sums it up: "Criticism of a writer is fair when there is something irrational and deprived in a story, and it isn't necessary."[94] We already touched on the first half of that, but the second is more important. Is the cruelty and brutality necessary? If it is not, it's open to critique. As Aristotle said, "Stories will dedicate their own appropriateness." Write away, just make sure it's needed to tell the story.

Artistic Standards: I've mentioned many times that you can write your book however you'd like. Structurally, sure. Stylistically, definitely. And I recommend you do. I applaud your courage. However, there are artistic standards in every craft. For writing, grammar, and such. For society, norms of the day. The latter is too big a topic to include in this book, but it's worth acquainting yourself with the culture to know when you're rowing against the tide.

Earlier, I mentioned some of those craft standards, like novel lengths for different genres, but there are plenty more, especially when it comes to hardcore grammar. If you break a rule, that's fine—in fact, I encourage it, I love rule breakers—but you have to be willing to take the potential criticism that comes with it. Taking chances is fun, but it's also risky. It's just part of the game. Or as one of my closest friends often reminds me about everything all the time, "it's just part of the action."

My favorite quote on criticism comes from legendary filmmaker Brian De Palma, a risk-taker for sure. In *De Palma*, a documentary about his life and films, he says, "You've always got to remember that you're being criticized against the fashion of the day. And when the fashion changes everybody forgets about that."[95]

Of course, he's speaking about critical public opinion(s), but for me, this has always been an important reminder that one should not chase trends, hot genres, or anything external. All that will change. You'll still be you. Your work will still be your work. You want to be proud of it. So instead, just follow your truth, the direction of that subtle breeze blowing inside you. Anybody who comes aboard to help bring your project to life should serve that truth, your vision for the work. The best collaborators, editors, and such recognize uniqueness of style as a strength, not a weakness.

And ultimately, they leave you better than they found you.

The 15th Principle

Novelists must write, read, and have courage.

Welcome to the 15th Principle. It is for novelists, not your novel. And, Aristotle didn't say it. I did.

Over the years, when asked for advice, I often say three words: *do the work*. I've updated that to "do hard things." Why? Striving and struggling is its own reward. Writing a novel definitely applies.

I realize this isn't super helpful, but honestly, doing the work is the most important thing. It is your ticket. Like Nabokov (sadly) writes in *Lolita*, "Words without experience are meaningless."[96] Or perhaps, more poignant, the great words of Morpheus, "There's a difference between knowing the path and walking the path."[97]

So, for any writer, that work consists of 1) writing, and 1A) reading. I recommend taking notes—on everything, all the time—whether it be on your phone or a pocket notepad. Trusting your memory is akin to searching the ocean for a shell you tossed back earlier that day. Even if you find it, you'll never be sure it's the same one.

But yes, you must write. Good words. Bad words. Any words. Just write.

I used to say write daily, but I've encountered too many writers who don't and still seem to produce wonderful work. In fact, I've loosened up a bit on writing every day myself. So much of writing happens when you're not writing. So, you don't *have* to write daily, but I'd still recommend it. At least to start, you must get in the habit of seeing the invisible become visible. Rusty fingers are the worst for a writer. Oil 'em up.

Just like a runner trains to get his miles up, I do the same with my words. For a month or so leading up to a longer project, I write stream-of-consciousness gibberish to prep my fingers and loosen up my mind—Julia Cameron calls this "morning pages."[98] It's a great tactic. Then, of course, I write the first draft. Oh, the first draft, how daunting it can be. That steaming pile of dung. It's gross, really, but it's also glorious. And you need it. Otherwise, you have nothing, and *nothing* is bad. Or, like Jodi Picoult reminded us: "You can't edit a blank page."

Reading comes in a close second, hence its 1A designation. It's the only way to know what you like and, maybe more importantly, what you don't like. Your writing will start to refine itself. I've seen my own writing change quite a bit over the last eight years and even more over the last two or three. I credit a lot of this to widespread reading. I do not trust any writer who is not a reader. You must be incessant. People ingratiate with what they like, what they know, what makes sense to them. To hedge against this, set time to read books that you normally wouldn't. Inspiration comes from places you least expect. Open-mindedness gets more difficult with age, but I still recommend it. Not just with your reading habits, but with your writing, as well. I created a short mantra: *tension in the plot, not in the pen.* A quippy reminder to just let it rip, baby.

And, like Aristotle has reminded us several times throughout this book, "The nature of the story itself teaches us what is appropriate." It means all you have to do is listen, pay attention, and have courage. Although, he never wrote about the courageous in *Poetics*, as I alluded to and noted in the Introduction, he wrote about it extensively as a virtue in *Nicomachean Ethics.* This is why I believe Aristotle would be on board with the 15th principle.

During an interview, I once heard the filmmaker Alejandro Iñárritu say, "Have the courage to be disliked." [99] For several reasons, many included in Principle #14, the advice is more difficult to follow than meets the eye. But oh, what advice it is. The best, really.

If you want to create art for commercial consumption, as in you're creating it to show the world and be sold, then you must have thick skin. There is no other way. The thought that you're creating something everyone will like is insanity. Or at the bare minimum, totally irrational. Rejection is normal. More people will dislike your art than like it. I've already encountered more than I care to remember. Fortunately, I've had the benefit of a nineteen-year selling career, so I'm equipped to handle it. Even so, I've never had so much skin in the game. Nassim Taleb said it better when he said, for an artist, it's not skin but "soul" in the game.[100]

All that to say, having the courage to be disliked is required for the novelist. For many, myself included, this is a learning curve. Right now, in art, the pressure to say the right thing has never been greater. You can't write *that*, can you? But if you say *that*, it also means *this*, right? Don't listen. It's the halo effect placed on stories and opinions. A cognitive bias that makes us believe if someone is nice, they are also smart or tall or a good leader.[101] You see what I mean: if you write *that* story, then you also must be *this* person. It's all nonsense.

In *Poetics*, Aristotle told us that writers are not bound to the same moral standards as non-writers (in the telling of their stories.) People who confuse art and morality miss the point entirely: art is about taking risks. Entertaining, sure, but pushing against the status quo has always been the thing that drives art forward. It's like what Stanislavski warned actors, "You must be careful in the use of a mirror. It teaches an actor to watch the outside rather than the inside of his soul."[102] Sure, he was speaking of rehearsing lines. But at some level, aren't we all actors?

I hope you have the courage to be disliked and to excavate the story from your soul, the one that needs to be told. That's the book we need. Risk it for the biscuit, as my buddy tells me. What comes from the heart goes to the heart. You already have all you need to write your novel. I promise.

Notes

A Little More Than an Introduction

1. Brian Duignan, "Plato and Aristotle: How Do They Differ?," Encyclopedia Britannica, Inc., last updated February 14, 2018, https://www.britannica.com/story/plato-and-aristotle-how-do-they-differ
2. "Aristotle," Biography, Hearst Magazine Media, Inc., last updated August 8, 2023, https://www.biography.com/scholars-educators/aristotle
3. "Aaron Sorkin Teaches Screenwriting," MasterClass, June 20, 2016, https://www.masterclass.com/classes/aaron-sorkin-teaches-screenwriting
4. William Goldman, *Adventures in the Screen Trade: A Personal View of Hollywood and Screenwriting*, (New York: Grand Central Publishing, 1983), 39.
5. Haruki Murakami, *Novelist as a Vocation*, trans. Philip Gabriel and Ted Goossen, (New York: Alfred A. Knopf, 2022), x.
6. Aristotle, *Poetics*, trans. Malcolm Heath (London: Penguin Classics, 1997), x.
7. Aristotle, *Nicomachean Ethics*, trans. Harris Rackham (Cambridge: Harvard University Press, 1926), 158-161.

Principle #1

8. "Kurt Vonnegut on the 8 'shapes' of stories," Big Think, Freethink Media, Inc., last updated June 13, 2022, https://bigthink.com/high-culture/vonnegut-shapes/
9. Aristotle, *How to Tell a Story: An Ancient Guide to the Art of Storytelling for Writers and Readers*, trans. Philip Freeman (New Jersey: Princeton University Press, 2022), xiv.
10. Aristotle, *The Poetics of Aristotle*, trans. Samuel Henry Butcher (London: Macmillan, 1922), 8.
11. David Mamet, *Three Uses of the Knife: On the Nature and Purpose of Drama*, (New York: Vintage, 2000), 22.

12. Aristotle, *How to Tell a Story: An Ancient Guide to the Art of Storytelling for Writers and Readers*, trans. Philip Freeman (New Jersey: Princeton University Press, 2022), 35.
13. Aristotle, *The Poetics of Aristotle*, trans. Samuel Henry Butcher (London: Macmillan, 1922), 8.
14. Anne Lamott, *Bird by Bird: Some Instructions on Writing and Life*, (New York: Vintage, 1995), 21-27.
15. Melody Joy Kramer and Marc Silver, "Jodi Picoult: You Can't Edit a Blank Page," NPR, last updated November 22, 2006, https://www.npr.org/2006/11/22/6524058/jodi-picoult-you-cant-edit-a-blank-page

Principle #2

16. Aristotle, *Poetics*, trans. Malcolm Heath (London: Penguin Classics, 1997), 3-6.

Principle #3

17. Aristotle, *Poetics*, trans. Malcolm Heath (London: Penguin Classics, 1997), xxv.
18. Jill Chamberlain, *The Nutshell Technique: Crack the Secret of Successful Screenwriting*, (Austin: University of Texas Press, 2016).
19. Ken Follett and James Altucher, "804 - How to Write Books That Sell 160-Million Copies with Ken Follett," December 12, 2021, in *The James Altucher Show*, produced by Jay Wujun Yow, podcast, MP3 audio, 1:11:52, https://open.spotify.com/episode/1iv-QYoTw5U2VZwbDeyCuLt?si=b8691f5f25154aa3
20. Aristotle, *How to Tell a Story: An Ancient Guide to the Art of Storytelling for Writers and Readers*, trans. Philip Freeman (New Jersey: Princeton University Press, 2022), 113-117.
21. "Son of a pitch," The Guardian, Guardian News & Media Limited, last updated March 12, 1999, https://www.theguardian.com/film/1999/mar/12/features
22. David Mamet, *Bambi vs. Godzilla: On the Nature, Purpose, and Practice of the Movie Business*, (New York: Vintage, 2008), 91-92.
23. Sylvester Stallone, in *Sly*, directed by Thom Zimny (US: Netflix, 2023).

Principle #4

24. Aristotle, *How to Tell a Story: An Ancient Guide to the Art of Storytelling for Writers and Readers*, trans. Philip Freeman (New Jersey: Princeton University Press, 2022), 53-55.
25. "How Many Words in a Novel?," *Reedsy Blog, Reedsy Ltd.*, last updated February 7, 2023, https://blog.reedsy.com/how-many-words-in-a-novel/
26. David Mamet, *On Directing Film*, (London: Penguin Books, 1992), 28.
27. Lenny Bruce, *How to Talk Dirty and Influence People: An Autobiography*, (Boston: Da Capo Press, 2016), 123.
28. Tara Brach, *Radical Acceptance: Embracing Your Life With the Heart of Buddha*, (New York: Bantam, 2004).
29. Marcus Aurelius, *Meditations*, trans. Gregory Hays (New York: The Modern Library, 2002), xxix.
30. Ernest Hemingway, *Death in the Afternoon*, (New York: Scribner, 1999), 50.
31. Aristotle, *How to Tell a Story: An Ancient Guide to the Art of Storytelling for Writers and Readers*, trans. Philip Freeman (New Jersey: Princeton University Press, 2022), 209.
32. Stephen King, *On Writing: A Memoir of Craft*, (New York: Scribner, 2010), 197.

Principle #5

33. Aristotle, *The Poetics of Aristotle*, trans. Samuel Henry Butcher (London: Macmillan, 1922), 30.
34. Aristotle, *How to Tell a Story: An Ancient Guide to the Art of Storytelling for Writers and Readers*, trans. Philip Freeman (New Jersey: Princeton University Press, 2022), 119.
35. David Mamet, *On Directing Film*, (London: Penguin Books, 1992), 67.
36. "What's Character Got to Do with It? (Full Session)," YouTube video, 57:42, posted by The Aspen Institute, July 1, 2015, https://www.youtube.com/watch?v=eucVNYQNGAs
37. Charles Bukowski, *On Writing*, (New York: Ecco, 2016), 124.

Principle #6

38. Aristotle, *How to Tell a Story: An Ancient Guide to the Art of Storytelling for Writers and Readers*, trans. Philip Freeman (New Jersey: Princeton University Press, 2022), 19.
39. Aristotle, *How to Tell a Story: An Ancient Guide to the Art of Storytelling for Writers and Readers*, trans. Philip Freeman (New Jersey: Princeton University Press, 2022), 87-89.
40. Aristotle, *How to Tell a Story: An Ancient Guide to the Art of Storytelling for Writers and Readers*, trans. Philip Freeman (New Jersey: Princeton University Press, 2022), 173.
41. "10 Questions for Elmore Leonard," YouTube video, 6:33, posted by TIME, March 19, 2010, https://www.youtube.com/watch?v=BuOgcbI59Xw

Principle #7

42. Aristotle, *How to Tell a Story: An Ancient Guide to the Art of Storytelling for Writers and Readers*, trans. Philip Freeman (New Jersey: Princeton University Press, 2022), 41.
43. Vladimir Nabokov, *Strong Opinions*, (New York: Vintage, 1990), 107.
44. Aristotle, *How to Tell a Story: An Ancient Guide to the Art of Storytelling for Writers and Readers*, trans. Philip Freeman (New Jersey: Princeton University Press, 2022), 41.
45. Aristotle, *How to Tell a Story: An Ancient Guide to the Art of Storytelling for Writers and Readers*, trans. Philip Freeman (New Jersey: Princeton University Press, 2022), 67.
46. Aristotle, *The Poetics of Aristotle*, trans. Samuel Henry Butcher (London: Macmillan, 1922), 11.
47. Charles Bukowski, *Hollywood*, (New York: Ecco, 1989), 92.

Principle #8

48. Aristotle, *How to Tell a Story: An Ancient Guide to the Art of Storytelling for Writers and Readers*, trans. Philip Freeman (New Jersey: Princeton University Press, 2022), 69-73.
49. Aristotle, *How to Tell a Story: An Ancient Guide to the Art of Storytelling for Writers and Readers*, trans. Philip Freeman (New Jersey: Princeton University Press, 2022), 109.
50. "Writing Advice from Matt Stone & Trey Parker @ NYU | MTVU's 'Stand In'," YouTube video, 2:15, posted by Fabian

Valdez, January 25, 2017, https://www.youtube.com/watch?v=vGUNqq3jVLg

Principle #9

51. Aristotle, *How to Tell a Story: An Ancient Guide to the Art of Storytelling for Writers and Readers*, trans. Philip Freeman (New Jersey: Princeton University Press, 2022), 69.
52. Aristotle, *How to Tell a Story: An Ancient Guide to the Art of Storytelling for Writers and Readers*, trans. Philip Freeman (New Jersey: Princeton University Press, 2022), 59.
53. Joel Cuthbertson, "In Praise of Melville's Whale Chapters," LITHUB., last updated October 16, 2015, https://lithub.com/in-praise-of-melvilles-whale-chapters
54. David Mamet, *On Directing Film*, (London: Penguin Books, 1992).
55. Sidney Lumet, *Making Movies*, (New York: Vintage, 1996).
56. Aristotle, *How to Tell a Story: An Ancient Guide to the Art of Storytelling for Writers and Readers*, trans. Philip Freeman (New Jersey: Princeton University Press, 2022), 99.

Principle #10

57. Aristotle, *How to Tell a Story: An Ancient Guide to the Art of Storytelling for Writers and Readers*, trans. Philip Freeman (New Jersey: Princeton University Press, 2022), 177.
58. Aristotle, *Poetics*, trans. Malcolm Heath (London: Penguin Classics, 1997), 41.
59. "Tom Clancy Biography," IMDb, accessed July 31, 2024, https://www.imdb.com/name/nm0002007/bio
60. Aristotle, *The Poetics of Aristotle*, trans. Samuel Henry Butcher (London: Macmillan, 1922), 15.

Principle #11

61. Aristotle, *How to Tell a Story: An Ancient Guide to the Art of Storytelling for Writers and Readers*, trans. Philip Freeman (New Jersey: Princeton University Press, 2022), 99.
62. Aristotle, *The Poetics of Aristotle*, trans. Samuel Henry Butcher (London: Macmillan, 1922), 24.
63. "Writing 101: What Is Chekhov's Gun? Learn How to Use

Chekhov's Gun In Your Writing," MasterClass | Articles, MasterClass, last updated September 2, 2022, https://www.masterclass.com/articles/writing-101-what-is-chekhovs-gun-learn-how-to-use-chekhovs-gun-in-your-writing

64. "Writing 101: What Is MacGuffin? Learn About MacGuffins in Film, Literature, and Popular Culture," MasterClass | Articles, MasterClass, last updated September 2, 2022, https://www.masterclass.com/articles/writing-101-what-is-a-macguffin-learn-about-macguffins-in-film-literature-and-popular-culture
65. "What Is a Red Herring in Writing? Definition of a Red Herring with Examples," MasterClass | Articles, MasterClass, last updated August 25, 2021, https://www.masterclass.com/articles/what-is-a-red-herring-in-writing-definition-of-red-herring-with-examples
66. Aristotle, *The Poetics of Aristotle*, trans. Samuel Henry Butcher (London: Macmillan, 1922), 14.

Principle #12

67. Aristotle, *How to Tell a Story: An Ancient Guide to the Art of Storytelling for Writers and Readers*, trans. Philip Freeman (New Jersey: Princeton University Press, 2022), 21.
68. Bruce Springsteen, *Born to Run*, (New York: Simon & Schuster, 2016), 42.
69. Alec Baldwin and Billy Joel, "Billy Joel," July 30, 2012, in *Here's the Thing with Alec Baldwin,* produced by WNYC Studios, podcast, MP3 audio, 57:03, https://open.spotify.com/episode/4XXtlIU7F7xMbgt7sBRJLc?si=c2c2b82ced8640d8
70. Elmore Leonard, *Freaky Deaky*, (Boston: Mariner Books, 2011), 127.
71. Jeff Tweedy, *How to Write One Song*, (New York: Dutton, 2020), 85-88.
72. Aristotle, *How to Tell a Story: An Ancient Guide to the Art of Storytelling for Writers and Readers*, trans. Philip Freeman (New Jersey: Princeton University Press, 2022), 173.
73. Elmore Leonard, *Elmore Leonard's 10 Rules of Writing*, (Boston: Mariner Books, 2007), 21.
74. Aristotle, *How to Tell a Story: An Ancient Guide to the Art of Storytelling for Writers and Readers*, trans. Philip Freeman (New Jersey: Princeton University Press, 2022), 155.
75. Aristotle, *How to Tell a Story: An Ancient Guide to the Art of Story-*

telling for Writers and Readers, trans. Philip Freeman (New Jersey: Princeton University Press, 2022), 161.

76. Aristotle, *How to Tell a Story: An Ancient Guide to the Art of Storytelling for Writers and Readers*, trans. Philip Freeman (New Jersey: Princeton University Press, 2022), 161.
77. Aristotle, *How to Tell a Story: An Ancient Guide to the Art of Storytelling for Writers and Readers*, trans. Philip Freeman (New Jersey: Princeton University Press, 2022), 161.
78. Charles Bukowski, *On Writing*, (New York: Ecco, 2016), 41-43, 115-116.
79. Rick Rubin and Rich Roll, "Rick Rubin: Modern Master Of The Creative Act," January 16, 2023, in *The Rich Roll Podcast*, produced by Jason Camiolo, podcast, MP3 audio, 1:34:42, https://www.richroll.com/podcast/rick-rubin-730/
80. Bob Dylan, *The Philosophy of Modern Song*, (New York: Simon & Schuster, 2022), 79.

Principle #13

81. Michaela Zee, "'Iron Claw' Director Didn't Include One Von Erich Brother Because His Death 'Was One More Tragedy That the Film Couldn't Withstand'," Variety Media LLC, last updated December 23, 2023, https://variety.com/2023/film/news/iron-claw-director-left-out-chris-von-erich-death-1235850087
82. Sidney Lumet, *Making Movies*, (New York: Vintage, 1996), 30-31.
83. Aristotle, *How to Tell a Story: An Ancient Guide to the Art of Storytelling for Writers and Readers*, trans. Philip Freeman (New Jersey: Princeton University Press, 2022), 181.
84. Joseph Campbell and Bill Moyers, *The Power of Myth*, (New York: Anchor, 2011), 3.
85. Chuck Palahniuk, *Consider This: Moments in My Writing Life after Which Everything Was Different*, (New York: Grand Central Publishing, 2020), 50.
86. Robert McKee and Mark Cecil, "Episode 14: Robert McKee," April 21, 2023, in *The Thoughtful Bro*, produced by Mark Cecil, podcast, MP3 audio, 1:16:18, https://sites.libsyn.com/412667/episode-14-robert-mckee
87. Aristotle, *How to Tell a Story: An Ancient Guide to the Art of Storytelling for Writers and Readers*, trans. Philip Freeman (New Jersey: Princeton University Press, 2022), 45.

88. Aristotle, *How to Tell a Story: An Ancient Guide to the Art of Storytelling for Writers and Readers*, trans. Philip Freeman (New Jersey: Princeton University Press, 2022), 41.
89. Aristotle, *How to Tell a Story: An Ancient Guide to the Art of Storytelling for Writers and Readers*, trans. Philip Freeman (New Jersey: Princeton University Press, 2022), 95-97.
90. Aristotle, *How to Tell a Story: An Ancient Guide to the Art of Storytelling for Writers and Readers*, trans. Philip Freeman (New Jersey: Princeton University Press, 2022), 97.

Principle #14

91. Douglas Vigliotti, *The Gap: The Little Space Between What You Know and Don't Know*, (Herndon: Amplify, 2019), 80.
92. Tyler Cowen and Douglas Vigliotti, "Tyler Cowen: On How to Improve Society and Change the World," November 11, 2018, in *It's Not What It Seems with Doug Vigliotti*, produced by Dave Lishansky, podcast, MP3 audio, 44:51, https://douglasvigliotti.-com/podcast/15-tylercowen
93. Aristotle, *The Poetics of Aristotle*, trans. Samuel Henry Butcher (London: Macmillan, 1922), 47.
94. Aristotle, *How to Tell a Story: An Ancient Guide to the Art of Storytelling for Writers and Readers*, trans. Philip Freeman (New Jersey: Princeton University Press, 2022), 199.
95. Brian De Palma, in *De Palma,* directed by Noah Baumbach and Jake Paltrow (US: Empire Ward Pictures, 2015).

The 15th Principle

96. Vladimir Nabokov, *Lolita,* (New York: Knopf Doubleday Publishing Group, 1989), 178.
97. Morpheus, in *The Matrix*, directed by Lana Wachowski and Lilly Wachowski (US: Warner Bros., 1999).
98. Julia Cameron, *The Artist's Way: 30th Anniversary Edition*, (New York: TarcherPerigee, 2002), 9-18.
99. Alejandro Iñárritu and Rick Rubin, "Alejandro G. Iñárritu," April 19, 2023, produced by Rick Rubin, in *Tetragrammaton with Rick Rubin*, podcast, MP3 audio, 1:41:21, https://open.spotify.-com/episode/5hf5isANA6DtUIqDD9SlXZ?si=e55f9800257b44fa

100. Nassim Nicholas Taleb, *Skin in the Game: Hidden Asymmetries in Daily Life*, (New York: Random House, 2018), 34.
101. "Halo effect," *Wikipedia*, last modified June 20, 2024, https://en.wikipedia.org/wiki/Halo_effect
102. Constantin Stanislavski , *An Actor Prepares*, trans. Elizabeth Reynolds Hapgood (New York: Routledge/Theatre Arts Books, 1989), 19.

Acknowledgments

I sort of hate the term *autodidact*—it sounds fancier than it is. Plus, knowledge doesn't arise out of nowhere. But if there was ever someone self-taught, then I would most definitely qualify. So first, I must thank every master of craft, editor, writer, or artist—living or dead—who has shown me how to create work that I believe in. My gratitude for you cannot be surpassed. For better or worse, your words are forever embedded in me. And quite literally, *Aristotle for Novelists* would not exist without you.

Second, thank you to my editor Chantel Goins, for holding me accountable to my own advice—trim the fat, keep it moving. This book wouldn't be the same without you. Your support is undying. Jeff Goins, your edits and direction prove to be stellar. Stacey Covell, thank you for all your early notes.

Also, I'd like to thank Abigail Taylor, Allan Nygren, Anna Weir, and anyone else who touched this book during the production process. Mike Cote, thank you for your sureness and fine eye. And of course, I cannot forget my folks, who listen to me rant every Sunday about books, movies, and TV shows. God bless them.

Lastly, I want to thank you, the reader. Not just for reading this book but writing for you has made me a better writer. I appreciate you more than you know.

30 Books to Read

In alphabetical order, below are thirty of my favorite books on storytelling, writing, and creativity. Each offers something a tad different, so I've also written a line or two describing how I think they might help you.

There are many great resources that didn't make the cut. I've read countless, but one must stop somewhere. You'll notice there are no novels, but you're a reader who likely has an enormous TBR pile. It's worth noting that novels make the best resources, especially for pure mechanics and/or style choices. Also, as of this writing, I have a podcast titled *Books for Men*, a pod to inspire more men to read, and every other Monday I share a novel talking about craft, themes, significance, etc. If you're looking for recommendations, just scan the back catalog at *BooksforMen.org*.

This list does not include *Poetics* by Aristotle, which is the first book you should read. One, to check my nonsense; and two, because it's quintessential reading for all storytellers. I've read three translations, and all have been referenced in some fashion in the notes.

Okay, now here's that list of thirty books. If you're short on time or bandwidth, I've bolded my take-to-the-grave top five.

1. *A Swim in a Pond the Rain* / George Saunders. Simply: how to read (and write).
2. *Adventures in the Screen Trade* / William Goldman. A bit dated, but an entertaining book on the movie business—as I've said, publishing's slutty cousin.
3. *An Actor Prepares* / Constantin Stanislavski. Great resource for developing characters.
4. *Bambi vs. Godzilla* / David Mamet. Another book on the movie business, but nobody writes about story better than Mamet.
5. *Before and After the Book Deal* / Courtney Maum. Tremendous resource for any writer, but especially those who aspire to be traditionally published.
6. ***Bird by Bird* / Anne Lamott. My favorite book on writing, and home of the shitty first draft and picture technique.**
7. *Consider This* / Chuck Palahniuk. Fun writing memoir with tons of tips and tricks.
8. *Create Dangerously* / Albert Camus. Mini manifesto on the essential nature of the artist.
9. *Do the Work* / Stephen Pressfield. Most prefer his *War of Art*, but this is my *Tao Te Ching*.
10. ***Elmore Leonard's 10 Rules of Writing* / Elmore Leonard. Exactly what it says.**
11. *Ernest Hemingway on Writing* / Kenny

Phillips. Much of what the outspoken ledge has said about the craft.

12. *Making Movies* / Sidney Lumet. Sure, about movies, but still one of the best on storytelling.
13. *MFA vs NYC* / Chad Harbach. Essays on the differences between the two worlds of fiction.
14. *Novelist as a Vocation* / Haruki Murakami. Essays the icon has written on the subject matter.
15. ***On Directing Film* / David Mamet. A small book that shows the power of intentionality.**
16. *On Writing* / Stephen King. Probably the most widely read memoir on writing—for good reason.
17. *On Writing* / Charles Bukowksi. Nobody has better quotes, and nobody is a bigger advocate for the writer.
18. *Page Fright* / Harry Bruce. Shows you how many ways there are to do this thing called writing.
19. ***Self-Editing for Fiction Writers* / Renni Browne & Dave King. It's one of my go-tos for line-by-line editing.**
20. *Story* / Robert Mckee. The most widely recognized book on storytelling.
21. *Strong Opinions* / Vladimir Nabokov. A bit stuffy for some, but a good juxtaposition of thought and theory for any natural minimalist.

22. *The Business of Being a Writer* / Jane Friedman. An "everything" manual for being a writer.
23. *The Compound Effect* / Darren Hardy. One of three non-writing books here, and yes, a bit cheesy, but the idea is universal and indispensable.
24. *The Creative Act* / Rick Rubin. Short, quippy insights on the act of creation itself.
25. *The Dip* / Seth Godin. A tiny book on when and why to quit—or, what it really takes.
26. *The Elements of Style* / William Strunk. The best of the bunch on grammar and style.
27. *The First Five Pages* / Noah Lukeman. Another book I love for self-editing fiction.
28. ***The Nutshell Technique* / Jill Chamberlain. My favorite storytelling resource on the Aristotelian method.**
29. *This is What I Talk About When I Talk About Running* / Haruki Murakami. Murakami twice? Yup, another writing memoir worth reading.
30. *Zen and the Art of Writing* / Ray Bradbury. So zestful, you'll want to write immediately.

About the Author

DOUGLAS VIGLIOTTI is the author of four books, including *Aristotle for Novelists* and *Tom Collins: A 'Slightly Crooked' Novel*, which is available to listen to on *Slightly Crooked: Good Stories, Told Well,* a podcast that also features his raw and unorthodox poem collection *mini heartbreaks (or, little poems about life)*. He is also the host of *Books for Men*, a podcast to inspire (more) men to read. He currently lives in New Haven, Connecticut.

*Available for speaking, interviews, and events. For more info contact him via DouglasVigliotti.com.

Cho

Within moments of Jeremy's l e snuggling down next to him, his li s mind's eye. And, with his new epiphanic perspective, he didn't like the look of it. Not one bit he didn't. The insistent question he kept asking himself as he writhed and sweated was: "What *have* I ever chosen?"

So down the list he went, starting with birth. Well, he hadn't chosen *that*, had he? What human or any other animal ever *did*? How could they, pre-embryonically? Mind you, parents Gloria and Ron hadn't exactly planned Jeremy's coming into the world either, by all accounts, notably those of his Auntie Maureen.

"Proper surprised they were when *you* came along," she'd once confided to Jeremy in a pub called The Hope and Horse after five Xmas gin and tonics too many. "At *their* age. Dearie me. Our Gloria must've forgotten her pills or sunnink. Probably reckoned she didn't need 'em any more. But then out you popped."

So, birth not planned, more a question of accident. A fumbled quickie, then the random workings of sperm and ova, and bingo a baby! Him. Fair enough, Jeremy could live with that.

But then on the list went: school, Oxford, the bank, Sophie. Had he ever chosen any of them? Of course he hadn't, quite the reverse. It was *he* who had been picked by *them* because he was either so bloody clever at maths (school, Oxford, bank) or, later when fabulously wealthy, Sophie.

"And where was free will in any of this?" he mumbled, clutching at his head and whacking at the palliasse. "Nowhere, that was *WHERE*," he yelled, which upset Pete who rolled onto his other side and grunted, "oink." What was *wrong* with this human?

But, being a pig, Pete had no answer to that. Didn't have the big brain to fathom such angst. Just found it irritating. Life for Pete was lived from one moment to the next without worrying about anything except where his next meal was coming from. As far as he was concerned, concepts like life and death, let alone who chose whom or why, had no meaning. Pete didn't even know that were he to venture unwarily out of his barn, he could be captured, killed, and turned into sausages, bacon, chops, or, in the worst case scenario, pork scratchings. Lucky Pete.

What They Are Saying About Chosen

An entertaining Kafka-esque fantasy. Pragmatic Jeremy Crawford is successful, wealthy and has everything laid at his feet. A genius in his work and force to be reckoned with, until the day he suddenly wakes up with a jolt. He recognizes the ephemeral life he's had over the years. Meaningless and all given to him. Not chosen. Questioning himself and his actions, Jeremy withdraws from the outside world and engages with philosophical conversations with a pig named Pete.

This is a very funny and cleverly-written book. The writing is fantastic. The dialogues just blew me away and I loved the way Paddy Bostock describes things. He's an author that anybody could easily love. If you're an adult or a teen, you would definitely enjoy this book. It's out of the ordinary, charming and extremely witty.

—Dawn Martinez
www.goodreads.com/reviews

After reading *The Hanging* by Paddy Bostock, I was thrilled when I got the ARC for *Chosen*. I like the unique style of Paddy where you not only have a good storyline and character-building, the writing style itself is very enticing.

The story revolves around the MC Jeremy who suddenly realises he's never Chosen anything in his life so far. He has conversations with his pet pig Pete about how his life is ... one-sided of course!

What he does and how he takes charge of his life…or does he is the rest of the story. I absolutely loved Jeremy. This is a wonderful change from hard and arrogant MC that seems to be a common troupe with Romance novels. Also, I loved Julie and she's an ideal match for Jeremy.

Want to know what happened and how? You've got to read the book, of course!

—Sherin Lloyd
www.goodreads.com/reviews

In this wonderful political fantasy, Paddy Bostock is back with a book that is unforgettable and mesmerizing. It is a book that I couldn't put down once I started reading it.

It is a story that most of us can relate to. We all get bored with our lives, regardless of what profession we are in. And sometimes, we feel that we have to make fairly big changes just to have a little bit of bliss and freedom. Jeremy Crawford wants to live a life he chooses and not one that is handed on by others.

Jeremy Crawford seems to have it all. He has a great life as a very wealthy banker. But he feels that something is missing in his life. He no longer wants to continue as he has for many years, living someone else's life. He wants to live a life than isn't mediocre and dull. He wants to be able to do other things of his own choosing.

It's hard to believe Jeremy would want to pursue something as different as politics. But he does. Much like our world, the world that Bostock has created in his book is just as out of control as ours is currently. But how can Jeremy resolve his need for freedom and autonomy through the world of politics? It seems that these goals do not cohere with each other, until we read Bostock's story.

I loved the story from start to finish. It is honest and raw. And it highlights the need that we all have as humans to be recognized and free. This story is so powerful it may just make the reader want to reflect on his own life and make some small and/or big changes. I'd love to thank Bostock for yet another great story! I can't wait to read your next book! Rating: 5 stars

—Irene S. Roth
irenesroth.wordpress.com
rothsbookreviews.wordpress.com

Chosen

Paddy Bostock

A Wings ePress, Inc.
Political Fantasy

Wings ePress, Inc.

Edited by: Jeanne Smith
Copy Edited by: Christie Kraemer
Executive Editor: Jeanne Smith
Cover Artist: Trisha FitzGerald-Jung

Wings ePress Books

ISBN 978-1-61309-629-1

Published In the United States Of America

Wings ePress Inc.
3000 N. Rock Road
Newton, KS 67114

Dedication

To the young ones: Anya, Dan, Ishbel and Theo. May theirs be a fairer and saner world.

One

It took Jeremy Crawford a good chunk of the twentieth century and almost two decades of the twenty-first to get sane. At least that's how he thought of it. Others—his wannabe actress wife, Sophie, his ageing parents, Gloria and Ron, his colleagues at the bank, fellow members of the squash club, assorted relatives and acquaintances—didn't. They all thought he'd lost his mind. Why *else*, on the spur of the moment, would a person quit his lucrative position as HAA (Head Assets Analyst) in the City and on the evening of the very same day, decamp from the sumptuous interior of his multi-million-pound mansion to a disused barn at the foot of the thousand-square-metre "garden" to sleep on a palliasse with a pig called Pete and "consider matters"? To do that a person *had* to have lost his marbles, reckoned Jeremy's relatives and friends.

Okay, a minor aberration for a day or two due to stress at work they might have understood. Such was frequently the outcome of high-pressure jobs these days. But once Jeremy had been in his barn for two whole weeks and refused to come out, they were pretty sure he'd lost the plot altogether. Food—he insisted on nuts and berries only—and water had to be left outside by Barry, the gardener, and were gathered in only when Barry was safely off talking to his trees and flowers. Jeremy trusted Barry. Apart from him, *nobody* was allowed within range, physically, telephonically, or cyber-technologically. It was Sophie who reported watching from their bedroom window as he tossed his three beloved smartphones, the ones he'd once termed his "lifesavers," into the stream bordering the estate and waving at them as they sank out of sight. "Bye, bye. Glug, glug, gluggity and fuck you for*ever*," Sophie reported him having screamed as a full moon rose.

Unsurprisingly, it wasn't long before Jeremy's relatives, acquaintances, friends and, leading the pack, his ex-boss Sir Magnus Montague, who hadn't a clue about assets analysis and was ruing the loss of Jeremy's expert advice, took to speculating about the desirability of psychiatric intervention to bring him back to his senses.

"Jeremy's evidently off his trolley and needs help, no question about it. Genius close to madness and so on," was Sir Magnus's view, as expressed at a private family powwow over canapés and champagne in one of the mansion's larger gazebos in a copse of silver birches a stone's throw from Jeremy's barn.

"Know a couple of trick cyclists myself, if that would be of any use," he added. "Top of the range Harley Street types. Would cost a few quid but I'm sure the bank would be happy enough to fork out to retain a fellow of Jeremy's talents. Wouldn't want *those* vanishing down the pan, now would we?"

"No we certainly wouldn't, Sir Magnus," was the joint response of Sophie, Gloria, and Ron, all of whose life expectations depended in one way or another on Jeremy's capacity to keep on earning as many shedloads of money as possible. Sophie, because she was a bimbo trophy wife who'd never done a day's work in her life and liked her mansion, and Gloria and Ron because their pensions were minuscule and they depended for their biannual private cruises to the Med and the Caribbean on their unexpectedly brilliant son's inordinate wealth coming their way at regular, monthly intervals. *Big* investments in Jeremy's continuing sanity *they* all had, and if this Sir

Magnus bloke could find a way to keep the cash flow flowing, *and* pay for Jeremy's treatment from bank funds rather than theirs, well he was their man.

It was Ron, a retired small-time failed entrepreneur, who piped up first.

"We're in your capable hands, Sir Magnus," he said. "Anything it takes to get poor old Jeremy back onto the straight and narrow."

A sentiment echoed by Gloria and Sophie.

"*Carte blanche* for me on the trick cyclist front then, eh?" said Sir Magnus.

"Of course," said Ron.

"Jolly good. It is in all our interests to see Jezza—that's what we call him at the bank—back in business when all is said and done. And I'm sure a few sessions with one of my psycho johnnies would do the trick. Probably just some little glitch in the wiring somewhere, eh? A few calmer-downers, a touch of the old talking cure, and he'll be back up to speed in two swishes of a pony's tail."

Sophie, Ron, and Gloria smiled happily.

"So then, many thanks for the nibbles and the bubbly, but now I really should be taking my leave. The car's waiting, so toodle-oo, I'll be in touch," said Sir Magnus, levering his large backside from the gazebo's finest wicker chair and opening the door.

"And don't fret, chaps, the shrinks will have old Jezza back to normal before you can say boo to a pelican," he called over his shoulder as he planted one large, brown, pointy-toed Oxford brogue onto Barry's carefully manicured grass and waved cheerily at the barn housing his ex-HAA before climbing into the back seat of the midnight blue Bentley 4x4 awaiting him.

Peeping through the gap between two loose barn planks, Jeremy watched on as his ex-boss took his leave, and overheard his parting comment.

"'Normal,' huh?" he muttered, returning to his palliasse. "Well, normal zormal. Eh, Pete?"

"Oink," said Pete, whom Jeremy now thought as his only friend apart from Barry.

~ * ~

And what, you will be wondering, had happened to Jeremy so radically to shift his lifestyle from one of extreme opulence to dossing in a barn with a pig? Hiding away from some indictable 2008-ish banking crime he'd committed which had suddenly been unearthed and was threatening to ruin his career and bring shame on him and his family and see him incarcerated for the foreseeable future?

Well, actually no. Jeremy had milked the markets with the best of them until the whole shebang went tits up and had been proud—as had Sir Magnus—of the firewalls he'd erected between himself and the bank to offset any threat of discovery or litigation. Due diligence was Jeremy's forte and he had his mansion and treasured white, latest model Mercedes E-Class Coupé to prove it. No, no, his current circumstances had nothing to do with any malpractice of that kind.

"So *what* then?" I hear you ask.

Well, in the nuttiest of nutshells, the answer is the past participle "chosen."

"'*Chosen*'?"

Yes. You see, Jeremy had awoken one morning after a night of agitated dreams—tossing and turning a bit like Gregor Samsa in Kafka's *Metamorphosis*—as an entirely new person, only mercifully not one transmogrified into a dung beetle. Call it an epiphany, call it anything you want, but overnight Jeremy Crawford had been reborn with whole new perspective on life. Whence the change had come he had no idea. But it *had* come. And the words echoing in his head when his eyes blinked open were: "In your whole life, Jeremy, *you* have never chosen *any*thing. All you've ever been is chosen."

Well, you can imagine the mental kerfuffle *that* caused. On the morning of his reincarnation, Jeremy had batted it away. Treated Sophie to her regular morning power fuck until she rolled over and went back to snoring as if she'd never noticed. Then did a few press-ups and knees-bends on the carpet for the cardiovasculars before power showering, dressing himself in his snazziest Master of the Universe outfit—the tieless, slinky, shiny, blue suit with the thin trousers and pointy shoes like Sir Magnus's—scarfing two energy bars with a *doppio espresso*, and heading to the Merc in the garage before hitting the highway City-bound to make his mark yet again on the international money markets.

It wasn't until he was only moments away from the office that he was forced to pull the Merc over, park illegally, and yoga-breathe.

"What the bloody *hell*?" he said to himself.

But the power breathing did nothing to improve his mood. Gone were his drive, his competitive edge, his desire to succeed, and, worst of all, his thirst for the status money guaranteed. And the bloody dream would...just...not...go...away. Normally Jeremy didn't dream at all. Out like a light he would go once he'd checked his three phones one last time before putting them under his pillow, then oblivion till six a.m. the next day, when the regular pattern would be repeated. As indeed it had been today *despite* the bloody dream, which, dammit, kept reverberating around his head. "Choose." "Be chosen." "Choose." "Be Chosen," the chanted words peculiarly counterpointed with the throbbing of The Sex Pistols' version of "My Way" and images that would have been familiar to Salvador Dali but weren't to Jeremy because Jeremy had never liked art. Reckoned it the escapist enemy of the capitalist work ethic, unless it sold for millions, of course. Then it had value.

It was as he was slapping his temples with both palms and banging his forehead on the Merc's horn that the cop car pulled up alongside and two officers jumped out asking if he was all right.

“Fine, and thank you for your concern, officers. You know how it can be on some days. Yakety yak from the missus, dog just puked on the kitchen floor, kids screaming—”

Jeremy had neither a domestic animal nor a child on the principle either would have deflected attention from him, and Sophie was usually too hungover in the morning to speak, especially after she’d been power fucked, but he imagined that was the sort of situation lower-class types like coppers might recognize.

And how right he was.

“Yeah, sounds just like my house,” said the PC, who introduced himself as Bill McGinity. Shaking his head and looking glum.

“Mine too, only we got cats who do the puking. All them mice they keep eating,” said PC Johnny Staniford, showing his badge. “Only, never mind all that, you still can’t park here, pal. So on your way, okay?”

“Okay. And thanks for the understanding.”

Which was an unusual thing for Jeremy to say, for two reasons.

Reason one: he never normally thanked anybody for anything, and,

Reason two: he operated in a workplace where emotional responses threatened performance and were thus discouraged.

Still the subterfuge had worked. No parking ticket. No warnings. Nothing. Nice enough blokes. Yet *still*, even as Jeremy gritted his teeth and pressed on towards the office, that godforsaken dream along with its Johnny Rotten soundtrack and its Salvador Dali fried-egg clocks kept flashing through what, he was beginning to fear, might have originated in his id. Fear because, as with art, Jeremy had always poo-pooed the possibility of explanations to life other than the super-ego awareness of profit and loss accounts, in Jeremy’s case always profit. So fuck Freud and his pals, right? Keep that kind of hooptedoodle safely where it belonged, in the basket marked “Basket Cases.”

But still something very weird was happening to him. It was hard to deny. So, illegally U-turning in a city street and waving V-signs at the ensuing blast of fellow motorists' horns, he headed straight back to the mansion, where, sidestepping Sophie's surprise at his early return, he heading to the barn, sent his immediate resignation to Sir Magnus Montague, laid his throbbing head on the palliasse, said "hi" to Pete, and hoped beyond hope the "Chosen" nightmare would go away.

Two

But it didn't, far from it. Within moments of Jeremy's head hitting the palliasse and Pete snuggling down next to him, his life so far began flashing before his mind's eye. And, with his new epiphanic perspective, he didn't like the look of it. Not one bit he didn't. The insistent question he kept asking himself as he writhed and sweated was: "What *have* I ever chosen?"

So down the list he went, starting with birth. Well, he hadn't chosen *that*, had he? What human or any other animal ever *did*? How could they, pre-embryonically? Mind you, parents Gloria and Ron hadn't exactly planned Jeremy's coming into the world either, by all accounts, notably those of his Auntie Maureen.

"Proper surprised they were when *you* came along," she'd once confided to Jeremy in a pub called The Hope and Horse after five Xmas gin and tonics too many. "At *their* age. Dearie me. Our Gloria must've forgotten her pills or sunnink. Probably reckoned she didn't need 'em any more. But then out you popped."

So, birth not planned, more a question of accident. A fumbled quickie, then the random workings of sperm and ova, and bingo a baby! Him. Fair enough, Jeremy could live with that.

But then on the list went: school, Oxford, the bank, Sophie. Had he ever chosen any of them? Of course he hadn't, quite the reverse. It was *he* who had been picked by *them* because he was either so bloody clever at maths (school, Oxford, bank) or, later when fabulously wealthy, Sophie.

"And where was free will in any of this?" he mumbled, clutching at his head and whacking at the palliasse. "Nowhere, that was *WHERE*," he yelled, which upset Pete who rolled onto his other side and grunted, "oink." What was *wrong* with this human?

But, being a pig, Pete had no answer to that. Didn't have the big brain to fathom such angst. Just found it irritating. Life for Pete was lived from one moment to the next without worrying about anything except where his next meal was coming from. As far as he was concerned, concepts like life and death, let alone who chose whom or why, had no meaning. Pete didn't even know that were he to venture unwarily out of his barn, he could be captured, killed, and turned into sausages, bacon, chops, or, in the worst case scenario, pork scratchings. Lucky Pete.

Meanwhile Jeremy continued to whack at his palliasse as into his troubled mind oozed a yet more vexed question, namely: "If—as I now suspect—I *were* chosen by school, Oxford, the bank and Sophie, was I *also* chosen by my best friend Mister Money and what he could buy? Using me as his puppet and jerking my strings. Not *me* who chose the mansion, therefore, but the mansion that chose me. Not *me* who chose the Merc but the Merc that selected me saying it was the best car on the market for a person like me to be seen driving. Ditto for the power clothes from top tailors, and even the Bankerese I spoke…or was *I* spoken by *it* just as I had been by the Oxford drawl I adopted when the public school brigade mocked my 'funny prole sayings'"?

And the answer to this was: "Yes to all of the above."

But it was the language issue that really stuck in his gullet. Spoken *by*? Never *speaking*? Parroting the words of others without ever examining the embedded agendas those words concealed? Jeremy also now "spoke" smatterings of tongues other than English—

bits of French, German, Italian and Spanish, all at restaurant level—and whenever he did it was like acting. The different body language, the different grammatical structures, the different nuances, until…he became a different person, which was fun but unreal. No wonder some actors no longer knew who they were and went crazy. So maybe he'd been chosen yet again, this time by the very instrument that supposedly separated him from the animals. And how was a person expected to *think* if he couldn't trust the very words supposed to carry meaning, if the only purpose of those words were some form of phatic psycho-babble? Find a whole new language? Well, maybe.

"Holy *SHIT*," said Jeremy, slapping at his head.

From his side of the palliasse, Pete said, "Oink, oink, *OINK*," which roughly translates as: "Shut the fuck up, will you? I'm trying to get a little shuteye here."

Jeremy calmed, nodded over at Pete, and smiled his first smile in a long time.

"Okay, pal. Point taken," he said. "Just trying to get the madness out of my mind, that's all."

"Oink," said Pete, who took to snoring.

~ * ~

No sleep for Jeremy, though, because the madness issue continued to torment him. What actually *was* madness, he asked himself. Clearly everybody he knew would conclude from his current behaviour *he* was the one who was mad because they were continuing to play the games required of them for social acceptance. So they would obviously consider themselves "normal" and him "mad." Jeremy saw that and didn't blame them for it. But that still didn't answer his central question.

Dimly, from an Oxford symposium he'd attended all those years ago, he recalled the words of a shrink called Laing. *R.D.* Laing, maybe? What was it he'd been quoted as saying again? That insanity was a perfectly rational adjustment to an insane world, something like that. Jeremy also remembered the work of a Frenchie called Foucault discussed at the same event. How it was that civilisation constructed ideas of madness—or "unreason"—for its own devious purposes but this said nothing about the condition itself. Indeed was fundamentally misleading. And had not the ex-Beatle Paul McCartney once been heard to remark, "I used to think anyone doing anything weird was weird. Now I know that it is the people that call others weird that are weird."

"Mmm, not *just* me then," Jeremy mused as Pete continued to snore contentedly.

Then there was a novel the audience been advised to read, by a writer called Ken Kesey, who'd been conned by his publishers and never made a dime from his work about a falsely diagnosed "mad" guy who gets lobotomized for causing trouble and telling the truth about the mental institution he's been incarcerated in. What was it called again? *One Flew Over the Cuckoo's* something. *Nest*? That was it. A fiction, but nonetheless a persuasive one when he considered the ways "madness" was used as a convenient excuse to ridicule or lock away opponents of political systems that brooked no dissent, *vide* the ways of the ex-Soviet Union or the current psychopath in the Kremlin. *Or* indeed the psycho in the White House whose routine response to criticism was to brush it off as "fake" and/or "insane" and fire its exponents.

"Sooo," Jeremy asked himself. "Is it *really* me that's mad, or *is* it the world?"

To address this question, he opted to narrow the focus to only recent history and take a cold look at the facts—if there were still "facts" in a post-truth society where lies were told with a "fuck you and your mother if you don't believe me" impunity. In which a mega-rich narcissist could get himself elected American president by lying through his teeth, abetted by his psychopath pal in the Kremlin and the corrupt social media. In which British electors had been conned into voting to leave the European Union through a campaign targeted to arouse xenophobic delusions of their specious grandeur. In which parliamentary democracies built across centuries were under threat from meddling personal data banks like Facebook and Cambridge Analytica. What sane person could contemplate such a scenario and think it anything but *in*sane? Not Jeremy, that was for sure, so maybe it was Laing's version of insanity he needed rationally to adjust to. And what better way to face up to this dystopian chaos than to confront it? How, he had no idea, but at least it was in his mind as a possibility.

"Better late than never," he muttered, covering his head with a smelly blanket and snuggling down on his palliasse. "Nightie, nightie, Pete."

"Oink," said Pete in mid-snore.

"Mmm, who knows?" Jeremy mumbled. "Meanwhile it's sleep for me too, perchance to have a happier dream this time. That would be a turn up for the book."

~ * ~

As fate would have it, Jeremy's first confrontational opportunity came with a tapping on his barn door at eleven thirty-five the following morning just as he *was* enjoying a happier dream. In it he featured as an elf called Yarume who could morph into any form he wanted, human or bestial, depending on the nature of the adventure he faced, and nobody ever called Yarume crazy and got away with it. Gurgling happily to himself, Jeremy slept on far beyond sunrise. Never, ever, even on a Sunday, had Jeremy slept so late, but now he was Yarume who was never defeated in any task he undertook, so let's enjoy the ride…

Then there came the tapping. Tap, tap, tap, tap, tappity *tap*, it went.

Followed by a knock, knock, knock, knockity *KNOCK*.

Jeremy snuggled deeper into his palliasse, terrified his only ever happy dream might have taken a turn for the worse. Worse even than the Kafkaesque one that had caused him so much trouble in the first place. You know how it is when you emerge from sleep betwixt and between one form consciousness and another. How you don't know what's real and what isn't, how long it can take for the mists to clear and "reality" to clutch you back into its grip.

"Ug? Grrrrr. Nnnnn?" he said, covering his head with the hay sack he used for a pillow.

Then came the voice. Blurred, distant, but nonetheless recognisable even to Jeremy/Yarume as a human voice, and one he had no desire to hear.

"Jeremy, *Jer*emy?" it said.

"Fuck off," moaned Jeremy into his hay sack pillow.

"Oink!!!" agreed Pete, who didn't like his sleep disturbed at the best of times, but certainly not at eleven thirty-five in the morning.

But on...and on...and *on* went the knock, knock, knockity, *KNOCK*ing. And the voice, now hiked in decibels.

"*JER-EM-Y*EEE. JEZZA. We *know* you're in there," barked Sir Magnus Montague, hammering harder on the door and wincing at Frau Professor Doktor Gisela von Strumpf, the Harley Street shrink he'd brought along at the family's behest to make Jeremy normal again.

"FUCK *OFF*," counter-barked Jeremy, finally recognising the voice and rising from his palliasse.

"OINK, OINK, *OINK*," said Pete.

"Clearly off his trolley, wouldn't you say?" whispered Sir Magnus to Gisela. "We'll need to tread very carefully."

"*Natürlich*," said Gisela.

Such were the circumstances leading to Jeremy Crawford's first attempt at asserting his sanity in face of a mad, mad world. And, recognising it as such in the nick of time, he pulled himself together, abandoned his fury at being awoken and, attired in one of Sophie's diaphanous taupe nighties with the frilly neckline, the only nightwear he'd managed to snatch from the laundry basket before heading to the barn, opened the door.

"Do step inside, I was expecting you sooner or later, Sir Monty," he said, bowing thespianly and waving inside his ex-boss and the sour-faced blonde bint accompanying him.

Three

"Sorry I can't offer you tea or biccies, it's all a tad spartan around here. But do take a pew anywhere you can find one," said Jeremy, gesturing vaguely at the pewless barn. "Or possibly a hay bale. Jolly comfortable things, hay bales."

Sir Magnus Montague and Frau Professor Doktor Gisela von Strumpf swapped meaningful glances while Jeremy pulled on the suit trousers he'd been wearing on and off for the last two weeks, then tucked Sophie's diaphanous taupe nightie into their waistband before cinching the ensemble with a Gucci belt. An unusual outfit, even Jeremy had to concede, but it would have to do.

Sir Magnus and Frau Professor Doktor Gisela exchanged even *more* meaningful glances, but, casting around for something authoritative to sit on and finding nothing suitable, went for the hay bales. Which were neither authoritative nor comfortable, but it was either that or standing. And, in the face of a loony needing life-changing therapy, standing/looming would have been threatening and counterproductive, soo...

"And to what do I owe the pleasure of your company, Sir Magnus, on this fine morning?" asked Jeremy. "Although I *could* hazard a guess."

"Oink," agreed Pete, who'd lumbered over to check out these unexpected and unwelcome visitors. Snuffling at their trouser cuffs—

Frau Professor Doktor Gisela was also wearing trousers, black shiny ones—and showing no evidence he approved of either of them. This he evinced by farting fulsomely, then sitting on Frau Professor Doktor Gisela's right, also black-shiny, shoe causing her to squirm, blink, blanch, and only just manage to prevent herself from screaming. But how could Pete have known that back in Swäbisch Gmünd as an adolescent, Gisela had developed a horror of the pigs on her father's farm and had herself needed long-term therapy to cope with it, hence her first introduction to psychiatric treatments, "face your fears" and all that. Which was now her professional, professorial mantra along with heavy doses of Meister Freud and anxiolytics, if push came to shove.

"Could you possibly persuade the pig to lever his bottom off the lady's shoe, Jezza?" Sir Magnus asked as politely as he was able.

"Pete?"

"You have a *name* for him?"

"Yes," said Jeremy, beginning to enjoy himself. "'Pete.' Also, who *is* the woman on whose shoe Pete is sitting? I don't believe we have been introduced. Does *she* have a name too?"

Sir Magnus took to grinding his molars. This wasn't going anything *like* the way he'd planned it. By now, Frau Professor Doktor Gisela's fabulous Freudianism and prescription mind changers should already have been at the very least *mentioned* as a means of healing Jeremy's clearly deranged mind. Persuading him to be normal and worship money again. Persuading him to get back to work and make shedloads of it for the bank—and his family, of course. It wasn't as if Harley Street Frau Professor Doktor Gisela von fucking Strumpf had come cheap either. Four thousand big ones he'd had to shell out just for her to agree to turn up. And all that now jeopardised by her evident hang-up over some pig called Pete farting, then sitting on her foot. In his long and distinguished career, Sir Magnus had faced all manner of crises—political, financial, fiduciary, *all* sorts. But this one took the biscuit.

"Yes, of course she does," he said, peering critically at von Strumpf who was attempting to overcome her *Schweineangst* by kicking Pete in the bottom with her free black-shiny shoe—the left one—which Pete wasn't appreciating.

"Oink, *oink*!!" he said, huffily. Shifting his prodigious weight such that his bottom immobilised *both* Gisela's feet, which caused her to shriek: "*Scheisse. Ach, meine liebe Götter* and collapse face forward over Pete's pink, bulbous, and prickly back.

Pete took that as the sign of the sorts of friendship and acquiescence which would allow him to forgive the lady, grunt, turn his head, and nuzzle her ash-blonde wig, thereby causing it to fall off and reveal a grizzled-going-on-white crew cut. Still Pete enjoyed chewing on the hairpiece. Made a nice change from hay and corn meal.

Jeremy chuckled. "And what is it...her name?" he asked Sir Magnus, whose face had turned puce, even more puce than normal. Sir Magnus's face was always puce-*ish,* given his proclivity for regular nips of five-star Courvoisier between high-protein luncheons and dinners mainly featuring *boeuf bourguignon* with *frites* and peas and two bottles of *Châteauneuf-du-Pape* to go with them. But this was a new and rare kind of puce bordering on vermilion.

"Frau Professor Doctor Gisela von Strumpf," he spluttered.

"*Long* name. And she is here why?"

"To help you out of the hole you've dug for yourself, you dumb prick."

Jeremy frowned.

"'Prick'?"

"Yes, 'prick.' Off you potter to live in a pigsty while your poor wife and parents are left bereft of cash? While the *bank*'s funds are dwindling in your absence. For *God*'s sake, man, get a grip of yourself."

"And you brought along this Frau Professor Doktor person to help me out with that?" said Jeremy, gripping himself in the crotch while waggling a pinkie.

"Yes."

"And she is a Frau Professor Doktor of *what*?"

"Psychiatry. You've gone bonkers, so you need a shrink, old chap. Simple."

"Simple, pimple. Tell you what, why don't you bugger off and take the lady with you? Looks to me like *she* needs a whole lot more help than I do," said Jeremy, raising both eyebrows in the direction of von Strumpf, who looked to be suffocating under the pressure of Pete's attentions, seeing as he was clearly beginning to think of her as his new best friend.

"Grrrurg, bleeerg, *Donner und Blitzen*," she said, having taken to weeping and gurgling once Pete began chewing at her grizzled crew cut after he'd swallowed her wig. But however hard she swatted at his muzzle, it made no difference, seeing as Pete reckoned she liked him and this was some form of foreplay. Watching on, Sir Magnus had little option but to agree with Jeremy on the buggering-off issue.

"Just call your pig off," he said.

So Jeremy did. "Pete. Enough," he commanded.

And, surprisingly, Pete obeyed. Stopped trying to eat Frau Professor Doktor Gisela von Strumpf's hair, climbed off her shiny shoes, and shambled back off to his hay corner.

"Okay. Thanks," said Sir Magnus, taking the distraught Freudian by a limp hand and dragging her to the barn's door.

"But I'll be *back*," he shouted over his shoulder as he and von Strumpf made their inglorious exit. "With reinforcements."

"Bring it on," Jeremy called back.

"Nice one, Pete," he then told Pete, but sapped by more human intercourse than a pig could be expected to tolerate on an otherwise perfectly normal day, Pete was already asleep.

~ * ~

"Mmm," Jeremy muttered to himself, pacing up and down the barn once Sir Magnus and the pig-challenged female had bowed out. "Gonna have to make a plan here."

His feisty performance with Pete's helpful intervention was all well and good at seeing off Sir Magnus and the peculiar Frau Doktor von Strumpet on this their first foray onto his territory, but would Jeremy be able to repeat the act? What if the next time Sir Magnus *did* come with reinforcements? Of shrinks all pre-tested and guaranteed porcine-phobia-free? Jeremy's playground bravado was one thing, but there was no good pretending it could frighten off a whole phalanx of Freudians armed to the teeth with not only gloomy ideas about sex and death but probably also hypodermics stuffed with benzodiazepine cocktails sufficient to fell a rabid rhino. There was little either Jeremy or Pete would be able to do to fend off *that* kind of attack, the very kind "Monty"—as Sir Magnus liked to be called whenever prating about his supposed role in government financial support for the Special Forces in Iraq and Afghanistan—which could include not only heavily armed mind benders but also heavily armed soldiers.

Mmm.

The problem was Jeremy didn't *have* a plan, or even the outlines of one, his strategy thus far having extended only to hiding in his barn and having a bit of a think about what choice and madness were or were not. Fine, so he'd decided he *had* been chosen but it wasn't him that was bonkers, it was the world, but no time had yet been devoted to considering his future. Short-termist? Well, you might say so but would *you* have had a plan up your sleeve in Jeremy's circumstances? I don't think so. Just let us say that since the unwelcome visit of Sir Magnus and the peculiar German, the ante had been upped. Think of it as a weather forecast in which the storm warning has been raised from amber to red.

Mmmm.

More pacing. And, irritatingly, Jeremy had taken to counting the number of paces. The mental calculator wouldn't stop: One hundred and thirty-one, one hundred and thirty-two, one hundred and thirty-three, and…so...on and *on*. Jeremy was beginning to feel like one of those health freaks with an electronic gizmo on their arm counting the number of steps they take on their fitness programmes. Crazy was what he used to dismiss them as. But now he was at it too. Did this mean, despite all his best efforts at asserting his sanity, deep, deep down *he* was batshit too and had only been deluding himself?

One hundred and fifty-eight, one hundred and fifty-nine...

"Oh, for *fuck*'s sake," he was saying, leaving off the pacing to bang his head on a flimsy wall for a bit when there came more tapping at the barn door. Only, mercifully this time it was coded. Two taps, pause; three taps, another pause; *six* taps—then silence.

"Barry?" whispered Jeremy, sidling to the door and nestling his ear against it.

"Everything okay in there?" said Barry, parking his wheelbarrow. "Only I seen them geezers what was just with you. Didn't like the look of then, did I? And I was just wondering..."

"*Barry*? Come in. Come *in*," counter-whispered Jeremy, opening the door a crack and peering over the gardener's shoulder at the estate behind him. "Have they gone?"

"The posh bloke and the weepy fräulein bint? Yeah, they're gone. Little chat on the doorstep with your missus and the parents, then they were off in 'is bleedin' great motor, weren't they?"

"Good. *Good*. Quick quick. Come *in*."

"You all right, boss, are you? Lookin' a bit peeky."

"I'm all right...well, sort of. Don't suppose you brought any supplies?"

"The nuts an' berries an' water? Yeah, got them in my barrow, haven't I?"

"Nothing...um...you know...*stronger*?"

Barry grinned.

"You mean, like...?"

Jeremy pinched his jaw between a thumb and a forefinger and rolled his eyes.

Barry smiled.

"You mean the little bottle of nettle homebrew I keep in my satchel for emergencies, boss?"

"Um..."

"Yeah, I got one of those. *Two*, matter of fact."

"Step this way, Bazza," said Jeremy.

'Bazza' was what Jeremy called Barry for fun. Me Jezza, you Bazza was one of their in-jokes. At least self-mockery made Jeremy feel a little better at having been a banker wanker for so long. And Barry got the irony. It evened things out between them.

"So, wazzup, bro? Where're you *at*?" he said, once he'd patted Pete on the head and broken open both bottles of the nettle brandy with significant additives of Barry's own design he refused to disclose to anyone, even Jeremy, claiming so to do would be to open his soul to the world. Which he wasn't going to. No way, Hozay, he wasn't.

It was later, in his cups, that Jeremy spilled the beans to Barry—*all* of them, including the whole choosing/chosen/madness nightmare. And, strangely, Barry seemed to understand.

Four

And what, you will be wondering, was the content of the "little chat on the doorstep" Sir Magnus and Frau Professor Doktor Gisela von Strumpf had with Sophie, Gloria, and Ron before hopping into the "bleedin' great motor"—the midnight blue Bentley 4x4—and being driven away?

Well, Jeremy had been correct in assuming they would be returning with backup. At least Sir Magnus would. Gisela von Strumpf reckoned she would only take part in an advisory capacity from a safe distance, but was prepared to recommend any number of her colleagues with more relaxed attitudes to pigs. And, to that contingent Sir Magnus was prepared to add some chums of his from his time as "financial counsellor" to the army's Special Forces in Iraq and Afghanistan.

"Not the sorts of boys you would want to mess with," he told Sophie, Gloria, and Ron. "No time for nutcases in their business, if you know what I mean. Wouldn't want a nutcase covering your back when there're crazed Islamist terrorists running about, now would you? So these boys sorted out their heads when they went wonky. Do a job on our Jezza *they* would, and no question."

Ron, who had once served six weeks in the Territorial Army, was impressed.

"Absolutely *not*," he said. "Spine, that's what that boy needs. And somebody to knock a bit of sense into it."

"Glad we're on the same page, old chap. Now, look, Frau Professor Doktor von Strumpf and I really should be taking our leave, so..."

But Sir Magnus and von Strumpf weren't allowed to leave until Sophie, after some umming, ahhing and looking sheepish, had unveiled to him the family's own plan for dealing with Jeremy should all other means fail.

"Just in case, narmean? Only as a last re*sort*," she said before wondering what Sir Magnus might think about "doing away" with Jeremy if—and only if, of course—he didn't respond to any of these "treatments" and got sane enough to go back to the bank and start making the kinds of money the family so badly needed to continue their "lifestyles."

"You mean *kill* him?" said Sir Magnus.

"And with any luck his pig too," thought Frau Professor Doktor Gisela von Strumpf, but didn't say so out loud.

"Yes," said Sophie. "Only not, like, *real* killing with a gun. Nothing we'd get blamed for. Just helping him along the way a bit. Some little pills in his nuts and berries that would make it look like suicide. After all, he *is* bonkers, so suicide thoughts would be normal, narmean? So..."

"And his very own *parents* would be agreeable to such skulduggery?" asked Sir Magnus, staring at Gloria and Ron for confirmation.

"We've talked it over with Sophie. Ain't we, girl?" Gloria admitted with faux glumness.

Sophie nodded with faux reluctance.

"And it seems to us, it would be best for all concerned."

"Mainly poor old Jeremy himself," said Ron. "Put him out of his misery. Same way you'd do with a horse after it's broken its leg. The kindest thing to do."

"And all this just for his inheritance?" said Sir Magnus.

Sophie, Gloria, and Ron checked with each other, and nodded.

"And his own *good,* seeing as he's gone bonkers," said Ron. "He's my son and I'll miss him. But a loony's a loony, right? And where're *we* going to get the money from to keep him in a loony bin for the rest of his life? Nowhere, that's where."

Sir Magnus could see Ron's point, but then there was self-interest to take into account too, namely Sir Magnus's which relied heavily on getting Jeremy back to work as soon as possible in order to ensure the bank's, and even more critically Sir Magnus's, continuing financial fluidity.

"It's a plan, chaps," he conceded. "It…is...indeed...a...*plan*, but not a very good one in my view. First little problem, the small matter of the goose and the golden eggs, eh?"

Sir Magnus raised both shaggy eyebrows. "In which scenario we would all be a lot better off with Jeremy alive. In my humble opinion, anyway."

Sophie, Ron and Gloria exchanged dubious glances.

"But if it's poor old Jeremy's life insurance pot you're hoping to get your mitts on," Sir Magnus continued, "I'm afraid you'd have to go whistle if it's his *own* life he's taken. Insurance johnnies are not at *all* keen on coughing up in *those* circs. Indeed, last I heard it was against the bally law."

Sophie, Gloria, and Ron exchanged gloomy glances.

"Soo...meantime, shall we perhaps continue with *my* little scheme? Clearly, should it not work out to the satisfaction of *all* our desires, one might need to consider alternatives, although Jezza's demise would not in my view be the most productive of them. But get him right in the head again and we can all look forward to *dec*ades of productivity before he pops his clogs."

Sophie, Gloria and Ron smiled, albeit rictally.

"Now...I'm afraid I really must dash. Busy, busy, busy. People to see. Places to go, so bysie-bye for now. I'll be in touch. Come on, Gizzly," said Sir Mortimer, taking Frau Professor Doktor von Strumpf by the hand and leading her away to the waiting Bentley.

~ * ~

Not such a *little* doorstep chat then, a pretty wide-ranging one. Just as well that Barry, having overheard it from his weeding duties in a cluster of giant hydrangea bushes around the corner, was in no hurry to pass on *all* of its contents to Jeremy. Poor bloke had enough on his plate already without family death threats to contend with, he reckoned. Sophie's, Gloria's, and Ron's desire to kill their husband/son he would therefore keep schtum about. But, having listened with empathy to Jeremy's bean-spilling version of recent chosen/madness issues and then his worries about further incursions by Sir Magnus, Barry felt obliged to confirm Jeremy's fears of threatened military reinforcements, although he emphasized they wouldn't be actual soldiers but only soldier shrinks.

"Soldier *shrinks*?" said Jeremy.

"Yeah, pals of his who've worked with soldiers in Iraq and Afghanistan who'd gone bonkers after all the killing out there. What's that thing they got again?"

"Post-Traumatic Stress Disorder."

"That's it. Anyway, these blokes' job was to shake 'em up good and proper, so they could get their heads straight and get on with the job of shooting the shit out of the bad guys again."

"Christ. And he's going to unleash those bastards on *me*?"

"That's what he said."

"And how d'you know this, Bazza?"

“Just doin’ the weeds around the corner, wasn’t I? Not listenin’ in on *pur*pose, like. Only he’s got a loud voice, that boss of yours, ain’t he?”

“*Ex*-boss. Tell me about it. Foghorns have nothing on Sir Magnus when exercised. A whole army of new shrinks, then?”

“What it sounded like. Another touch of the nettle brandy?”

Jeremy took the proffered bottle and swigged hard. “I don’t fancy meeting up with *that* bunch,” he said, peering at the empty bottle and shaking it. “Any ideas, Bazza?”

“Well in the circs, if it’s a plan you’re askin’ for, maybe the best thing right now would be for us to get the hell out of Dodge before he comes back with this psycho army of his and shit hits fans.”

“Us? You mean you *and* me?”

“Yeah.”

“You would be prepared to help me? I wouldn’t want to cause *you* any trouble.”

Barry shrugged. “No trouble.”

“Sure, sure, *sure*?”

“Positive.”

“Okay. And leave all this behind?” said Jeremy, gesturing out at the estate and the mansion.

“I reckon you’ll have to if you want to avoid the bother. And after all you told me about that ‘chosen’ business of yours, I don’t reckon you’d miss it.”

Jeremy nodded and smiled. Bazza was right. If he were to live up to his newly discovered version of sanity, the logical next step into the future would be precisely to leave the past behind.

“And where would we be *going*?”

“You’ll see. It’ll be fine.”

“And can Pete come too?”

“Of course he can. Just let’s wait until darkness falls and we shall all take our little trip.”

Five

It was at midnight beneath a gibbous moon, when Sophie, Gloria and Ron were all too pissed to notice or care after a dinner of lamb shank and all the trimmings plus two bottles of Jeremy's special cellar reserve Ruinart Rosé RV champagne, that Barry, Jeremy and Pete made their clandestine exit from the barn. Barry had his extra size, extra deep, four-wheeler wheelbarrow waiting at the door.

"Just hop in and snuggle down," he told Jeremy. "And once you're comfy, I'll chuck some twigs and branches and stuff on top of you. Nobody will ever suspect. Not that there'll *be* anybody out this time of night. All off in the land of nod, as usual."

"And Pete?" said Jeremy, climbing into the niffy barrow and curling himself into a ball.

"Don't worry about Pete. He'll follow me anywhere I tell him. Now you just settle yourself down while I chuck this stuff over you."

"Okay."

And so it was, once satisfied with the camouflaging, that Barry hefted the wheelbarrow's shafts and off they set along the banks of the stream behind the barn, Pete trotting behind, tied to Barry by a long rope. Along the way, Barry sang excerpts from Bob Dylan's "The Times They Are-A-Changin'."

"Oink, *oink*," chorused Pete.

Jeremy would have joined in too had it not been for the need for absolute secrecy. Who knew what rumours might have circulated around the village had any neighbour chanced *not* to be asleep, stopped for a gossip, and come across a singing wheelbarrow?

Across the little bridge over the stream Barry trundled, taking his usual route. Then it was along the hamlet's hundred yard main drag, past the only pub, The Wigeon With Wings, past the ruined Norman church and a couple of cottages, until he reached open fields and, leading through them, the wild-hedged, leafy path that ended at the copse of sycamores in which nestled his white Shepherd's Hut mobile home, which was only marginally larger than Jeremy's barn, although it had an upstairs too. There he laid down the wheelbarrow's shafts, tied Pete to a handrail of the three-step staircase leading up to the porch, and told the fugitive he could come out. The whole trip had taken no more than half an hour.

But there was no response from Jeremy, no sign of movement in the wheelbarrow, nothing.

"Jezza?" he called, delving into the canopy of leaves, branches, and other detritus. God help him if the bloke had suffered a heart attack or something.

But no, once Barry found a foot and waggled it, Jeremy gurgled a bit, sat bolt upright, and took to peering about.

"Bloody hell, must've nodded off," he said, swiping twigs from his hair. "Brilliant ride, Bazza. Really enjoyed it. Like all the weight of the world had been lifted. Wow, is that your *house*?"

"Such as it is. But you'll be safe here. Nobody ever comes without an invitation. Which I rarely extend. And the postman leaves any letters in a hollow oak down the end of the path we just came up. Otherwise it's just me. Oh, and Shirley."

"Your partner...or whatever?"

Barry grinned and pointed at the two forepaws drumming on his front window and the shaggy head with pricked-up ears between them.

"You might think of it that way. My best friend, that's for sure. Only she's a Labrador/Afghan Hound cross. Hi there, Shirl," he said, waving. "Be with you in a minute."

"Raaf, raaf, *RAAAFFFF*," said Shirl. Muffledly.

Jeremy climbed out of his wheelbarrow and waved too.

"D'you reckon she'll get along with Pete?" he said, patting the pig on his pink head.

"'Course she will. Knows Pete already from the couple of times I took her over to your place with me when you and the missus were off in Barbados or wherever. Best of pals, these two, aren't you, Pete?"

"Oink, oink, *OINK*," said Pete, his two front trotters already on the staircase and his curly tail twitching.

"Look, why don't we all go inside and get settled in?" said Barry. "It's late, but a drop or two of my nettle brandy, or the burdock version if you'd prefer, would do us no harm. Plus maybe a slice or two of pizza? What d'you reckon?"

Jeremy reckoned that was a *very* good plan. And so it was that he and Pete took their first steps into a new life.

Shirley was delighted, planting both paws on Jeremy's shoulders—on hind legs she was as tall as him—and slurping at his nose and chin, before saying hi to Pete, who rolled over on his back and kicked his four trotters in the air.

"So, here's to us all," said Barry, after dispensing the burdock brandy Jeremy had opted for as a change. "Let only good things come of this."

"Hear, hear to that. And thanks so much for all your help," said Jeremy.

"*De rien. Je t'en prie*," said Barry raising his glass. "*À ta bonne santé*."

The French surprised Jeremy. But that was only the first of the surprises Barry had in store.

~ * ~

It was two days later when Sir Magnus Montague returned to Jeremy's ex-house and pulled the rope that operated the wind-chime bell. Gloria and Ron had returned to their own place, so a fidgety Sophie was home alone, dusting things that didn't need dusting because Nina, her eager-to-please Bulgarian "housekeeper," did all that. And the vacuuming, and the bathroom scrubbing, and the kitchen parquet floor swabbing, and indoor window cleaning, and the floor-to-ceiling mirrors polishing. And anything else Sophie instructed her to do while the mistress of the house sashayed off to relax in the jacuzzi. But this was Nina's day off, so, with nobody to boss about and her breadwinner having relocated to the barn, Sophie was at a loose end and twitchy.

"Who the bloody hell's *that*?" she muttered, dropping the dustless duster on the bedroom floor, primping her platinum-dyed hair, checking her eyeliner in her vanity case mirror, marching over to the window, and peering out.

Sir Magnus tugged the bell rope again, this time holding it while the wind chimes hit their mega-decibel levels.

"Bloody woman," he grumbled, thrusting a hold-it-right-there hand behind him at his hastily assembled army of Jeremy healers, which consisted of two sex-and-death Freudians, plus two Jungians just in case Jeremy were to be tempted by a spot of the collective unconscious. Behind them stood three further shrinks clothed in battle dress. These were not *real* military personnel because, despite his fictitious boasts of involvement in the "freeing" of Iraq and Afghanistan, Sir Magnus didn't know any real military people, so he'd hired these guys—Kevin, Duncan, and Caitlin—from an out-of-work actors Internet site called JFJA (Jobs for Jobless Actors). He hadn't expected a girl to be included in the deal, but she looked good in khaki and green, even Sir Magnus had to admit, a bloody sight fiercer than Kevin and Duncan, that was for sure. Despite their crew cuts, faux scowls, stick-on war wounds, and toy AK-47s, Kevin and Duncan didn't look frightening at all. Especially not when holding hands, which a furious Sir Magnus had forbidden them never *ever* to do again while they were in his employ or they'd be *fired*, civil partnership or no bloody civil partnership.

"Bloody hell," said Sophie, gawping through her bedroom window. "Who are *that* lot?"

Sir Magnus tugged at the bell rope yet again. Chimey, chimey, chimey it went. Then the rope came off in his hand and the chiming came to an abrupt halt.

Behind him, the troops were getting restless at the delay. And quarrelsome. You know how it is with Freudians and Jungians, how little respect for their rival philosophies they have at the best of times. Well, this bunch—Friedrich and Marcus, the Freudians and Carl and Milly, the Jungians—were already swapping snide glances when first introduced to each other on what Sir Magnus had described as "a joint mercy mission." Now, despite the currency-stuffed brown envelopes in the pockets of their white coats, they were barely on speaking terms.

When Marcus said, "What the fuck's going *on* here anyway?" for example, Carl told him to calm down and shut his gob.

"Calm down? Calm *down*?" sneered Friedrich. "Just the sort of unhelpful, unempathetic, un-thera-*peut*ic bollocks one would expect of a *Jung*ian."

Behind them, Kevin and Duncan continued holding hands despite Sir Magnus's homophobic command. Some bum job *this* was for act*or*s who had once played Hamlet (Duncan) and Iago (Kevin). Okay *only* the once in both cases because of their disastrous first-night performances at repertory theatres in Middlesborough and Slough respectively. But even so, they had trodden the boards. And now they were reduced to *this*.

Caitlin and Milly stared off and tut-tutted. It was Milly who broke the ice.

"Boys, eh? Don't s'pose you've got a ciggie on you?" she asked Caitlin, who said she didn't have a regular one, she rolled her own. But she'd be happy to make them both one.

"With a little extra?" she asked, nodding at the cellophane pouch of weed she took from her pocket. "Always find it helps."

Milly giggled. "Go on then."

To calm the "boys," Caitlin also rolled *them* what she termed "wee mind enhancers" to keep their spirits up and, in the case of the shrinks, bury hatchets. Which, once they were all toking happily, they agreed to do...at least *pro tem*.

By the time Sophie eventually managed to teeter downstairs and open the door and be commanded by Sir Magnus to lead his "army" to the barn to confront Jeremy, his army was in a pretty playful mood. Glassy-eyed and giggly.

It was little wonder, when there came no response from Jeremy even after repeated hammerings, and the soldier shrinks Duncan and Kevin and Caitlin were reluctantly, and now on wobbly legs, dragooned into breaking down the door, that Sir Magnus's grand plan met its fruitless end.

"Come out, come out, you bastard, wherever you are," he called.

And called. And *called*. But to no avail.

"Even the bally *pig*'s gone," grumbled Sir Magnus, striding around the barn, tossing hay bales hither and thither.

Following in behind him, Sophie tugged at her platinum-dyed hair and wept.

"Oh, my poor Jeremy," she snuffled hypocritically. "Where have you *gone*?"

Mind you, she calmed down a bit after a couple of puffs on the spliff Caitlin offered her.

Sir Magnus didn't calm down at all though, far from it. Stamping up and down, he fired all his "trick cyclists" and "military men" on the spot, and then, swearing he'd come back with sniffer dogs, stalked off in a huff, banged on the roof of his waiting midnight-blue Bentley 4x4, opened the passenger door, and told the driver—Boris, a distant cousin of Nina's—to hit the road.

Which would have made for a powerful and dramatic exit for Sir Magnus had Boris's idiomatic English been up to scratch. But, while having an excellent command of the regular everyday aspects of the language, Boris hadn't bothered much with idioms and, interpreting his new master's order literally, leapt from the driver's seat and took to beating the asphalt and shale with his fists, thereby rendering Sir Magnus's departure even less powerful or dramatic.

His by-now pretty well stoned mishmash of shrinks and actors loved it. Even Friedrich, Carl and Marcus linked arms and punched air, while Milly, Caitlin, Duncan, and Kevin hopped about in Kevin's idea of The Dance of the Clowns in the last act of *Midsummer Night's Dream*. Sophie joined in too, leaping about in a manner she considered balletic. Until she fell flat on her face and had to be helped up by Milly.

Understandably, Sir Magnus was apoplectic.

"Get back in the fucking *car* and stopping hitting the road, you fucking foreigner," he shrieked xenophobically. Sir Magnus was a devoted Brexiteer, except when he could hire foreign labour on the cheap, that was.

"What I do wrong?" Boris wanted to know, lifting himself from his knees.

"Just get back in the fucking car and goose the fucking gas," Sir Magnus told him.

"Goose the...?" said Boris, flapping his arms a bit.

Which was when Caitlin, still in faux battle dress, marched over, slung an arm around Boris's shoulders and told him not to worry, everything would be fine if he joined her friends behind her. Pointing at the still cavorting Dance of the Clowns people. So off Boris happily went. He liked dancing.

Then Caitlin turned her fire on Sir Magnus.

"About time *you* fucked off, knobhead," she told him. "Drive your *own* fucking car."

Sir Magnus blustered a bit as is the way with blusterers, but left with little option other than ignominy, climbed into the Bentley's driving seat and slammed the door.

"But I'll be *BACK*," he hollered through the open window before flooring the accelerator and spraying shale all over the place.

Six

While his host had been off in his tiny kitchen fetching the burdock brandy and fiddling with glasses, Jeremy experienced the first of the many surprises Barry had on offer. Wide-eyed, he stood before the floor-to-ceiling shelves lined with tomes from Plato to Bertrand Russell, and even including works—in French—by Frenchie thinkers such as Barthes, Derrida, Baudrillard, Foucault and Cixous normally poo-pooed by the British academy. Although Jeremy had been more interested in the economics part of his Oxford PPE programme than the philosophy or politics, at least he could tell a logical positivist from a poststructuralist. But what was a humble gardener doing with such heavyweights in his meagre home? And this was just the philosophy section. Jeremy hadn't had time to check out the poetry and fiction.

It was close to one a.m. when they took to swigging at the burdock brandy, but after their adventure with the wheelbarrow, neither felt sleepy, although Shirley and Pete had already snuggled down together in Shirley's super-size dog bed at her invitation. You know how it is with animals. When it gets dark, they go to sleep till it gets light again, then they wake up and start all over. If the humans wanted to stay up and chat, that was their business, meanwhile Shirley and Pete were getting their normal shuteye.

"Didn't know you were a..." said Jeremy, carefully avoiding any reference to humility or gardeners but nodding nonetheless at the bookshelves.

"Reader?"

"Um...well...yes."

"As opposed to just a humble gardener?"

Barry smiled, uncorked a fresh bottle of burdock brandy, and refilled their glasses.

"An understandable confusion," he said in a quite different register from the one he'd used while working on Jeremy's estate. "I have lived a number of lives already, and have yet to reach the government's new retirement age."

"How old...?"

"Am I? Sixty-eight."

"You don't look it."

"Thanks. Flattery will get you everywhere."

"And listen, when I mentioned the books, I didn't mean to imply..."

"Of course you didn't, old chap, so don't beat yourself up over it. You were what *you* were, and *I* was the gardener. Okay, I was also "Bazza," for fun. Yet I am *still* the gardener, albeit in a perhaps more metaphorical sense."

Jeremy blinked. "And the books?"

"Are my best friends, possibly my *only* friends. Seen me through some tricky times, those fellows have. Ever read any Voltaire?"

Jeremy shook his head as Barry levered himself from his chair and headed to the Vs in his carefully alphabetised philosophy section.

"Ah, here it is. My old pal *Candide*." He chuckled, taking down the ancient hardback, blowing off the dust and flicking to the last page.

"Many troubles the poor fellow had to endure in his young life: The Seven Years War, the seventeen fifty-five Lisbon earthquake.

But what does he conclude? That '*Il faut cultiver notre jardin.*' Not *quite* the Leibnizian optimism he started out with, but still a way forward, eh? In any case, you may think of this as my own take on life's messiness. Mine, and that of my old mate Voltaire. And so it is, as I said, that I was and still am a gardener."

"And you *were*?"

"A professor of philosophy at the very university *you* once attended, old man. But that was only during the second of my lives and didn't last very long. In feline terms, I'm now nearing my seventh, so we shall see what happens by the time I get to my ninth, eh? It's never too late to learn a new trick or two. And, as I said, if I can help *you* along the way at all, you'd be most welcome. A top-up of the burdock?"

~ * ~

While Pete and Shirley slept the sleep of the innocent, Jeremy and Barry talked through the night. Unaccustomed although he had long been to conversations of an even vaguely abstract or personal nature—all bankers ever talked about was spread sheets, targets, and numbers—it was surprisingly Jeremy who kicked off this part of the conversation. After all, he remembered having confessed his choosing/chosen conundrum to Barry who had seemingly understood, so now it was perhaps Barry's turn to offload.

"And what made you quit Oxford?" he asked.

"I became tired of teaching already hyper-privileged chinless twits how to become even more hyper-privileged chinless twits by developing their 'mental muscles' so they could be adapted to any other subject on the planet. That was the bizarre notion on which the place still operated."

"Twits like me?" Jeremy raised an amused eyebrow.

Barry laughed. "Twits like you, my friend. Only worse. Have you any idea how many prime ministers, foreign secretaries, home secretaries, and chancellors of the exchequer were ex-Oxbridge?

Twits who'd pumped up their mental muscles studying Classics and then turned their big brains to running a country without the first idea how to do so? Twits who'd have trouble distinguishing an idea from a hole in the road and couldn't count beyond single numbers without a calculator, but happily pontificated their way through the Westminster parliament to Downing Street on the back of their Oxbridge 'educations,' the very same sorts of twits who are currently the laughing stock of Europe over Brexit. And who, apart from them, stands to gain most from such privilege?"

"Oxbridge," admitted Jeremy who, through his alumni association, had been invited on a regular basis to contribute large sums to the "refurbishment and re-development" of his alma mater.

"Quite. Enough of which I had soon had once I twigged to this unholy arrangement between the ancient universities, the sons and daughters of the already mega-rich, and ill-gotten power. Bally country run by the posturing buffoons whose 'minds' *I* was helping develop? No, thank you very much."

"So you left."

"With some aplomb, and indeed ephemeral notoriety in the media, as it happens. You know hacks. How half of them *were* educated at Oxbridge and the other half weren't, so both sides make up all manner of defences for their positions. As evinced through my resignation being leaked by a post-doc student of mine and the bastions of the press having a, mercifully short, field day debating whether I was a whingeing wet or a working-class hero. And those were the days well before Facebook and Twitter. Imagine how it would be in *these* story-ballooning times with all their mindless chatter. Anyway, interest in me died down soon enough to be replaced with some war or another. Excuse me just a sec, old man, I think I need a pee. Bladder not working quite the way it once did. Not the full flush, if you know what I mean, although you probably don't."

While Barry was off trying to pee, Jeremy checked out the poetry and fiction shelves in his library and found them to be as representative of top writers as those of the philosophy section. And not just with texts from the Eng. Lit. canon. It also included contributions from the French, the German, the Spanish, the Italian, the Russian...most in translation, but not all.

"Holy shit," he was muttering to himself as he heard Barry returning.

"More friends?" he said, gesturing at the bookshelves.

"Indeed. Always need the balance of the literary and the logical to feed *both* sides of the old brain," Barry replied, struggling with the flies of his khaki gardener's pants. "Fancy a smoke?" he added, taking a battered Old Holborn tin from his pocket.

Jeremy hadn't smoked since varsity where it had been *de rigueur* to smoke, whatever the health Nazis said. Would probably make him dizzy after all these years. But, hey, what was a little dizziness in addition to his other problems? Might even help.

"Sure. That'd be great."

"A fatty or a thinny?" said Barry, extracting his green Rizla cigarette papers.

"A thinny or my head might blow off."

"Okey dokey. Now, where *were* we?"

"You quitting Oxford."

"Right. And you know why?"

"Because of the chinless twit business."

"Yes, the chinless twit business. But that was only the surface reason," said Barry, carefully tamping and rolling Jeremy's "thinny" before handing it over along with a red plastic lighter. "May I quote my old pal Socrates?"

"Quote away."

"'The unexamined life is not worth living,' a concept which failed to penetrate even the most brilliant minds in academe, all of which appeared to be so concentrated on self advancement no room was left for the question: Why exactly am I doing this?"

Jeremy nodded as the tumblers began to fall.

"It was on this basis I found your questioning of the 'choosing/chosen' dyad so interesting," said Barry, head bent as he concentrated on rolling up his "fatty."

"Because you had done the same thing yourself."

"Precisely, old fellow. Took a long hard look at myself and, like you, concluded it was time to put an end to singing from other people's hymn sheets. To examine very carefully the power games secreted in their subtexts. And when I looked, again like you, what did I see?"

"Lies? Fantasies? Delusions?" Jeremy nodded, puffing on his roll-up.

"Exactly so. Belief systems swallowed whole. As you said, folk chosen by the cars they drove, the smartphones they changed every five minutes, the fashionable clothes they wore. All the while fooling themselves into thinking it was *they* who were doing the choosing. It was you who also gave the example of 'speaking' languages as opposed to being spoken by them, if I remember."

Jeremy nodded again. Some memory this bloke had.

"But sadly how else are we to communicate, except through our always already infected grammars and lexises?" Barry continued. "What was it George Bernard Shaw said? 'The single biggest problem in communication is the illusion that it has taken place.' Something of the sort. I now think bees are more capable of sending effective messages than us poor humans. We could learn from bees."

"And the rest should be silence," muttered Jeremy, misquoting a line from the only Shakespeare play he'd ever watched, the one at the local church hall in which Sophie played Ophelia badly.

"I wish it were," said Barry lighting his fatty. "So much better than the gibberish we are given to think of as reason. Once one becomes aware of these things, life changes. It *must*. Which is why you find me where I now am."

Jeremy stubbed out his roll-up in the ashtray Barry proffered for the purpose.

"And you're happier now?"

"Ah, happy. A problematic notion, happiness. You may recall Basil's line in *Fawlty Towers* when asked by his wife, Sybil, whether something was the matter because he wasn't looking very happy. 'Happy?…happy?...Oh, *happy*?' Basil replies delving back into ancient memory."

Barry chuckled and crushed out his own cigarette.

"So rather than 'happy,' let us just say I am at peace with myself and leave it at that, shall we? Now, look, you've had a long day, old chap. I've been gassing for far too long and there's still a lot to think about. So why don't we call it a day and hit the hay?"

"Call it a 'dawn,' maybe," said Jeremy, as slants of light started filtering through the Shepherd's Hut window and Shirley and Pete began showing signs of life.

"Possibly literally *and* metaphorically," said Barry. "In any case, let me show you to your quarters."

Seven

Nobody made a mockery of Sir Magnus Montague and got away with it, and he was going to make damn sure Jeremy Crawford, the maths genius upon whom the bank's future depended, wasn't going to succeed where others had so frequently failed. First the little blighter had gone bonkers and lived in a barn with a pig. Then he refused psychiatric assistance. *Then* he had the audacity to disappear altogether, leaving Sir Magnus the laughing stock of his very own army of shrinks and thespians. At least he'd had the pleasure of firing *them*. But what was his next step to be? That was the million-dollar question.

Back in his City office, he twirled around and around in his high-backed, maroon-leather swivel behind his mahogany Chippendale desk and, sucking on a Havana Tranquillity cigar, rehearsed what he knew so far. He'd checked with Sophie and found that all three of Jeremy's cars were still in the garage, so he couldn't have skedaddled in one of those. Scrub *that* escape plan then. Unless he still had his credit and debit cards on him. But Sir Magnus had also checked that possibility with Sophie. The cards were in his wallet in the bedside table where he always kept them. And, when Sir Magnus dialled, his smartphones only made funny, gurgling, watery noises, so no chance of his having used *those* to facilitate his escape. He was on foot then, which meant he couldn't have got far. Great! So call in the sniffer hounds. But by then, the trail would have gone cold, however many pairs of Jeremy's soiled underpants and socks the hounds were given to sniff. And the last thing Sir Magnus needed after the risible failure of his dimmo hired army was a pack of bemused hounds setting off in different directions sniffing each other's bottoms for want of anything better to do.

So what *was* his next step to be? Call the rozzers, possibly? But no. Too many of Sir Magnus's business dealings were far too shady to get those blighters involved. Ditto for private eyes. Alert the press? Also no, for the same reason. So what *was* he to do? It was a conundrum indeed for a person of Sir Magnus's limited intelligence, and frustration soon set in.

"*FUCKKKK*," he ululated, the Havana Tranquillity having failed to live up to its name.

It was this racket—plus the same expletive being repeated six fold, each time accompanied with what sounded to Julie Mackintosh, Sir Magnus's PA, a lot like headbanging—that persuaded her first to knock tentatively at the door, then, at the seventh ululation, to open it.

And what Julie saw wasn't a pretty sight. Never had she witnessed her boss so *out* of it. Flinging his arms about while nutting the Chippendale and continuing to mutter profanities.

"Everything okay, Sir Magnus?"

You know how it is with us British. How we ask people who've just been run over by a pantechnicon if they're okay, and expect the answer: "Yes, fine, thanks."

But Sir Magnus, his silver expensively coiffed hair all askew, said nothing of the sort.

Instead, he ululated *FUCKKKK* for an eighth time and took to headbanging his antique desk yet again.

"Cup of tea, perhaps?" asked Julie, also Britishly.

But then, from one second to the next, Sir Magnus stopped spinning around in his high-backed, maroon leather swivel and thumping his head on his desk, and shrieked "*EU-RE-KA*!!!" before calming down, taking a cerise silk handkerchief from the top pocket of his navy blue, pin-striped, Savile Row suit jacket and using it to dab at his fevered brow.

"Tea, Julie. Earl Grey. Milk and two sugars as usual," he barked.

"Coming right up, Sir Magnus."

Julie was relieved at having no more than a cup of tea to deal with.

And why had Sir Magnus calmed down so quickly? Because, using what he thought of as his "ingenious" mind, he had, out of nowhere, come up with an extremely cunning ruse. Which was, in his missing-persons search for Jeremy, to by-pass the old-fashioned media whom he didn't want poking their noses into his nefarious business anyway and hit the unregulated *social* ones, which, as he'd learnt from America's new president whom he much admired, was the new-fangled way to get to hearts and minds...in...an...*in*stant. Twittering, he believed it was called. There was only one problem: Sir Magnus didn't know *how* to twitter.

But once Julie came back with the Earl Grey, that could be easily rectified. Julie was young and was sure to know how it worked. He had seen her thumbing her smartphone when she thought he wasn't looking. It would mean taking her into his confidence on the Jeremy issue, of course. But, if the girl wanted a future at the bank, she would know on which side her bread was buttered, wouldn't she?

"*Ju*lie, thanks soo much for the cuppa," he therefore said as his PA came back into the office toting a tray holding both the tea *and* a plate of the Hobnobs she knew Sir Magnus favoured. She was pleased to see him looking less loony.

"Sir feeling a little better, is he?" she said, easing the tray onto the antique Chippendale number like the Savoy-trained waitress she had once been to help pay back her London School of Economics student loan fees. Truth be told, Julie Mackintosh was far better qualified to run a bank than Sir Magnus, but a girl had to climb the greasy pole somehow.

"*Tons* better, thanks, sweetheart."

Julie didn't like being called "sweetheart," but what was she to do?

"Glad to hear it. Anything else I can do for you, sir?"

There were plenty of other things Sir Magnus would have liked Julie to do for him, fellatio top of the list, but currently there were even more pressing issues on his mind. Which was how Julie learned of the unexplained disappearance of Jeremy Crawford with whom she'd had sex, just the once, in a closet during an office party and Sir Magnus's need to locate him soonest. By means of "twittering."

"A tad behind the times on the actual method*o*logy though," Sir Magnus explained while dunking a Hobnob into his Earl Grey. "So one would be *aw*fully grateful for a little help in the matter. *Very* grateful...if you know what I mean," he added, hoisting his hirsute eyebrows. "I'm sure you're cut out to be more than a mere PA, eh, Julie?"

Julie smiled rictally.

"Thought so. Now, if I give you my script, perhaps you'd do me the small favour of twittering it into the Twitter zone or wherever it is twitters go. Ready? Got your instrument on you?"

"Yes, Sir Magnus."

And so it was that Julie took from the secret back pocket in her leggings her latest model Apple iPhone and hit all the sites—Twitter, Facebook, Instagram, Google Plus etc on which she (under the alias Jackie Lamur) had accounts—and posted Sir Magnus's dictated message: *MEGLOMANIAC BONKERS BANKER ON THE LOOSE, MILLION-POUND REWARD FOR INFO LEADING TO HIS CAPTURE*. To which, at Sir Magnus's behest, she attached the photo of a smiling Jeremy taken from the bank's in-house "Top Troopers" page.

"That should do it, sir. Now we just wait for responses."

"Wonderful, sweetheart! Fan*tas*tic," said Sir Magnus, extending an arm to stroke Julie's bottom. "I don't suppose...?"

"Oops, I think that's my office phone," said Julie, scuttling from the room. "Good luck on the Jeremy front."

A shame, from his point of view, that Sir Magnus hadn't thought through all the implications of employing the Internet, naively believing it was inhabited by kindly folk ready and willing to help him in his cause. A bad case of "duh," Julie could have told him, but it was no good telling Sir Magnus *any*thing when his dander was up.

~ * ~

It was at the behest of Gloria and Ron, plus her parents, Vince and Val, and two of Jeremy's squash club buddies, Harry and Jonah, that Sophie called the police to report her husband missing. Sir Magnus had proudly told them of the tweet announcing Jeremy's disappearance and insisted that under no circumstance should they involve the law, but none of them was happy with that.

"No good leaving it to the Internet, Babes," said her father, "Honest" Vince, the local bookmaker and small-time crook. "Full of bleedin' nutters *it* is. Ain't that right, Val?"

His wife flicked back her shoulder-length, peroxide blonde hair. "Spot on, Vincey. Tell any old story for a million quid, some of them shysters would. *Gawd* knows."

Gloria and Ron nodded in agreement.

"Most of 'em even nuttier than our Jeremy," said Ron. "And could be foreigners to boot. All over the bleedin' *world* those messages go. China, Russia, India, North Korea…"

"Right. And look what happened in the US," said Jonah, at which Sophie, Gloria, Vince, and Val exchanged perplexed looks seeing as their preferred view of any news outside village gossip was "noise in the system." This had even included 9/11, never mind the 2016 election.

"A tweeting dickhead president elected by *Russians*," Harry explained.

"And by even more tweeting dickheads in…his...*own*...country." Jonah was on a roll. "Populism it's called. And look where it's got *us*. How else would Brexit ever have happened?"

But neither Sophie's parents nor her in-laws had any answer to that—more noise in the system—and so didn't encourage Jonah or Harry to continue with their exegesis. For them, it was enough to establish that the Internet was infested with dangerous lunatics, or, as Gloria put it: "Nasty spidery people who try to con you out of your money with fake emails."

"Right, that's it, then," said Vince, passing Sophie his phone. "So it's agreed we call the cops. And make sure you cry a lot, Babes. Coppers don't listen unless you cry a lot. Think you're wasting police time."

*Any*way, to Sir Magnus's fury when he found out some days later, that's how it was that Sophie came to call the local cop shop.

It was shaven-headed, heavily bearded, six-foot-three PC Dennis "Shorty" Dawkins who picked up.

"Fanbury Police. 'Ow may I be of hassistance?"

Were weeping an Olympic sport, Sophie would have bagged the gold medal. All her (failed) actress cravings she put into the performance—wailing, snuffling, back-snorting, spluttering, eye-dabbing even though she wasn't on camera, the whole shebang.

"Problem, missus? Pussy got stuck up the chimney or sunnink?" said an unimpressed Dennis. "In which case, it's the fire brigade you need," he added, all set to hang up after a long day of tedious village crime fighting shared between him and his fellow officer Billy "Dustbin" McCann—Fanbury could only afford two policemen. Silly old biddy, Hattie Duchamps, known to the local cops as "Batty Hattie" at Chestnut Cottage reckoning she'd spotted an ISIS terrorist pissing up an oak tree in her garden. Ninety-four-year-old egregious grump, "Earl" Montmorency Fortague calling to tell Dennis and Billy that if one more "urban interloper" cyclist came within six inches of the 1958 Rolls Royce parked outside his front gate and almost scratched it, he would feel obliged to shoot him with the Boer War rifle he'd proudly inherited from the first earl of Fanbury, Earl Basil. The list of geriatric time wasters went on…and on, and *on*. Fanbury was a small village, which was boring Dennis and Billy into practical catatonia. Both had applied for transfers to *any*where in the vicinity with proper crime.

Faced with Dennis's unempathetic response, Sophie cranked up the decibels.

"*WAH, WAH, WAH, WOOH, WOOH, WOOH,*" she went, until Vince nudged her and whispered, "Time to *say* something, Babes. If that's Dennis you're onto, crying's not his bag. Should've warned you. Sorry."

So, only microseconds before Dennis hit the Quit Call button, transferred all further incoming calls to NAT (the Nighttime Assist Team), and closed up the cop shop for the night, Sophie got the slimmest of windows to tell of her husband Jeremy's disappearance.

Dennis sighed. "Go on then. But be quick about it."

Which was when Sophie, resurrecting the (poor-going-on-zero) thespian skills she'd had before Jeremy Crawford lured her from a promising stage and TV career with his money, moved swiftly from the horrorshow to the blunt and pithy.

Dennis was stopped in his tracks.

"Say that again, missus."

"I just told you, my banker husband went bonkers, lived in our barn with a pig called Pete for a bit, but...now...he's...disapp*ear*ed."

"Description?" said a newly interested Dennis, pulling a smartphone from his Kevlar vest and jabbing at it. For, yes, being a social media addict, the "megalomaniac bonkers banker" story resonated somewhere in the depths of Dennis's normally switched-off mind. And, when Sophie gave Jeremy's description and it matched exactly the pic of Jeremy Crawford Jackie Lamur had attached to Sir Magnus's dictated post, little bells distantly chimed in Dennis's otherwise blank mind and he became interested. Nothing Dennis would have liked better than a million quid bung in a brown envelope *and* promotion to *D*C for having cracked the case of the missing megalomaniac bonkers banker. Better not to tell Billy McCann anything about it, though. A million quid shared two ways was, after all, only *five* hundred thousand quid each.

"I'll be right over," he whispered, signalling to Billy it was time he packed his bags and went home.

Ron, Gloria, Vince, and Val breathed sighs of relief when Sophie passed back the phone to her father and announced her triumphant result.

"He'll be right over," she said.

Eight

It was only as the result of Barry's interest in worldwide flora and fauna that he and Jeremy also became aware of the Jackie Lamur post. Philosophically, Barry had no time for social media, particularly given recent evidence of their pernicious effect on the erstwhile reliable processes of representative democracy. By "the moron" in the White House's psychotic use of Twitter, he was particularly exercised. Outraged, in fact, especially once the addiction had spread to politicians across the globe. Even to those of his once beloved Labour Party, which he had recently quit in protest at its use of such tools as a means to achieve cult status for its leader. No, no, Barry was no fan of what he termed "technology for zombies." Unlimited choice, sharing, openness and connectivity it seductively offered, but who was *really* doing the choosing? Especially given the recent revelations of Facebook's collection of personal data and the way it had been used to sabotage elections.

Nonetheless, and despite these visceral misgivings, Barry remained a user, although no longer of Facebook. Why? Because he couldn't bear to lose the remaining contacts he'd made all around the world as a compulsive photographer of local plants and animals using the latest Canon DLSR. Repulsive though the medium was, it had provided him with a unique means of sharing his pics with "friends" all around the globe and, in exchange, seeing theirs. His photo app was full to bursting with snaps taken by fellow enthusiasts from even the remotest of regions of the planet, regions Barry would never visit if he lived two hundred years. How he loved the insights he gleaned from these exchanges. And how proud he had been when *his* images of a badger sett in construction had won plaudits from even professionals in the field. In this regard, and this regard *only*, Barry found the activity an addition to his understanding of the aspects of life on earth that most interested him, his excuse being he chose *it* for specific benign purposes rather than it choosing *him* for random *mal*ign ones. And never had he posted personal information beyond the very basic requirements.

Even so, he couldn't resist the odd peep at other folks' pages, just in case there was anything he should know about. And Jackie Lamur was one of his favourites. A girl from Liverpool who could make him laugh even in some of his darkest moments, and Barry had had plenty of those.

"Hey, Jezza, take a look at *this*," he said, as the pair settled down to breakfast after returning to the Shepherd's Hut from taking Pete and Shirley for their morning walkies.

"Bloody *hell*," said Jeremy, peering at the screen announcing the million pound reward for info on the whereabouts of the escaped megalomaniac bonkers banker. "That's *me*," he added, with a sharp intake of breath, pointing at the picture clipped from the bank's in-house "Top Troopers" page. "What the *fuck*?"

Barry raised a perplexed eyebrow. "Hard to say, but there're thirty-four thousand, eight-hundred and sixty-two hits already."

(Including one from Dennis "Shorty" Dawkins using the sobriquet "Betty" and saying she was "on the case.")

"According to this, you've already been sighted in Minsk, Sausalito, Prague, St Ives, Beijing, Mumbai, The Outer Hebrides, and..."

"*Christ*. Any clue who posted this crap?"

“Jackie Lamur. She’s a regular.”

Jeremy blinked. “Jackie *Lamur*?”

“You’ve read her too?” said Barry, surfing the site for more places Jeremy had been spotted—Helsinki, Cairo, Knotty Ash, Kansas City, Knotty Ash again...

Jeremy swallowed hard and nodded. “Yes. Her real name is Julie Mackintosh. Jackie Lamur is her alias.”

“And you know this how?”

“Because she’s PA to Sir Magnus fucking Montague, my ex-boss.”

“Ooops.”

Marie in Montmartre, Fritz on the Kurfürstendamm in Berlin, Anon in Knotty Ash *again*, Salah in Cairo...

“Ooops is right. The old bastard has no idea how to use the Internet, so he must have got Julie to do it for him,” said Jeremy, calming a little. “No doubt his idea of a clever plan to scare me back onside after the shrink idea had failed and I’d scarpered. What he won’t understand is what ‘viral’ means and the can of worms *that* can open.”

Jaime in Barcelona, Norman in The Maldives, Gianfranco in Naples, Anon in Knotty Ash yet *again*.

“Still, at least we now have a clue as to who’s behind all this,” said Barry, still scrolling.

“For all the good it will do if I’m to become the subject of a million-pound manhunt. And now *you’re* sucked into this nonsense too.” Jeremy sighed. “I’m sorry. Maybe the ‘chosen’ business was just a piece of foolishness and I should have stayed put and got on with it.”

“I think not, old chap. ‘Should haves’ don’t count. The past *is* a foreign country and there’s no point in revisiting it and wondering how one might have behaved differently and to what end. The conditional perfect is a pointless tense and should be elided from grammar. We are where we are and that's all that matters. No good trying to re-live what we have already lived and attempting somehow to rearrange it. That way only madness lies. And you are *not* mad. Remember?"

Jeremy smiled.

"And as for my part in this little adventure, you've no need for regrets. Who knows, it could be fun," said Barry, still scrolling.

Mike in Montreal, Isabel in Tenerife, Gunnar in Reykjavik, Samantha in The Scilly Isles...Anon in Knotty Ash...

"Still, strange of the old bastard to use the social media. You'd have thought his first option would be to call the cops."

Jeremy shook his head. "Not him. *Far* too much to hide. A major player in the two-thousand-and-eight banking fiasco and as yet still undetected."

"And you, Jezza?"

Jeremy winced. "I was his right-hand man. That's why he needs me. For my famous maths, but also to stop me singing."

"I hadn't realised."

"Yup, Bazza. You have a reprobate on your hands. So sorry to have landed you in this mess, like I said."

"No worries, old fellow. Between us we'll find a way."

Titch in Toronto, Dan in Damascus, "Horse" in Brooklyn NYC, the moron in The White House in Washington DC, Kitty in Nebraska, Giorgio in Calabria, Jim—named at *last*—in Knotty Ash.

"We'll just need to put our thinking caps on, that's all. And, to be square with you, Jezza, at my time of life there's nothing a chap needs more than a bit of a challenge. Now, how about a nice bowl of my famed porridge with honey-roasted peanuts? Going to need to keep our strength up."

Jeremy laughed for the first time in a long time. The devil's laughter, was it? He no longer cared, just dipped his spoon into Barry's special breakfast and took a bite.

"Yum," he said after the first mouthful.

~ * ~

Sophie, Vince, Val, Gloria, Ron, Jonah, and Harry were astonished to find that when PC Dennis Dawkins said he'd be "right over," he'd meant "right over." Once he and Billy McCann had switched all incoming calls to Nighttime Assistance and closed down Fanbury Police Station, he'd told Billy he'd see him tomorrow then feigned his own departure by climbing on his bike and starting to pedal. When Billy was safely out of sight on his way back to Mrs McCann and their brood of mini-McCanns, however, Dennis—aka Facebook's "Betty"—had swiftly backpedalled, dismounted, stowed his bike in its shed, fired up Fanbury's only cop car, and, with blue lights flashing and wah-wah-wahs on full blast, burnt rubber to Jeremy's ex-mansion, before which he skidded to a stop, showering gravel all over the place.

"Bloody hell," said Vince, watching through the lounge curtains as Dennis climbed from the car, smoothed down his uniform, and headed to the door. "Never seen The Dork in such a hurry before."

"The Dork" was what Vince called Dennis, both because he thought it a witty take on "Dawkins," and because he reckoned Dennis to *be* a dork, given he'd never sussed even a single one of Vince's shadier bookmaking schemes. Mind you, so much the better for Vince.

"Looks like he's got ants in his pants," said Val, as Dennis marched to the door and pulled the chime bell rope, which was still broken because nobody had thought to fix it after Sit Magnus's yanking.

"I'll let him in," said Sophie. "This is my house and I'm the one who called."

"S'cuse us if you wouldn't mind," chorused Jonah and Harry as they sidled out of the lounge into the abutting kitchen area, dimmed the lights over the six-foot-long "eating island," and checked the back door for an escape route through the solarium/conservatory and into the "garden." Why? Because, upstanding citizens though they might have appeared to be, there were certain little past misdemeanours—Internet banking fraud, for example—Jonah and Harry did *not* want broadcast around their new hideaway in Fanbury. It was one thing for them to agree to the coppers finding their pal, Jeremy, but quite another to meet one of them. Not when their mug shots were still on Scotland Yard's computer.

"Missus Crawfish?" Dennis said as Sophie opened the door.

"Craw*ford*"

"Ah-*hah*," said Dennis, taking a notepad from his top pocket and scribbling at it sinistrally. "You called about your missin' 'usband. Mind if I come in?"

Sophie stood aside and obliged. Never having had dealings with the local constabulary, she'd not before encountered Dennis and reckoned he was pretty funny- looking for a policeman, what with the bushy beard and everything. But then she supposed practically all young men had to have beards nowadays in order to prove they *were* men. Still, at least he was tall. She liked her policemen tall. There were far too many undersized ones knocking around, in her opinion.

"This way, Detective," she said.

"*Con*stable, missus."

"Never mind. Do take your boots off and follow me. I'll introduce you to the family."

"*Boots* off?"

"House rule. We don't allow muck on the carpets."

Dennis frowned. Given the nature of the socks he hadn't changed for two days, this wasn't going to be a good start to the investigation.

"Don't worry. We have guest slippers," said Sophie as Dennis struggled with his laces. "Oriental to fit all sizes," she added, peering down at his immense feet. Still, to be tall—and therefore reliable—she assumed a person also needed big feet. For balance.

"Blue or red?"

"Blue. To match the uniform, innit?"

"Mmm, I like a man with dress sense," said Sophie as Dennis finally unbooted himself and, as fast as possible, slipped his size twelves into the slippers Sophie held out at arm's length while averting her nose. "*Now* you can follow me and meet the family."

And so it was that PC Dennis "Shorty" Dawkins made his way into the luxurious depths of the Crawford mansion.

"Careful not to bang your head on the chandeliers," Sophie advised him along the way. "They were very expensive."

First the boots, now the head, bit of a bleedin' bossy bitch this Missus Crawfish, Dennis reflected, inching his way along behind her, head bowed.

"*Women*," he muttered *very* sotto voce as he followed Sophie. Bloody glad *he*'d never got married. Especially not to Gladys, the barmaid at The Wigeon With Wings for whom he'd once carried a torch. Wonderful bottom, and the sorts of knockers a man would pay money to jiggle—but finicky. Pernickety even. Beer mats always needing to be re-arranged on the bar, beer-pump handles always having to be wiped for fingerprints, glasses so clean they were unhealthy. No, no, a fine bedmate Gladys would've made, but not a wife.

"Hi there, Dennis," said Vince, choking back any dork-related slips-of-the-tongue when the copper finally made it into the mega-lounge. "So glad you could spare the time to join us in our hunt for Jeremy. Do take the weight off your feet," he added gesturing at a faux Louis Quinze green velvet armchair.

"Jeremy?" said Dennis, lowering himself carefully onto the seat for fear of breaking it.

"Sophie's husband? The missing one? The reason you're here? Name of Jeremy?" said Vince, still fighting off dork references.

"Ah-*hah*, Je-re-my," said Dennis, taking the notebook from his top pocket and again scribbling sinistrally at it. "So...and his whereabouts are now unknown, you say?"

"Unknown," Vince confirmed.

"And, apart from bein' our village bookmaker, you are?" said Dennis.

"Vince, Sophie's dad. And this is her mum, Valerie," said Vince, wafting a hand at Val, who was looking pale and distressed as instructed by Vince.

"Okey dokey," said Dennis, scribbling some more. "And these?" Nodding across at Gloria and Ron, who were also looking pale and distressed as instructed by Vince.

"We're Ron and Gloria, Jeremy's poor parents," said Ron.

"We want him back. Wuh-we nuh-*need* him back," said Gloria, dabbing at her eyes.

"Right then. An' Missus Crawfish is called Sophie, I deduce."

"Correct, Constable," said Ron. "Our darling daughter-in law. And it's Craw*ford*."

"Ah-hah," said Dennis, turning pages in his notebook, jabbing his pen at them, and thinking, "Christ, what with the Sophie bint as a missus an' this lot as mums an' dads, no bloody *wonder* the poor bloke did a runner."

"And Jeremy was last seen?"

Which was when Dennis learned from Vince Jeremy hadn't actually been *seen* by any of them for two whole weeks, during which time he'd been living in a barn with a pig called Pete and refusing anybody admittance.

"*Pete*?" asked Dennis, pen poised.

"Pete," Sophie confirmed. "We'd been planning on eating him, but now it's too late."

"Pete has vanished too?"

"Yes. Been spirited away."

"Jeremy *and* Pete? *Both* of them 'spirited away'?"

"Yes."

Dennis's largely ineffective brain was starting to hurt.

"By demons?"

"Wuh-we duh-don't nuh-*know*," said Gloria. "Tell the nice policeman about Sir Magnus, Sopha." That's what Sophie's mother called her daughter: Sopha.

So, while Dennis scribbled sinistrally, Sophie recounted at length both failed attempts by Jeremy's boss Sir Magnus Montague and his team of trick cyclists to heal Jeremy's evidently deranged mind.

"And the second time, huh-he wuh-wasn't even *there*," she wailed.

"No Jeremy? No Pete either?" said Dennis.

"Nuh-*no*. *Both* of them...*gone*."

"An' this Sir Magnus geezer? Wanna spell that for me? Might need to contact him."

And so it was that Dennis "Shorty" Dawkins learned the family version of Jeremy Crawford's disappearance. Not that he didn't already know Jeremy *had* disappeared, of course. As "Betty" on Facebook, he already knew about and coveted the million quid reward for clues leading to his discovery. But it was always good to get details from the horses' mouths.

Not that Dennis was much impressed by *these* horses. Snobby dipshits, he reckoned. And again, as he pocketed his notebook, made his excuses, headed back to Fanbury's only cop car and burnt rubber away from the estate, he felt sympathy bordering on empathy for poor old Jeremy. And Pete. Dennis had always rather liked pigs. But, wherever they were, at least they were safe from their loony family.

Nine

Sir Magnus Montague was startled and baffled at the global response to "Jackie Lamur's" plea for information as to Jeremy's whereabouts when Julie plugged him into his little-used desktop iMac and showed him her results.

"Bloody *hell,*" he said as she scrolled up and down from "Maxim" in Minsk to "Jim" in Knotty Ash and back again. "Stop going so damn *fast*, woman, you're hurting my eyes."

"I thought sir would be pleased," said Julie, faux pouting. "What with it going viral and everything. So many to choose from."

"Viral? Sounds like a bally disease. And sir is *not* pleased. Sir is confused."

"Sir con*fus*ed?"

"Yes," Sir Magnus was forced to admit, grabbing at his box of Havana Tranquillities. "How the hell am I supposed to pick any *one* from this lot? And you're not telling me Jeremy bloody Crawford has been all over the *world* in the last seven days. What am I supposed to think, that he's Superman or something? Some damn bollocks this Internet business has got to be. Talk about finding needles in *hay*stacks."

Julie shrugged and stared off. "Only doing my best for you, sir."

"Well, your best isn't bally good enough!"

"Sorry, sir."

Sir Magnus held a Havana Tranquillity to his ear, twizzled it between a thumb and a forefinger, then, satisfied it was up to scratch, cut off its end with a Donatus Gold-plated V- cutter, stuck the cigar in his mouth, and fired it up with a St Dupont Slim 7 lighter. Julie wafted her hands before her eyes and coughed thespianly, but Sir Magnus puffed on regardless.

"And where *is* this Knotty Ash place that keeps coming up? One has heard of most of the other places. But Knotty *Ash*?" he said from within the cumulus of Tranquillity smoke swirling around his head. "Sounds like some joke town."

Julie went on with the hand wafting but, having grown up in Liverpool, she was also smiling. Sometimes wished she'd never left the place. And in a way Sir Magnus was dead right. It *was* a joke town. You had to be a comedian to live there, some said. But not a day went by without her remembering the times when things had gone wrong and somebody would come up to her, throw an arm around her shoulders and say, "C'mon, love, give us a smile and you'll be all right. If you don't laff, you cry, right?" And she'd laffed, and every time the pain had gone away. When did that ever happen in London? Never, that was how often. Everybody too busy, busy, busy and locked up in themselves. Well, more fool them.

"It's a suburb of Liverpool," she said. "Made famous by Ken Dodd. Remember him?"

Sir Magnus frowned. "Ken...?"

"Dodd, the comedian with the big teeth and the tickling stick? The one with the diddymen and more than his share of happiness?"

Sir Magnus stopped frowning and, for once in his life, chuckled.

"Oh, *Doddy*," he said. "I rather *liked* him. Completely off his trolley, of course, but, how shall I put it...?"

"Funny?"

"That's it. *Funny*. A proper clown. And he's a Knotty Asher, is he?"

"Was. He's dead now. But yes he was a Knotty Asher all right. Born and bred. Wouldn't leave the place for a big clock. They made him a sir before he died."

"A *sir*? Like me?"

"Like you, Sir Magnus."

"Good Lord. Still, it takes all sorts, I suppose. *Any*way, back to the point at hand. Namely what we are to *do* with this deluge of improbable information concerning the whereabouts of Jeremy Crawford? Do you *know* this 'Jim' chappie from Knotty Ash, for example? Could he be a reliable source? Or is he perhaps just another diddlyman?"

"*Diddy*man. Too early to say, sir," said Julie, who had no Knotty Ash 'Jim' in her address book. Mind you, as far as she was aware, she hadn't befriended 'Maxim' in Minsk either. Or any of the other oiks who'd swamped her pages with self-evident lust for a million pounds. Some hacking must have gone on somewhere, but Julie had no idea how or where.

"Perhaps sir would just like to leave the problem to me?" she suggested. Betty in Fanbury, whose post had only just pinged into the list, looked like a person of interest, for example. Especially as Fanbury was where Jeremy had lived before disappearing. But then Jim in dear old Knotty Ash was also tempting.

"Indeed sir would," said Sir Magnus, as the Havana Tranquillity this time had its desired effect and he flopped forwards across his mahogany Chippendale desk, whispered "aaaahh," and took to snoring for England.

"Sleep tight, bossy boy," whispered Julie, heading for the door.

~ * ~

After they'd put their thinking caps on, Jeremy and Barry debated at length Jeremy's dilemma in face of the deluge of Internet interest in his whereabouts, which had by then spread to the conventional media. After all, newspaper editors aren't proud when it comes to hooking a big fish in case somebody else hooks it first. They too have smartphones and aren't the types to ignore a viral when it smacks them in the face, especially if it can be hitched to a human-interest story. Within a day or so of it airing, therefore, Jackie Lamur's post and its global response had been spotted. And tweaked a little to give it more oomph. In its first revised version, Jeremy became the lone parent of six children whose drug-addicted mother had abandoned the family home to become a porn star in America, where she was hoping to have sex with the madman in the White House. And now the bonkers banker had done a runner too, the six children were in the care of a grandmother, herself suffering from dementia.

But that was only the first tweak, featuring as a mere taster in a few inside pages.

Once *The Daily Truth*'s editor, Simone de Vérité, spotted the legs such a story might have, however, it took on a whole new—international—dimension. No more bother with such fripperies as children and porn star wives for Simone. No siree. Instead she was able to reveal as headline news that she and her team of "undercover experts" had been able to link the disappearance of megalomaniac bonkers banker in question to not only the 2008 banking crash but also ("tellingly") to Maxim in Minsk who, it was believed, had CIA-confirmed connections to Bratva, Russia's Mafia, and thereby direct links to the Kremlin.

Similar and yet more inventive interpretations were to follow in *The Daily Grunt*, *The Sunday Planet* and other organs across the nation, all of them directly linking the unexplained vanishing of what had become the "renegade *Trotskyite* megalomaniac bonkers banker" to Russian president Igor Ripurpantzov himself. According to these accounts, not satisfied with the Internet fiddling of the election of a paranoid narcissist to The White House and the destabilization of the UK's age-old parliamentary democracy by flooding the social media with pre-Brexit referendum bot-generated pro-Leave posts, Ripurpantzov's quest for world domination had sunk to the level of tempting into his inner circle Britain's top talent, possibly by doping them. *The News* described the phenomenon as "BRITAIN'S NEW BRAIN DRAIN," while *The Morning Scrutiny* asked: "IS THE BONKERS BANKER THE BURGESS AND MACLEAN FOR THE TWENTY-FIRST CENTURY?" and, in similar vein, *The Evening Informer* wanted to know: "IS THE BONKERS BANKER THE NEW EDWARD SNOWDEN?"

And so on...and on...and *on* as the story took flight and was further amended to suit the tastes of readers in places as far flung as Australia where normally it was only cricket or rogue kangaroos that made the headlines. Back home even supposedly balanced heavyweight titles and respectable TV and radio channels pounced on the story, careless of the danger of yet again arousing the same xenophobic angst that had caused voters to rally to such specious concepts as "Britishness" and "sovereignty" in the 2016 Brexit referendum.

"Some imaginations these guys have," said Jeremy as he and Barry surfed the net for updates on his situation.

Barry nodded. "But possibly not so far off the mark. Who would bet *against* the Ruskies having had a cyber pop at Western democracies and then trying to lure away their top talent? Was it an American who built the first atomic bomb or was it an imported ex-Nazi?"

"Why *me* though?" said Jeremy. "All I wanted was a life away from my old life. And now *this*."

"To sow uncertainties, promote fake news, and sell newspapers, my friend. You are simply the latest convenient catalyst for a good story. You know the other meaning of that word, don't you?"

"Lie."

"Exactly. And you have been chosen as the unwitting subject, object, whichever way you want to look at it, of someone else's narrative."

Jeremy sighed. "Again?"

"Afraid so. Just let us say you have been framed as the latest player in the age-old game called: 'Sod the truth if porkies can make more money.'"

"Just when I was trying to be the *real* me. And now I get to be someone *else's* toy?"

"It seems that way."

"Fuck."

"Don't worry, old chap. News never lasts longer than a femtosecond these days. Should the moron in the White House get himself nuked overnight and suspicion fall on either the pudgy bloke with the funny hair in Pyongyang or the Kremlin's latest version of Stalin, you'll be yesterday's news just...like...*that*..." Barry snapped his fingers. "And be free to plough your own furrow. Won't he, Pete?"

"*Oink*," said Pete.

"Another shot of the nettle brandy, old chap?"

Jeremy sighed and held out his glass.

Ten

Dennis "Shorty"/"Betty" Dawkins wasted no time in his hunt for the internationally sought fugitive megalomaniac bonkers banker, Jeremy Crawford. The very next morning, claiming to Billy McCann, he was off in search of the egregious local poacher, Squiffy O'Donnell. He freed from their kennel his ace sniffer dogs, Colin, an English Cocker Spaniel, and Hans, a German Shepherd, leashed them up, and set off. Ostensibly he was heading in the direction of Squiffy's caravan, but his real goal was the Crawford mansion again, this time in search of clues.

Having been caged up and not done any proper sniffing for a long time, Colin and Hans were excited, along the way leaping up trees where they suspected squirrels may be hiding, sniffing at fallen branches and leaves then pissing on them. And, embarrassingly for Dennis, although mercifully for him no villagers were watching, on one occasion yanking so hard on their restraints in pursuit of a cat called Maxine sitting stock still in the middle of the lane staring at them, that their master fell flat on his face and was dragged ten metres along the tarmac before he could regain control.

Maxine, still sitting sphinx-like with the dogs only inches from her face, thought it was very funny as Dennis finally managed to scramble to his feet and holler at Colin and Hans they were *VERY*

BAD BOYS who wouldn't be taken walkies any time again soon unless they behaved themselves.

"No treats for *YOU* unless you be*HAVE*," he told them, as Colin and Hans did their best to look repentant by sitting on their bottoms and giving Master the doe-eye.

Maxine shook her head and stalked off into a hedgerow, saying "*Dogs*!"

The problem Dennis faced, however, was that, despite their misdemeanours, Colin and Hans refused to budge unless they were given treats, both of them eyeing Dennis's Bonios-For-Good-Dogs satchel meaningfully.

"But you haven't *been* good dogs. You've been very *bad* dogs," Dennis explained, reading their eyeballing.

Colin and Hans exchanged puzzled glances that translated as: "Some weirdo, this human. What's a dog sup*posed* to do when it sees a cat? Go up and say, 'Hi there, Cat. How you doin' today?'"

The other problem Dennis faced was that, despite being their supposed master, he wasn't actually very masterful at all. Never had been. The dogs knew that; *he* knew that. And so it was he relented, dug into his Bonios-For-Good-Dogs satchel, and, breaking all the rules of reward-for-good-behaviour dog training, gave Colin and Hans one each.

The rest of trip to the Crawford mansion was to all intents and purposes a mobile picnic for Colin and Hans. Every three paces they would sit, beg, and be given a new Bonio. But at least Dennis and his "highly trained sniffer dogs"—as he introduced Colin and Hans to Sophie when they eventually arrived at the Crawford mansion—were on hot on the trail of her errant husband.

Well, hot-*ish*. Actually more like lukewarm. Fine, the dogs sniffed around the barn picking up scents of its previous occupants for a bit, but once outside again, they lost much of their interest and took to rambling about the estate, pissing on plants.

"Omi*god*, *stop* them doing that on my begonias, will you?" Sophie barked, reminding Dennis of the irritating 'no boots in the house' line she'd come out with on his last visit.

"They're checking," he said. "Maybe they've picked up a trace of your 'usband. Maybe *he* pissed on the begoonias too."

"Beg*o*nias."

"Whatever."

"And Jeremy *never* did his business on begonias."

"Not even late at night when you were asleep? Hard to tell *what* a bloke might do when he's gone bonkers. Plus there's the pig to think of, innit?" said Dennis as Colin and Hans took an unnatural interest in a blackberry bush and pissed on that too.

"Oh...my...*GOD*. We'll *never* eat those now. I was going to get the cook to make a pie out of them. With apples," said Sophie pointing out a Bramley tree in which Colin and Hans, following what they took to be her instructions, also took an unnatural interest in and pissed on too.

Losing the will to live, let alone any faith in Dennis and his filthy dogs having a snowball's chance in hell of finding Jeremy, Sophie faux wept, stamped a foot, tugged her hair theatrically, turned, stormed off back to the mansion, and slammed the door, causing the newly repaired door chimes to start ding-a-ling-a-linging at full volume.

"Hmm," said Dennis. "Not the best of starts, boys."

Which Colin and Dennis took as a sign of them needing more Bonios-For-Good-Dogs.

"Hardly any *left* in here," said Dennis, ferreting about in his satchel. "And we've got a whole morning's sniffing ahead of us."

But Colin and Hans weren't buying any of that old "hardly any left" bollocks, and remained resolutely on their bottoms with their tails swishing at the grass. Obediently.

"All right then. But if I give you these last two..."

Colin and Hans smirked at each other, knowing full well Master was bluffing and there were at least another *twenty*-two hidden in the satchel.

"...You'll have to promise to be *good* boys and do what Master tells you."

"Raaf, raaf," chorused Colin and Hans, sitting up straight.

Mind you, even when they left the Crawford estate and headed to the stream along which Dennis surmised Jeremy might have beaten his retreat, there was still no response from the dogs. More squirrel chasing, more pissing on vegetation—mainly ferns and suchlike—but little indication of a human or porcine trail to follow. And, let's be quite clear about this, Colin and Hans *were* in fact pretty expert in such matters. Colin had once led Billy McCann to a heroin stash worth two million pounds in a disused warehouse, and Hans had a gold medal for his part in a counter-terrorist sting in a town near to Fanbury leading to the arrest of the anti-Brexit protesters Hugo de la Zouche and Janet Googlesbury (both aliases) who had been letting off fireworks the local police mistook for AK-47 rounds.

No, no, the lukewarm trail Colin and Hans were being asked to follow wasn't just lukewarm. It was, as Sir Magnus Montague had suspected when he'd thought of employing sniffer dogs, stone cold. A fact Dennis was also forced to concede after no more than three hundred yards of pointless pissing, and some pooing, by which time the Bonios-For-Good-Dogs satchel really was empty.

"Bugger," he said, before calling Billy McCann to come and get them in the cop car.

"No sign of Squiffy O'Donnell in these parts," he told Billy, loading Colin and Hans into the hatch at the back when Billy drew up alongside.

"Always was a touch nut to crack, old Squiffy," said Billy.

"Tell me about it. Wanna turn on the old-time radio? My brain's hurtin'."

And so it was that Dennis "Shorty/ "Betty" Dawkins returned to base empty-handed. Colin and Hans liked the ride though, particularly the part when the radio played Patti Page singing "How Much is That Doggie in the Window?"

"Raaf, raaf," they sang along, both wondering how much longer they'd have to go on being sniffer dogs. Dreaming dreams of a better life in Hollywood.

~ * ~

"*Any*way, real me or no real me," Jeremy asked Barry, "what if neither the pudgy bloke with the funny hair in Pyongyang nor the new Stalin in the Kremlin nuke the moron in The White House and nothing else earth-shattering happens to divert attention from me? If the worldwide media have my story, you can be sure MI5 and MI6 will too. Brooding on it, they'll be. And how long will it take *them* to find me? No time at all, that's how long."

Jeremy's was a perfectly legitimate concern. The HQs of MI5 and MI6 at 12, Millbank and Vauxhall Cross respectively were abuzz with rumours, counter-rumours and suspicions, some even connecting the megalomaniac bonkers banker's objectives not only to aiding and abetting the Kremlin's clear desire to "fuck" with "our sacrosanct British democratic values," but also—this was only a conjecture, but it was "on the table"—to aid and abet homegrown ISIS fighters back from Syria in *their* quest to "rock the boat."

"We live in interesting times, eh, Muriel?" said Sir Hubert Humphreys, Head of MI5, to Dame Muriel Eggleshaw, Head of MI6, over tea and crumpets in the sequestered drawing room of Dame Muriel's club in one of the back streets behind Park Lane.

"Indeed so, Hubert. One needs to be on full alert, does one not?"

"Indeed one does, Muriel."

"Any indications so far from your chaps where the megalomaniac bonkers banker chappie might have gone? Moscow?

Damascus? Holed up in some foreign embassy claiming diplomatic immunity like that Wikileaky chappie."

"Not a one," said Sir Hubert. "Internet over*flowing* with sightings. But you know how it is..."

"Staff stretched? Budget cutbacks?"

"Cutbacks, my dear. Downing Street still scrimping and saving in line with their austerity mantra, protesting insufficient moolah to go around if we're to pay off the bally Europeans for our divorce settlement even though we were supposed to *save* money on the deal, so..."

"No progress."

"None at all. Little blighter could be *any*where so far as we at Five know. Any better news from *your* lot?"

"Ditto. Do help yourself to a crumpet, Hubert. A top-up of tea?"

"No chance of a snifter of something stronger, I suppose?"

Dame Muriel clicked her fingers and a flunkey called Jackson tapped on the door in secret tapping code, three taps in quick succession followed by four with intervals of ten seconds each.

"Enter," said Dame Muriel. "Ah Jacko, brandy for our guest and possibly a splash for me too, if you please."

"Dark days, Hubert, eh?" she added, once Jackson had bowed out.

"Dark indeed, Muriel. Shifty tactics and terrorists wherever one looks."

Silence as Jackson returned with a bottle of Asbach Selection 21 and two crystal brandy glasses engraved with the legend *Honi Soit Qui Mal Y Pense*.

"Frankly, just between the two of us and these four unbugged walls, of course..." said Dame Muriel, pouring the brandies when Jackson had again bowed out.

"*Mais bien sûr ma chère. Ça va sans dire.*"

"Let's face it. We haven't a bally clue *what*'s going on. Let alone where to find this megalomaniac bonkers banker blighter."

Which top-secret conversation would have been music to Jeremy Crawford's ears, except, like everybody else in the (Dis) United Kingdom, he wasn't party to it and therefore continued to ask Barry what he was to do if attention *weren't* diverted from him by either the little pudgy bloke with the funny hair in Pyongyang or the new Stalin in the Kremlin nuking the nutter in the White House.

"Well," Barry replied, smoothing down the wispy grey tresses that hung to his shoulders. "The way I see it we only have two options."

"*We*?"

"You don't think I'm going to leave you to fight this battle on your own, do you?"

"Well I...Thanks so much," said Jeremy, who'd never before had a friend of this order. Acquaintances yes, hundreds of them. But they had all been too busy with their own interests to concern themselves with anybody else's.

"I appreciate it. Really I do. I..."

"No need for hyperbole, old fellow. If one is involved, one is involved, and that's that. Now, to the two options?"

"Okay, shoot."

"Pretty simple, really. Either we do a runner or we stick around and face the music. In either scenario, we would, of course, need to be heavily disguised. Many years ago, in a brief moment of vanity back in Oxford, I saw myself as something of a thespian. Even appearing as Macbeth on one occasion, the poor player that struts the stage before being heard of no more and so on. Explaining life as 'a tale told by an idiot, full of sound and fury, signifying nothing.'"

Jeremy smiled. "A fair description of *my* tale."

"Nobody like old Shakey when it comes to hitting nails on heads. But I wasn't for a second imputing idiocy to *you*, my friend."

"Although the worldwide media are. And indictable idiocy to boot."

Barry shrugged. "And what do they ever signify *except* for sound and fury?" he continued. "As I said, it's their bread and butter. *Any*way we're getting off-track here. My point is that I have a nice little stash of costumes down in my cellar. Never thought I'd have a use for them again, but, you know how it is with old friends, how you just hate to dispose of them."

Jeremy nodded, although until recently the concept had been alien to him. Having been born into a throwaway society then becoming wealthy beyond even his expectations, he had never kept anything past its sell-by date. If his last year's 4x4 Merc developed a glitch, he bought a new one with all the latest gizmos, keeping only the A1 JC vanity plate from the old one. Image was everything and needed to be constantly renewed. Now, of course, he knew better. Understood it had never been *him* choosing the car, but him having been chosen by *it.* The memories lingered.

"All from Shakespeare plays, the costumes?" he said.

"No. Not all of them. Wouldn't want you wandering about looking like Puck, now would we? No, no, there are items in there from productions of Beckett, Ionesco, Pinter, Pirandello, Brecht and even rock musicals. Just in case I hit the big time. Which, of course, I didn't."

"Must be a big cellar you have."

"It is. *Now*, are we to run? Or are we to hide in plain sight? That is the question," Barry was saying, as there came a knock at the door.

"What the…?" said Jeremy, wide-eyed and fearful.

"Damned if I know. I'd better answer it, though. Go and hide in the kitchen."

"Anybody home?" came a voice through the unused letterbox as the knocking continued.

"Just a mo," Barry called until he was sure Jeremy was shut in the kitchen with the door locked.

"Ah, PC Dawkins, and what may I do for you this fine afternoon?" he said when he opened the door. "And what nice dogs you have," he added, patting Colin and Hans on their heads. Which they liked. "Raaf, raaf, *raaf*," they said, sniffing the scents of both Shirley and Pete and wagging their tails meaningfully at Dennis "Shorty"/"Betty" Dawkins.

It was as the animals were getting to know each other that Barry again asked the purpose of Dennis's visit. "Pleased to see you, of course, but I'm a little busy just now and…"

Which was when Dennis explained he had reason to believe Barry may know something about the whereabouts of the megalomaniac bonkers banker everyone was making such a fuss about and would be obliged if he could step inside for a moment. At which Barry was forced to weigh his options. The easiest course of action was to deny all knowledge of bonkers bankers, wish Dawkins well in his enquiries and close the door. But what if—somehow, God only knew how—he had evidence of some sort and came back with a warrant to search the premises, in which case the whole bally police force would be involved? The very last thing Barry needed. Simpler by far to deal with just the one copper and come clean by explaining the true nature of Jeremy's presence at the Shepherd's Hut and the manner in which it had been blown out of all proportion by the media. That should take to wind out of his sails.

"Step this way," he therefore invited Dennis.

Colin and Hans were very pleased.

~ * ~

And how, you will be asking yourselves just as Barry had, did Dennis, Colin and Hans finally track down Jeremy even when the trail had apparently gone stone cold and they'd all returned to the cop shop empty handed? By Dennis telling Billy McCann he was damned if he was going to give up on finding Squiffy O'Donnell and intended to give it one last try, that was how. Then by him and the dogs setting off, again on a false track in case Billy got suspicious, before knocking on the doors of each and every one of the villagers on Fanbury's main drag and asking if they'd spotted anything at all unusual on the night of Barry's and Jeremy's escape from the barn. And of course, they all had. UFOs, ISIS lookalikes creeping up to their windows, crazed cyclists about to scratch their cars. The list went on...

But there was something in Batty Hattie Duchamps's story that eerily rang true. It was her report of having been unable to sleep, "Because of my *age*, young man," and, parting her lace curtains as per usual in the wee small hours in case of any threats to her or the local community, having espied the Crawford's gardener—Barry, she believed was his name—trundling an oversize wheelbarrow along the main (only) road. With...a...pig...in...tow!

"Pretty damned un*usual*, would you not say? Fellows walking their *dogs* for pees and poops before beddy byes a person can understand. Better than their poor beasts peeing or pooping on the carpet. But, walking a *pig*?"

"Pig?" said Dennis. The Crawford geezer had lived with a pig, hadn't he? And what if…? It was a long shot, but one worth taking when there were no other options on the table.

"Pig," Batty Hattie confirmed. "Filthy creatures."

"I don't suppose you have any idea where this Barry person might live?" Dennis had quizzed Hattie, who, batty though she was reputed to be, came up with specific directions.

"Shouldn't be allowed to live there. It's against all the regulations. I've told the Council enough times," she called after Dennis. "And now he's harbouring *pigs*."

But, having thanked Hattie profusely for her help, told her she had assisted in a major crime investigation, and wished her at least *some* sleep tonight, Dennis was already on his way with Colin and Hans.

"Sleep, peep," said Hattie, closing the door behind him and shifting on arthritic legs to her "radio room" for the afternoon's episode of The Archers in which Ben was forecast to have become worried by claims of Alf Grundy's historic paedophilia.

Eleven

Sir Magnus Montague was underwhelmed by Julie Mackintosh's progress in the hunt for Jeremy Crawford when she reported back.

"Not even a hint of a *sniff* of a trace, girl?" he said from behind his Chippendale desk.

Julie shook her head.

"One hopes you checked *all* the twitterings or twootings or whatever they're called. Good money I'm paying you. Wouldn't like to think of it going to waste."

"No, Sir Magnus."

"No *what*? 'No, I didn't check all the twootings, Sir Magnus.' Or, 'No, I wouldn't like to think of your good money going to waste, Sir Magnus.'"

"The latter," said Julie, although the salary she was paid was a pittance by comparison with the male staff in the office.

"Should jolly well think so, girl. Need to be careful which way the wind's blowing when it comes to possible promotions, eh? In the light of which, one hopes the answer to the twootings question wasn't also a 'no.'"

Which of course it was. No way had Julie intended to waste her precious time scrolling through thousands of clearly bananas tweets. But she wasn't going to fess up to it. Not to Bossy Boy, anyway. On the other hand, nor was she going to lie. "Never tell lies, our Julie," her dad, Steve, had always told her. "They'll always catch up with you in the end, luv. Particularly if you can't remember *who* you told *which* lie to." And Steve would have known after all those years of working the Mersey docks and being told he'd never lose his job...until the night before he did and Julie's mother left home. Yet still he'd somehow managed to send her to university down in The Smoke. They said in Liverpool the only good things to go south were rain clouds, but Steve had nonetheless believed such a move would give his only child the chances in life he'd never had. And Julie loved him for it.

So she never lied. On the other hand, largely through exposure to the very academics in whom Steve had so much faith, she had quickly learnt how to obfuscate. Getting a straight answer from an academic was like extracting truth from a politician. Never reply to the question you're asked was the maxim. Always hum and haw for a bit, then come up with an abstruse answer to the question you *wanted* to be asked instead.

The preferred question Julie framed for this occasion was: "How hopeful are you of *future* progress in the hunt for Jeremy Crawford, Miss Mackintosh?"

Dodging precise details of Bossy Boy's tweetings/twootings enquiry, therefore, Julie nodded and said the material was certainly interesting and she was working day and night on a complex algorithmic formula she was confident would, within next to no time, deliver the very goods Sir Magnus had requested: viz Jeremy Crawford's whereabouts. She would report back in a few days.

"Gosh...well...um," said Sir Magnus, perplexed just in the manner Julie wanted him. "All-go-rhythmic, eh? And a *for*mula to boot. Sort of dancing while you work, is it?"

Swallowing a giggle, Julie claimed she needed to get on with the job ASAP and excused herself.

"I shall be out of the office for a few days," she called over her shoulder. "Anything urgent, you've got my mobile number. Have a nice day."

What Julie hadn't told Sir Magnus—which wasn't a lie, just a matter of withholding the truth—was that, during the "research" in which she hadn't contacted million-pound-seekers worldwide, she *had* been in touch with both "Jim" in Knotty Ash and "Betty" in Fanbury in regard to their claimed sightings of Jeremy Crawford.

"Jim" had been friendly enough and even given Julie his Skype number "so's we can have a proper chat," but, when she made the connection, she'd concluded he was either an out-of-work Sir Ken Dodd impersonator or, more likely, off his trolley. Same straggly hair as Sir Ken, same protruding teeth although they looked false, same tickling stick being wafted about, but not funny. Far from it. Gloomy and self-pitying, more like. Before Julie could get a word in edgewise, he was telling her about how life had kicked him in the teeth even though he was an obvious genius. How he could have been in The Beatles if he'd wanted, but he hadn't reckoned them good enough to play his songs. How he could have been one of the Liverpool Poets along with Roger McGough, Adrian Henri, and Brian Patten, only his poems were better than theirs. Deeper and more complex. How his plays compared with Shakespeare's. How at least two of his kitchen sink novels were far better than "Saturday Night and Sunday Morning," only...

That's when Julie had interrupted and asked about the sighting of Jeremy Crawford, to which "Jim" had replied: "Who?" before embarking on a rant against Margaret Thatcher and all subsequent Tory governments, especially the latest one led by a woman called Maggie May, before launching into his version of the song about the whore who wouldn't walk down Lime Street any more.

Leaving "Jim" to his world, Julie had thanked him for his time and disconnected.

The correspondence with "Betty," by comparison, had been more interesting. No Skype this time, just a phone number and a cryptic one-liner, saying: "You can find me in Fanbury." Impressed indeed had "Betty" Dawkins been at having been contacted by the very Jackie Lamur who'd posted the original bonkers banker tweet. Best to stay in her good books, he reckoned. Might even help with his investigation.

That was why Julie Mackintosh was to be "out of the office for a few days."

~ * ~

Barry deferred any further enquiries into the purpose of PC Dawkins's visit by plying him with several glasses of nettle brandy and then launching into a lengthy off-the-wall disquisition on the manner in which simple and innocent stories could be hyped out of all recognition by the regular and social media.

"Take this bonkers banker tale, for example," he said. "Local chappie, as I understand it. It would take an idiot to believe there is any truth in the wild accusations about *him*, wouldn't it? Especially not the million pound reward for his capture. Pure fabrication and pernicious tittle tattle in my view. "

"Um," said Dennis.

"I assume an officer of the law would share such a view," said Barry.

"Erm," said Dennis.

"Don't tell me you *don't*."

Dennis hummed and hawed some more, swallowed hard and semi-nodded. "I just thought…"

"Well, I suggest you think again, PC Dawkins. I wouldn't like to think your unexpected visit to my humble home was in any way related to *that* nonsense."

"But it *was* you who brought this pig to your house at the dead of night?" said Dennis, unwilling to concede the game just yet. "The one over there," he added, nodding at Pete, who said, "Oink."

Barry rubbed at his stubbly chin. "Yes, that was I," he said after a pause.

"The pig who'd lived with the Crawford geezer in his barn," said Dennis, encouraged by the admission.

"So the story goes. Probably apocryphal but…"

"Although it is true that you are the Crawfords' gardener and might know him if you saw him."

"I can't deny it, Constable."

"And why would you have been stealing the pig at the dead of night?" said Dennis/"Betty" hoisting both eyebrows. "Especially as from what I heard, anywhere the pig went Crawford would follow. Don't s'pose you had anybody hidden in the wheelbarrow you was pushing that night, did you?"

Forced onto the back foot by a copper who wasn't as daft as he looked, Barry was left with no option but to tell the truth.

"Ha-*hah*," said Dennis/"Betty." Triumphantly.

But Barry wasn't giving up on the falsehood of media narratives.

"Crawford's story is not what you think it is, PC Dawkins," he stressed. "It is of the simple and innocent kind I mentioned at the beginning of our discussion, now blown out of all proportion. All I was doing was helping a fellow human being in some distress," he added before explaining why it was that Jeremy had left his millionaire lifestyle and wife for a leap into the unknown.

"Nothing to do with politics or international plots. He was just sick and tired of the life he was leading, that was all."

Dennis nodded. He could understand that part of the story. Sympathize even. "No-boots-on-carpets" Missus Crawford seemed to him a perfectly understandable reason to do a runner. What took him a little longer to get his head around was the choose/chosen argument Barry then explained, especially if it led to penury. Who would want to live without all that money, chosen or not bloody chosen, he wanted to know.

"Me," said Jeremy, emerging from behind the kitchen door. "Thanks for doing your best to protect me, Barry, but I reckon it's time I took up the tale."

Dennis's jaw dropped at the sight of one million pounds on legs. Not that he looked worth the money, mind you. Bonkers, yes, all messy and dishevelled and everything. But valuable…? Dennis/"Betty" didn't think so. Almost felt sorry for the bloke.

"It's all quite simple really," Jeremy continued. "Barry was right. I just ran away from my old life, that's all. Never been to Russia. Never had anything to do with spying or politics or anything like that. Believe the press, clap me in irons, and claim your reward if you want to, but you'll never get your money because, like everything else about me out there, it's a fiction."

Dennis/"Betty" squinted back and forth between Barry and Jeremy like a spectator at Wimbledon.

"And just while we're on the subject of money, perhaps I might further explain my current attitude to it? That be all right with you?"

Dennis/"Betty" nodded.

"What was that Dickens' quote you came up with the other day, Barry? The one with Mister Micawber in it," said Jeremy.

"'Annual income twenty pounds, annual expenditure nineteen pounds nineteen shillings and sixpence, result happiness.'"

"That's it. Thanks. So you see, Mister policeman, it's just a matter of cutting one's clothes according to one's cloth. Money is not the be all and end all of everything. A little more than you need is ample. But, in my experience at least, too *much* of it can be a burden. What was it your friend Karl Marx said, Bazza?"

"'If money is the bond binding me to human life, binding society to me, connecting me with nature and man, is not money the bond of all bonds'? And that's the last of my quotes if you don't mind, Jezza. I'm not just a quote ma*chine*, you know. Also it gets boring."

But it seemed Dennis/"Betty" had got the point.

"Mmm," he said.

"Before long," said Jeremy, "you're doing what *it* tells you to do. Dancing to its rhythms. Needing this and needing that, fancy cars and suchlike, even though, if you think about it, you don't really *need* them at all. You just *want* them. To show the world how successful you are. That's how you get chosen by them, rather than making your own choice. That's why..."

"You did the runner," said Dennis.

Jeremy nodded. "Enough was enough. Arrest me if you must. For what crime, I don't know. But that's why you're here, right?"

"That's why I *was* here. Don't s'pose there's any of that nettle brandy left in the bottle, Mister...?"

"Just call me 'Barry.'"

"Okay, Barry. And I'm Dennis. Look, I need a loo break. Could you show me where it is?"

"No problem. Step this way. I'll fetch a fresh bottle while we're at it."

It was Dennis who returned first from the nether regions of the Shepherd's Hut and, after the considerable thought he'd put into the matter while peeing, sheepishly confessed to Jeremy his recent Twitter activities. How keen he'd been on collecting the million-pound reward offered for any information leading to the capture of the megalomaniac bonkers banker on the loose. He even fessed up to his alias.

"*Betty*?" Jeremy laughed. "Some name for a copper with a beard."

Dennis blushed.

"Anyway, Betty, it's your call. Like I said, I'm here if you want me. Get the handcuffs out and go for the big bucks, if you still believe in them. But before you do, a further word of warning. The prime reason for suggesting that the million pound reward is a fiction is that Barry and I know the origin of the bonkers banker post and I should tell you Jackie Lamur's boss isn't the most reliable when it comes to shelling out that kind of money. Probably just offering one more of his rubber cheques to suck in the punters. But, like I said, it's your call."

"Here we are," said Barry, returning with the fresh bottle. "Top-ups for everyone?"

To which everyone gladly agreed.

"'Betty' here is one of the tweeters who swallowed the Lamur post," Jeremy told Barry when the topping-up was over.

"*Betty*?" said Barry, peering around the room.

Dennis blushed again.

"That's what Dennis is called when he's on Twitter."

Barry frowned. "Some name for a copper with a beard."

"That's what *I* said."

Dennis re-blushed and this time also squirmed. "Spur of the moment thing, wasn't it? Copper's pay ain't all that brilliant. Surprised you didn't have a go yourself, Barry. Gardening can't bring in much."

Barry nodded and smiled. "Like Mister Micawber, I make ends meet."

"Also, Barry wasn't *al*ways a gardener," said Jeremy. "Used to be an Oxford professor before he thought better of it."

"Bloody 'ell. The two of you make a proper pair. Anyhow, look, I've made up my mind, innit?"

"To take me in and claim your mythical reward, Betty?"

Dennis sucked at his nettle brandy. "Quit it with the 'Betty,' okay?"

Jeremy and Barry shrugged and nodded.

"No, I ain't goin' to take you in. And I ain't goin' to claim no reward neither. Enjoyed our little chat, didn't I? Made a lot of sense to me."

"Raaf, *raaf*," chorused Hans and Colin who'd been listening in.

"So, what I was thinkin' was..."

Barry and Jeremy exchanged squints.

It was Barry who spoke up. "Yes?"

"See, only if you was willin'...I wouldn't mind...only for a few days like…"

"Dossing with us?" said Jeremy.

"Well...um..."

"You'd be very welcome, old fellow," said Barry. "It's not a big house, but there's room for all. There might be a few questions asked at your place of employment, of course. But that would be for you to negotiate. Let us just say we wouldn't want any more strangers knocking on our door."

Dennis dropped his head into his hands and fiddled with his beard. "See, the thing is, I've never *liked* being a copper all that much. Wouldn't take me nothing to toss in my badge altogether and I'd never say nothing to nobody about where I'd gone. Honest Injun."

"Raaf, *raaaaafff*," said Hans and Colin, who were as bored with being police sniffer dogs as Dennis was with being a police*man*. Hans was particularly pleased if the boss's words meant he could spend some quality time with Shirley.

"Oink," said Pete, more as an expression of general support than from any self-interest. Pete just liked it when humans got along with each other.

"Well, it's an interesting idea and you'd be welcome," said Jeremy. "Keep me out of the pokey for a while anyway."

"Thanks. I'll pull my weight, and there's plenty of that, as you can see," said Dennis, patting his belly. "There's one other thing I haven't told you, though. And you're not going to like this. Before I came looking for you, I had a message from Jackie Lamur on my phone sayin' she'd fancy a chat with me."

"And?" said Jeremy.

"She sounded kosher and said she could be in Fanbury in two shakes of a dog's tail. That was yesterday. But…"

"But?" said Jeremy.

"While I was in the loo just now, she *called* me. Seemed like such a nice girl and I'd always liked her tweets, so…"

"You told her where you were," said Barry.

"Yes. Look, I'm sorry. Must've been the drinks you gave me that made me talk but she'd already been speaking with Batty Hattie who'd told her about funny goings-on in the village and talking to me and how she'd sent me to this address and…"

"Like you, she's found us," said Jeremy.

"Yes. Sorry. Look, I'd take it back if I could, only now it's too late, and..."

Which was when there came another knock on Barry's door.

"Popular chap I am all of a sudden," he said, levering himself from his chair.

"Yes indeed, my dear, *do* come in. We've been half expecting you," were the muffled words from the door.

"Oops," said Dennis.

And so it was, after pedalling the metal in her beaten-up pre-Satnav VW Golf all the way to Fanbury that Julie MacKintosh finally met up with her Twitter buddy "Betty."

And then, to her astonishment, she also re-encountered her one-time-only sex partner, the rogue megalomaniac bonkers banker, Jeremy Crawford.

Twelve

Back at Jeremy's ex-home, his soon-to-be ex-wife, his parents, and his in-laws were gathered together in the solarium discussing progress so far and getting antsy— Sophie most of all. She still had her credit and debit cards working, but for how much longer once Sir Magnus cut off Jeremy's enormous salary, which he had sworn to do if "the bounder" weren't caught soon? Hardly any time at all, that was how long. Then what? Go to work her*self*? No way, Hozay. But life would be soo different. She would, for example, have to let "the help" go. No more cook, no more cleaning lady, no more hairdresser, no more pedicurist, no more manicurist, no more beauty therapist, no more interior design adviser, no more personal shopper, no more free credit for Harrods' food, wine, and couture deliveries. *None* of the benefits Jeremy's money had bought, and to which his "loving wife" had become accustomed.

"Just im*a*gine how the queen would feel if someone said they weren't going to pay for her palaces no more," she complained to Ron, Gloria, Vince, and Valerie. "Proper pissed off she would be. *Proper*...pissed...fucking...*off*." Faux tears dribbled down her rouged cheeks and smudged them.

Ron, Gloria, Vince, and Valerie stroked their chins and nodded.

"Terribly hard for you to bear, my dearest dahling," said Valerie, eyeing Ron and Gloria with the suspicion she felt they deserved for having spawned a failed banker. Implying there might have been something amiss with either their genetic materials or their parenting skills, or both.

"Spot on, babe," said Vince, taking his wife's hand and, while squeezing it, also giving Ron and Gloria the malocchio.

It was Ron who fought back against such thinly veiled accusations.

"There was always a darker side to our Jeremy. A side we could do nothing about. Used to hide in his bedroom playing mathematics computer games all night long, and..."

"You just *let* him?" said Vince.

"The boy was a genius," said Gloria. "That's all we knew. It's what his teachers all said."

"Phooey," said Valerie, taking her daughter's limp hand and massaging it while also faux weeping a bit.

"*Bastard*," spat Sophie.

"Let's just hope the coppers find him soon. At least we've got that nice PC Dawkins on the case," Gloria said.

"Dawkins porkins," Sophie re-spat. "Never *met* such a dickhead. Didn't even know Jeremy's *name* till we told him. Okay, so he was tall. But with that horrid beard..."

"A dork's a dork," Vince agreed. "Dawkins always was one and still is. Couldn't investigate his own bottom without a bottom map."

Which was just as well given "Honest" Vince's nefarious gambling transactions—horse doping, jockey bribery, and suchlike—but this wasn't the time or place for such an admission.

"Seems to me," he continued, "although I'd never have thought it before, it looks like our best hope's gotta be the bleedin' Internet, innit?"

"Also it's all over the telly and the newspapers too, ain't that right, Vince?" said Valerie.

"Right as night, darlin'. Bound to be *some* bugger out there who's seen him."

"What I think we should all agree on," said Ron, "is the sooner we get poor Jeremy back to the heart of his family, the better."

This was a sentiment with which nobody could disagree, given the extent to which they all depended one way or another on Jeremy's capacity to print money. Ron and Gloria owned their home—mortgage paid off and everything—but a joint state pension and a couple of piddling work-related ones weren't going to fund any more Caribbean cruises, were they? And thriving though Vince's bent betting business currently was, he wasn't getting any younger. Plus he had *no* pension, seeing as wide boys didn't go for pensions, did they? And as for Sophie, life was unimaginable without a consistent cash flow. She would *even* be prepared to forgive Jeremy his "blip" and let him have morning sex with her again just so long as the big cheques kept hitting her bank account.

They were all agreed, therefore, that Jeremy should be found as soon as possible. But none of them had the least idea how that might be achieved and were becoming gloomy and distraught as they sucked down one of the few remaining bottles of Jeremy's cellar-preserved bottles of Larent Perrier Cuvée Rosé.

"Tell you what," said Ron. "Why don't we phone the Sir Magnus bloke and see if he's found out anything? He was the one who started off the Twitter campaign, wasn't he?"

"Well actually no, that was Jackie Lamur," said Vince, whose bent betting business depended heavily on multiple tweets from thousands of equally bent sources.

"Jackie *who*?" chorused Ron, Gloria, Valerie, and Sophie, all of them suspecting a secret mistress of Jeremy's who might have some claim on his money.

"Lamur," said Vince. "Look, why doesn't *some*one just call the Sir Magnus geezer and find out what's goin' on?"

"How about *you*?" said Ron, "I've got his number if you haven't."

But Vince did have the number and was surprised at how quickly Sir Magnus picked up.

"Yes?" said the Lord of the Realm, who'd been awaiting on his landline phone a call from Julie to report progress.

"Oh," he said. "It's *you*."

Vince and Sir Magnus had a shared, albeit covert, interest in horses. And greyhounds. *And* the likelihood of a further Brexit referendum. Who might win it were it to recur and by what margin. Sir Magnus had a complex three-thousand-pound, win-either-way stake with Vince at odds of 20:1 on both the possibility of a further plebiscite and the repeat of the anti-European vote by margins varying between 2-30%.

"What d'you want?"

Which was when Vince asked Sir Magnus if he had any updates on Jeremy's whereabouts. Any results so far from the Jackie Lamur tweet?

"None so far," Sir Magnus replied. But not to worry because his Personal Assistant was on the case with a specially tailored all-go-rhythms formula, which she guaranteed would provide results.

"She...being...*who*?"

But, knowing Vince as he did, Sir Magnus wasn't prepared to divulge *that* sort of sensitive information.

"Trust me, it's all under control," he said before cutting the call.

"It's all under control, he says," Vince reported back to Sophie, Ron, Gloria, and Valerie, who—seeing as Sir Magnus was a Lord of the Realm and everything—breathed sighs of relief and polished off the penultimate bottle of Jeremy's cellar-preserved Larent Perrier Cuvée Rosé.

"Well, thank the Lord for *that* then," said Ron.

~ * ~

Julie Mackintosh blushed when she was ushered into Barry's parlour and saw Jeremy sprawled across a sofa. The closet party sex she'd shared with him hadn't been great, just swift, slurpy and perfunctory, but it *had* happened and Julie wasn't one to forget such things.

"Oh, um, *hi* there," she said with a little wave. As if Jeremy weren't the most sought-after megalomaniac bonkers banker on the planet.

"Hi, Julie. So you found me."

"Looks like it."

"Do take your coat off and have a seat, my dear," said Barry. "Cup of tea or coffee? Something stronger perhaps?"

"Stronger please," said Julie, struggling out of her jacket and wondering where to put it as Hans, Colin and Shirley bounded into the room to welcome their new guest. Just as well Julie had grown up with dogs or else she might have been knocked over by the six forepaws vying for her attention. But, doing the right thing, she dropped the jacket, squatted, and offered her hands for confirmatory sniffing.

"Hi there, boys. Oh, and a girl," She laughed as Hans, Colin and Shirley recognised her as a pal and took to extensive face-licking, soon to be joined by Pete, who didn't do any face-licking but did say "oink" to draw attention to his presence.

"Blimey, a *pig* too," said Julie, reaching out to pat Pete. "Proper little zoo you've got here, Jeremy."

"They're not mine, Julie. They're his and *his*," said Jeremy, wafting a hand at Barry and Dennis. "Look, let me pick up your coat before we go any further, okay? And maybe you could call the dogs off, Barry?"

"No, no, leave them," said Julie. "And the pig. They make me feel at home."

"Whatever you prefer, young lady," said Barry, taking the jacket from Jeremy and hanging it on a hook behind the parlour door. "Now, *if* the beasts will allow it, why don't you take a seat? And you did say 'something stronger,' did you not? Dandelion wine be suitable?"

Julie smiled. She hadn't drunk dandelion wine since back home in Liverpool where her dad, Steve, had brewed it to save money during his time "between jobs." Somehow, as if in a dream, this weird little house to which "Betty" had given her the directions, was already starting to feel like back home too.

"Dandelion wine would be smashing."

"Okay, coming right up. Now why don't you take that seat? I'll be back in a mo to make the introductions."

It was only then it struck Julie that the sole person she knew in the room was Jeremy. Who the bloke who'd answered to door was or who the tall grinning bloke in police uniform with the straggly beard was, she hadn't a clue. And where was "Betty"? Also, now she looked a little closer, *why*, she wondered, was Jeremy wearing a woman's nightie over his old suit trousers?

The answer, which Julie couldn't possibly have known, was that Barry had offered him a change of clothes since the escape from the barn, but none had fitted. Barry sporting a boxer's chest and a waistline of thirty-four, by comparison with which Jeremy was skinny. All far too baggy and, it had to be said, smelly Barry's outfits had been. A wardrobe refurb was part of future plans, but hadn't been addressed yet.

"Okay then," said Julie, flopping into an armchair with sprouting stuffing, around which clustered Hans, Colin, Shirley and Pete, all of them eager to see the new arrival feel right at home.

"Here we are then," said Barry, returning with a brimming glass of dandelion wine and passing it to Julie. "Hope the Château Broadbent 2015 Premier Cru is to your taste."

"Château *Broadbent*?" said Jeremy.

"It's my second name, old chap."

"Ah," said Jeremy, who'd only ever known Barry as "The Gardener."

Julie sipped the wine and wondered. Not only did she not know who these other blokes were, but apparently they didn't either. And still no sign of "Betty."

It was Jeremy who picked up on her confusion. "Probably time for those introductions, Bazza? And possibly a little backstory first?"

And so it was, on the strict understanding his narrative would never be relayed beyond those walls, to which Julie nodded her full consent, that Barry told the tale of his part in Jeremy's escape from the barn in which he'd been living with Pete the pig after deciding his life needed re-examining. And, loathing circumlocution as he did, Barry's account was to the point in its description of the actual events, although he was unable to resist a footnote indicating how much he agreed with both Jeremy's and Socrates's precept about the unexamined life not being worth living. Beyond his part in Jeremy's escape, of himself—let alone his past life as an Oxford professor—he made no mention.

"So I am Barry, and this is my house, and Jeremy is my guest for as long as he wishes to stay," he concluded.

It wasn't just Julie who listened wide-eyed to this history. Dennis was equally glued. Neither said anything, however.

"And the policeman over there," said Jeremy, "is PC Dennis Dawkins, the one who finally tracked me down to my hideout."

Julie smiled at Dennis, who looked back sheepishly, fiddled with his beard, and felt the need to re-tie his bootlaces.

It wasn't for nothing, however, that Julie Mackintosh had achieved straight starred As in her A-Level subjects of Economics, Politics, and Music—Julie was also a Grade 8 cellist. As her dad Steve had always said, "The girl's got brains comin' out of her ears."

"So *you're* 'Betty,'" she said.

"Yup," said Dennis, not quite sure where to put himself

Thirteen

In the big bad world outside Barry Broadbent's Shepherd's Hut, interest in the megalomaniac bonkers banker story and his potential role in worldwide political shenanigans had slipped from the headlines, just as Barry had predicted it would if the pudgy bloke with the funny hairdo in Pyongyang tried nuking The White House. Which he *had*, only the Hwasong-17 super-intercontinental missile had experienced an unforeseen glitch over the Pacific, blown up, and flopped into the ocean a few nautical miles north of San Francisco. But there was no question of its intended target. On some, the fragments rescued from the seabed by US Navy Seal Chuck Chambers in his submersible and later reassembled by experts were written the words BYE BYE WHITE HOUSE in North Korean characters. At which the mentally deranged US president was reported by a deep-throat Washington DC source to have gone "apeshit" and only been restrained from using the nuclear football codes by being hit on the head by his Secretary of State with a lead pipe.

So it was that Jeremy's story had been relegated to a footnote in history, at least for the time being. Mind you, there were also plenty of other juicy tales knocking around to take its place, specifically the explosion of sex pest scandals engulfing both Hollywood and the Westminster parliament. *GOTCHA GROPER* blazed *The Daily*

Snitch, for example, while Simone de Vérité in *The Daily Truth* went for *MITTS OFF TITS* beneath which she ran an article jam-packed with first-hand lurid accounts of ageing, obese American movie moguls and senior British parliamentarians from all parties lying naked on couches commanding female underlings to strip to the waist and blow them. A case of "kiss my dick or kiss your career goodbye."

There were counter protestations from the accused, of course there were, the most frequent being "the sex was always consensual," and "for crissakes, this kinda stuff's being going on since ancient Athens and even before that, so what the *fuck*?" Which gave rise to a barrage of pro-and anti-tweets and posts from across the whole Twitter zone, *even* one from the madman in The White House once he'd recovered from being hit over the head with a lead pipe after attempting to start World War Three. "Pussy's ther for the grabbin'," read his tweet.

And these were just the sex stories. Within a week of their unveiling came news of offshore investment paradises in which it was claimed the queen and the whole of her otiose family, never mind the nation's other superstars, had for years been squirrelling away trillions and never paid a penny in tax to the Treasury. *DAYLIGHT ROBBERY* screeched *The Daily Snitch*, for example, above an editorial asking what the government intended to do about it.

~ * ~

Anyway, *any*way, what, you will be wondering, did all of this have to do with Jeremy Crawford?

Answer: 10 Downing Street was getting its collective knickers into so much of a twist it needed to divert public attention soonest from its litany of woes with a spanking new story of the PM's unequivocal success at something or another, *any*thing would suffice. Quite apart from the—justifiable—fears of being branded sex pests or tax dodgers themselves, cabinet ministers were experiencing failures in more or less every avenue of their responsibilities caused largely by a pig-headed refusal to ditch their austerity mantra. On and *on* the budget slashes went, including those of MI5 and MI6 as noted by Dame Muriel Eggleshaw and Sir Hubert Humphreys, and even then government borrowing was still *way* off its target of 0%. The National Health Service was on its knees but its bosses were told that was their fault and to make further cuts. The army, navy, and air force chiefs ditto, even though the defence of the realm was, to quote Sir Ronald Biggins, Head of the Armed Forces: "In severe jeopardy."

As were the lives of those worst affected by reductions in welfare benefits. In all the major cities, homelessness was rife, especially amongst the young, and street crime statistics were up as the result of the ongoing frustration caused by the disparity between the incomes of the super rich and those of the super poor. Why should *we* suffer, objected the latter, when the mega rich, including the two-faced politicos and Missus Queen, could hide their trillions from the taxman in offshore accounts instead of paying their fair share into the wealth of the nation? And all this at the same time as Westminster ponces had porn on their computers and groped any staffer that took their fancy. Revolution was in the air, no doubt about it.

Added to these widespread woes, there were two other specific factors causing the PM increasing angst. These were:

1) The ignominy of her hubris in calling a general election to boost her majority in parliament to hundreds, and instead seeing her government finishing up with a majority of only two.

2) The debâcle of the Brexit negotiations with Brussels, which, by any definition, were at best faltering and at worst fucked because the Brit negotiators were considered by bemused Europeans to be historically deluded gung-ho Brit prats to whom they were unprepared to offer any concessions whatsoever. Yet more embarrassingly, there remained the suspicion that the 2016 Brexit referendum itself had been compromised by interference from Russian president Igor Ripurpantzov and his team of Internet hackers

in St Petersburg. In short, the UK government was pretty much on its knees, in the light of which it's not hard to imagine how keen the PM was on the creation of *any* media story, however mythical, to deflect the public gaze from the morass of sewage through which she and her government were currently wading.

In a blessed moment one sleepless night, however, what the PM thought of as her "super-acumen" was catalysed. It was while watching re-tweets of the madman in the White House that she suddenly spotted light at the end of this awful tunnel. "Switch the story and find a worse one with a real *BAD* guy to blame" was the essence of the madman's messages, which, albeit attributed to a madman, didn't seem *so* mad at all.

"Mmm," she mused as the woes reverberated through the few neurons still functioning in her ditsy brain.

And then, bingo, just like that, she had it. Of course, of *course*, the Trotskyite megalomaniac bonkers banker with links to the Kremlin! *That* should do the trick all right. Nothing the nation would love her for more than a spot of mudslinging at the old Ruskie enemy, especially if it involved one of the nation's much-hated City bankers. A win-win situation, no question about it. All she needed on board now was the latest model 007 from MI5 or MI6 to hunt down the demon and haul him up before the courts to validate her tale. From zero to hero she could go overnight.

"*YESSSS*," she yipped, punching her pillows and, by accident, her snoring husband who said, "Oh, for fuck's *sake*, Clarissa."

That was what all this had to do with Jeremy Crawford, who had been chosen yet again.

~ * ~

It was the following morning that the PM addressed an emergency meeting of her twitchy cabinet with her new brainwave idea.

"What we need at this historic juncture in our proud history, chaps and chapesses," she told them, "is a dose of true British grit to steer Mister and Missus Joe Public's attention away from all the smears and fake news threatening to envelop us. Instead we shall have the *true* story of roguery, treachery and international intrigue undertaken by the Trot megalomaniac bonkers banker chappie—only to be thwarted at the critical moment by the sang froid, suavity, sharp-shooting skills, and dare one say it *all*ure, of the Secret Service's top agent who will be answering directly to...*me*."

"Jolly dee, tip top, Pee Em," barked the home secretary, Janus facedly, seeing as she nurtured aspirations of ousting the PM and becoming PM herself.

"Great, triff, brill," echoed the foreign secretary. Also Janus facedly, given he had exactly the same ambitions as those of the home secretary.

And, to her gratification, the rest of the ministers happily trilled along to the same song sheet, praising the PM with statements such as "genius," "gosh," "super," and "go for it." That was the measure of the hypocrisy of the British cabinet, *all* of them, unbeknownst to either the home or foreign secretaries, running covert campaigns to unseat the PM and replace her with *them*selves. And this latest batty idea looked the perfect means of achieving just that, a classic case of hoisting herself by her own petard, thus leaving the path wide open for any one of them to succeed her.

"Righty-*ho*, then," said the PM, as oblivious to such internecine plotting as she was to practically everything else. "I'll get right on it. Cabinet dismissed."

At which the fractious bunch trudged out of the chamber swivel-eyed and muttering to each other behind their hands, while the PM picked up the phone to a top secret joint line shared by Dame Muriel Eggleshaw at MI6 and Sir Hubert Humphreys at MI5 to demand they appoint to the case the newest and most improved 007 they had on their books to serve up the head of the megalomaniac bonkers banker on a platter.

~ * ~

Initially when the PM got "right on it," her call to MI5 and MI6 went unanswered as the result, so a recorded message told her, of a "temporary but catastrophic failure in the communication system caused by government austerity cuts."

"Fuck," said "Phoebe." That was the Clarissa's codename when calling the Secret Services.

But then she had another of her brilliant ideas and surprisingly this one worked.

"I know what I'll do, I'll call Milly on her smartphone," she muttered, dialling the super-encrypted number. "Milly" was Dame Muriel's secret codename. Sir Hubert's was "Hubby."

And, sure enough, the boss of MI6 answered on only the second replay of Vivaldi's *Four Seasons*, portentously the winter one.

"Yes, Phoebe?" she whispered, seeing the PM's also super-encrypted number on her screen.

"A small favour I have to ask of you, Milly."

"Hrrmph," said Milly, who'd never liked Phoebe, and not only because of her fatuous politics. While they'd been undergrads at Girton College Cambridge together, Phoebe had stolen away Milly's targeted inamorato, Nigel Jeffreys-Joynson, and had flagrant sex with him on a punt. "Flagrant" because the episode had been caught *in delicto* on camera by the punter, fellow undergrad Simon Snodgrass, and published across the university in the very next edition of *Varsity*.

Uncharacteristically for her, Phoebe intuited this lingering opprobrium and responded with what she thought of as Prime Ministerial gravitas.

"Listen, Milly. We're both big girls now. I'm Pee Em and you're head of Em-I-bally-*Six*, so let's draw a line under the past, shall we?"

"Hrrmph," repeated Milly, frowning meaningfully at Sir Hubert "Hubby" Humphreys with whom she was again sharing an intimate conversation at her club in the hinterland of Park Lane. That wasn't all she was sharing with Sir Humphrey these days, but neither her current husband nor Hubby's current wife needed to know *any*thing about *that*.

"What we're talking about here is a national crisis," Phoebe continued.

"Your job on the line again, is it?"

"You can be a real bitch, you know that?"

"So I've been told. It's more or less why I was appointed to MI6. Now, this 'national crisis' you spoke of?" said Milly, switching the phone to super-hushed speaker mode so Hubby could listen in. "Care to elucidate?"

Thinking she'd made a little progress, Phoebe explained—as long as you could equate lengthy specious periphrasis with "explanation," which Milly couldn't. Reckoned it to be the usual half-arsed politicospeak, the next best thing to lying.

Which was why she interrupted halfway through the PM's verbiage and said, "Cut the crap, Phoebe. We all know you're on a hiding to nothing and looking for any which way out you can find. Get to the point or I'm hanging up."

Hubby nodded, sipped at his Dom Pérignon and flipped Phoebe the finger. Just as well they weren't on Skype.

So it was that Phoebe finally hit the bottom line: how much she needed the sang froid, suavity, sharp-shooting skills, *and* allure of the latest model 007 Milly and Hubby had on their books to hunt down the Trotskyite megalomaniac bonkers banker clearly in cahoots with the Kremlin and bring him back from wherever he was to face justice. *This* was the only tiny favour she was asking.

In the following hiatus, Milly and Hubby swapped amused, knowing (and coded) glances, and allowed Phoebe to continue blethering down the line about the way her government was close to having its back broken by "false disinformation" under which she needed to draw a line smartish.

"*Well*?" she practically shrieked as the blether was drawing to a close.

And so it was that the deal was done. In exchange for an unprecedented hike of £2bn in the budgets of MI5 and MI6, Milly and Hubby were prepared to release into Phoebe's command the very best operative they had come across in all the years they'd been in the Secret Services.

"Heavens. Heck. Thanks *soo* much," said a humbled Phoebe after agreeing to the sum in question. "And his name and number?"

Milly and Hubby exchanged smirks.

"He answers to Casanova," said Milly. "We think of him as Double-O Seven*teen*. Speaks the usual four European languages, plus Russian, Arabic, and garage-level Mandarin. Also he has computer skills Silicon Valley would die for, shoots like Wyatt Earp, *and* has black belts in karate, judo and taekwondo."

"And does he also possess the sang froid, suavity, and allure I require? The kind of thing one associates with Roger Moore, my personal favourite Double-O Seven?"

"In spades. The sexiest beast on the planet," said Milly.

Which was a minor distortion of the truth because OO17 Maurice Moffat/ "Casanova" was five foot seven and chubby, his argument being it was quality that counted, not quantity.

"Thanks soo much," said Phoebe, practically genuflecting as Milly whispered his contact number on the secure line.

"Just make sure the money hits our accounts by close of business tomorrow, though," said Milly. "Otherwise it's no Casanova Double-O Seventeen for you."

"You got it. Done deal," said Phoebe, in what she thought of as American.

But by then Milly had already cut the call and taken to sipping at *her* glass of Dom Pérignon.

"Here's to us, Hubby." She giggled as the pair clinked flutes. "Poor old Phoebe though, eh? Not *exactly* what she had in mind, our Maurice, but I'm sure he won't let the side down."

Fourteen

Unlike James Bond, who never had a home address, "Casanova"/Maurice Moffat lived in a three-bedroom terraced house in Tooting, South West London, which he shared with a confused tabby he'd rescued from Battersea Dogs and Cats Home and named Terpsichore but only ever addressed as Tiddles, hence the cat being confused. But what was in a name? All Terpsichore/Tiddles cared about was getting her dinner on time and being allowed to sleep on Maurice's bed.

Also unlike James Bond, Maurice didn't drive an Aston Martin. If he drove at all, which he seldom did unless to stock up at Tesco once a month, it was in the classic Morris Minor Traveller he'd inherited from his father, Malcolm. In Maurice's eyes, the car *was* his father. Whenever he switched on the ragged old engine, he felt his dad's presence—on the driver's seat, on the waggly gear stick, on the handbrake. But mainly the four-wheeled Malcolm was parked outside the house under a specially designed weatherproof blanket. If Maurice really wanted to go anywhere, he went by bike. And not on some latterday iron-man mountain-climbing monstrosity with thirty gears, on an old sit-up-and-beg called Janet with a wicker basket on the handlebars and a Sturmey Archer three-speed gear mechanism. That's how Maurice liked life...slow and easy.

So how, you will ask, did *this* bloke get to be a top secret service agent? Because, unlike the hyped-up hero in the Ian Fleming stories, he was very, *very* secret, that was how. All his lights—and there were many of them, Milly hadn't been lying about that—were so hidden under so many bushels, nobody would ever suspect he was anything more than an undersized, chubby, middle-aged man eking out his days on a small private income and causing no trouble to anybody. That was what his neighbours at numbers eleven and fifteen Oakshot Street thought, an oddity unquestionably but kindly and always with a good word to say about everybody. If they needed help, it was Maurice to whom they, and others in the street, would turn.

As had Milly and Hubby whenever they needed someone deep, deep undercover in capital cities across the world where there was suspected nastiness going on they needed to know about. Who better than OO17 to lurk and skulk unnoticed on the peripheries of Moscow, Beijing, Damascus, Tel Aviv, Paris, Rome, Berlin, Brussels et al when you wanted to know what was *really* going down? Not some conspicuous Beretta-toting dude with a gambling habit and a liking for flashy women and even flashier cars, that was for sure. That was all well and good for cinema audiences, but not for the real spymasters and mistresses. What *they* needed was a practically invisible person with a working knowledge of all the relevant languages and an eidetic memory who only tossed baddies off tall buildings or shot them when absolutely necessary. Which on occasion Maurice had been obliged to do, but never with maximum (or even minimum) machismo. Insignificance was his stock in trade, and it had opened all sorts of doors for him.

Posing as a Brit diplomat's dogsbody, for example, Maurice had been deployed to Washington DC as a White House wine waiter shortly after the madman had been "elected" president and had relayed back to MI5 and MI6 in super-encrypted code the conclusion:

"This fellow has the mind of a sewer rat and should never—double understroke *never*—be invited to our shores, let alone to meet Missus Queen or address parliament. He's a catastrophe waiting to happen and if he's to be shot, let it at least be someone on his own turf to do the dirty deed." It was this sort of advice, amongst a plethora of other examples from all corners of the planet, for which Dame Muriel and Sir Hubert had been deeply grateful.

So that was Maurice Moffat for you. Unassuming, unknown to anybody but his neighbours, who thought he was called Michael, but nonetheless one of the most effective players in the world of global espionage. Alerted by "Milly" and "Hubby" to the possibility of a pleading call from "Phoebe" on his mega-encrypted, government-issue smartphone, "Casanova" was therefore ready and waiting.

"Phoebe," he said. "What a pleasure."

"Miaow," said Terpsichore/Tiddles, who reckoned it was time for her dinner.

~ * ~

At much the same time as Casanova was getting his brief from Phoebe, Julie Mackintosh was beginning to feel ever more comfortable at chez Barry. After several more rounds of the Château Broadbent 2015 Premier Cru, Dennis had fessed up to being Betty on Twitter and even had a good laugh about it, saying he was like the bearded lady in the circus.

"Tell you what, if I can call you Betty, you can call me Jules," sang Julie to the tune of the Paul Simon song her dad liked so much. "But thanks for telling me where Jeremy was. It's been a real relief seeing him again. Knowing he's okay."

Jeremy smiled lopsidedly.

"And not even asking for the reward," said Barry, refreshing glasses.

"Yeah. Why *was* that?" said Julie.

Which was when Dennis recounted the conversation he'd had with Barry and Jeremy after he'd found his way into the Shepherd's Hut.

"See, it's all about choosing or being chosen," he concluded. "Like, having a good hard look at the life you're livin' and thinkin' to yourself: Did I choose *it*, or did it choose *me*?"

Julie stared and frowned as little twinkly signals pinged backwards and forwards between the lobes of her cerebral cortex and occasionally into her hippocampus.

"Old Barry here used to be a prof at Oxford bleedin' uni*ver*sity," Dennis continued. "Only he gave all that up to be a gardener. Didn't you, mate?"

Barry's turn to smile lopsidedly.

"And Jeremy used to be a banker wanker, but he's been havin' second thoughts too. Right, pal?"

Jeremy nodded.

"And me, I'm not a copper anymore."

Julie's eyes widened as the little twinkly signals intensified.

"So, who're you all *now*?" she asked, when the twinkly signals abated sufficiently.

"Ourselves. Just ourselves," said Jeremy, speaking on his, Barry's and Dennis's behalves. "Isn't that right, Betty?"

"Couldn't have put it better meself," said the ex-copper.

"So, all *three* of you are...?" said Julie.

"No longer who we once thought we were," said Barry. "Now how about a little supper? Homegrown carrots, asparagus, potatoes, runner beans and sprouts all whisked together in my blender to make a decent soup? Plus bread and rice, of course."

"Sounds great," said Julie.

And it was. As was the coffee and the *Apfelstrudel* from homegrown apples with Cheshire cheese course to follow. So was the tiny bunk bed she was offered when night began to fall. So were the sweet dreams that followed until the next day when she was awoken by Hans, Colin and Shirley snuggling up around her. It made for a packed bunk bed—even *more* packed when Pete made his way upstairs—but it was fun. And it had been a long time since Julie Mackintosh had had fun. *Never* in all the time she'd been working for Sir Magnus fucking Montague, that was for sure.

~ * ~

Speaking of whom, this was a man who, having already experienced a series of unaccustomed bad days, was losing the will to live. First his valued HAA (Head Assets Analyst) had gone bonkers and decamped to a barn before vanishing altogether, bequeathing to Sir Magnus his batty family. And *now* his all-go-rhythmic Girl Friday, who was supposed to be following up a red-hot lead to the ingrate Crawford, had also vanished. At least that's how it seemed. No answer had there been to any of Sir Magnus's furious phone calls demanding progress updates. Nothing from the Jackie Lamur Twitter, Facebook, Instagram, Google Plus sites, all of which Julie's pro tem replacement, Jenny, assured him had been deleted. A case of "no such number, no such zone," if Sir Magnus remembered the line from Elvis Presley's "Return to Sender" correctly, which he was pretty sure he did. For, believe it or believe it not, back in the previous century when Sir Magnus was young, he'd been an Elvis fan. Had the oiled quiff, the sideburns, the wiggly hips, the tight trousers, the brothel-creeper shoes, the whole nine yards. But that was before he'd become a banker and, in the next century, been knighted by an ebullient "Third Way" Labour government for his contribution to "The Welfare of the Economy." No such rock 'n' roll fripperies after *that* ennoblement. But still the songs resonated. Such is the way of the songs of one's youth.

*Any*way, what with one thing and another, Sir Magnus was royally pissed off. *So* pissed off, his heart was starting to fibrillate all over again, which was not...a...good...sign. At least according to the wisdoms of his grossly overpaid Harley Street cardiologist, Professor Doctor Hugo Printemps, who'd warned him years ago his stress levels were far too high and to knock off the booze and the Havana Tranquillity cigars *immédiatement*.

"Bugger it all to buggery," Sir Magnus said from the sanctuary of his high-backed, maroon-leather swivel behind his Chippendale mahogany desk before pouring himself six fingers of his favoured five-star Courvoisier which he downed in one, and firing up a fresh Havana Tranquillity. "Self-medicating" he called it and sod Professor Doctor Hugo poncy Printemps.

Feeling a little better, he left the office on wobbly legs, telling underlings he was going out and was under no circumstances to be disturbed by phone calls or emails. Heads turned and eyes strayed from desktop computers as he stumbled through the plush accommodation muttering to himself and twice banging into cubicle dividers, but the underlings knew better than to question the boss when in a bad mood and/or legless. That way lay instant dismissal as they'd witnessed to their chagrin when, in similar circumstances, junior assistant under-secretaries Mildred O'Flannery and James McCloud had asked Sir Magnus if he was okay and been told to clear their desks and fuck off out of his sight forever.

Out on the street, where his midnight-blue Bentley 4x4 was parked on a double yellow line, its windscreen plastered with multiple fine and towaway notices, Sir Magnus took several deep breaths, none of which eased the fibrillations, and leered lubriciously at the direction he would take, namely to the Soho establishment of Madame Francine La Fouette. If *any*one could ease his troubled mind, if would be Francie or one of her girls. There were always several to choose from. Yellow ones, black ones, pink ones in see-through schoolgirl uniforms with ribbons in their hair. Do anything you asked them, they would, and all for a mere two hundred quid per half hour.

"Yesss!" said Sir Magnus, tearing the multiple fine and towaway notices from the Bentley and tossing them into the gutter as the fibrillations pleasingly shifted from his chest to his crotch. And into the midnight blue 4x4 Sir Magnusmobile he climbed.

A pity its battery was flat. You know how it is when you climb into your car feeling powerful, turn the key and goose the gas in full expectation of an explosion of energy only to hear a dull thud, then nothing. How you turn the key and goose the gas some more, but all that produces is a winking red warning light...then even *that* is extinguished. Crap, that's how you feel, disem*power*ed. Which is when you succumb to fury, climb out of the car, and take to kicking it. Or, if you're Basil Fawlty in *Fawlty Towers*, giving it a damn good thrashing with a tree branch.

Well, that was pretty much how Sir Magnus Montague reacted when the midnight blue Bentley 4x4 failed to start, although there were no tree branches on hand to thrash it with, so he was reduced to kicking at its wheels, hammering on the roof, and screaming it was a "useless piece of shit" he wished he'd never bought.

"This year's fucking *model* too," he was hollering when the wah-wahs and the flashing blue lights started up in an adjacent street, and then, only moments later, drew up right alongside him.

"Care to stop doing that, sir?" said PC Jason Humphreys. "Only you're disturbing the peace."

"FUCK the FUCKING *peace*," shrieked Sir Magnus, making the big time mistake of punching PC Humphreys on the nose, then, as the fibrillations headed back heartwards, collapsing onto the pavement in a cardiac arrest which was only prevented from becoming terminal by PC Humphreys administering CPR until the paramedics arrived.

But cardiac wasn't the only arrest Sir Magnus was to suffer. Attached to a defibrillator though he was in the ambulance on his way to Intensive Care, Jason Humphreys also read him his rights where the assault of police officers was concerned. And such rights were few and far between, so Jason wished Sir Magnus well on the heart issue but added he'd be seeing him in court when, and if, he recovered.

Not one of the best days in Sir Magnus Montague's life so far therefore.

Fifteen

Maurice Moffat had never liked "Capricious" Clarissa, as he'd dubbed the prime minister. Too wishy-washy even to run a laundrette never mind a country, he reckoned. The sort of person who'd be hard put to organize footballs to roll down a hill let alone corral her cabinet into obedience. And this at the very time the UK needed a canny leader to see it through its worst crisis in modern history, a subject Maurice was able to speak about with authority, given his Oxford starred triple first PPE and the chats he'd shared with Prof Broadbent in his rooms after tutorials. Like the professor, Maurice was no xenophobe, but since the fiddled Brexit vote he *was* beginning to rue the way Britain had become the laughing stock of not only Europe but the rest of the world. Capricious Clarissa could say what she liked about Russian meddling in "democratic" elections and how we would stand firm against it, but did the Kremlin give a monkey's when the United Kingdom was at its least united in living memory and seeking divorce from very economic bloc to which the Kremlin might pay attention? Of course it didn't. Ripurpantzov just rubbed his hands, chuckled, and advised his top brass to go on laundering their ill-gotten rubles by continuing to buy up empty mansions in London's most salubrious enclaves.

But Maurice wasn't paid to be political. He was a spy. And thus it was only with Terpsichore/Tiddles he shared such thoughts as the pair sat on their late evening sofa channel surfing for relevant news. Well, that's what Maurice did. Terpsichore/Tiddles just nodded off. As did Maurice when the news became too tedious to bear.

Nonetheless, when "Phoebe's" call came through as expected, he was as polite as he was able. Almost felt sorry for the woman as she told him a cock and bull story about the "vital importance to the nation at this critical juncture" of finding the megalomaniac bonkers banker Jeremy Crawford and thereby diverting attention from as many of lies told about her government's "achievements" as conceivable. Even possibly blaming *him* for them. How, for example, his involvement in covert money laundering and systematic tax evasion on behalf of rogue regimes worldwide was depriving the Treasury of billions of pounds annually and threatening the demise of "our beloved NHS." How his collaboration with the Russian Internet Research Agency to produce Twitter bots had destabilized not only the entire banking system but also threatened the very Mother of Parliaments herself.

"What we require in Downing Street, Casanova, is an incredible story," she said, as this fiction ran away with her and became practically a faction. "But first we need to catch the blighter. And it is to you, on excellent recommendations from Milly and Hubby at Six and Five, that we have chosen to entrust this noble, dare one say it, 'nation saving' enterprise."

"Most honoured I'm sure, Milady," said Maurice in his best Uriah Heep voice.

"And so you should be. Upon your shoulders shall fall responsibility for the maintenance of the very fabric of the British society we all so cherish and in which we trust, the unflinching backbone that has seen us through so many centuries of turmoil and always ensured we came out victorious. The never-say-die Dunkirk spirit and reliance on the wisdom of our noble queen, who..."

Maurice held the phone from his ear. As if this mumbo-jumbo weren't bad enough, there had to be mention of the bally queen. Many a time Maurice had wished Charles II had never been invited back from France after England's only ever successful revolution and then spawned the better part of four centuries' worth of totemic wastrels.

A hiatus, therefore, while OO17 struggled to retain his *sang froid.*

"You still *there*, Casanova?"

"Still here, ma'am. So it's more fake news we're going to be spreading, is it? Always assuming I can *find* this megalomaniac bonkers banker chappie."

Another hiatus while Capricious Clarissa attempted to compute what sounded to her a lot like disbelief, possibly even an objection. But then she hit her rhythm again.

"There's fake news, Casanova, then there's fake news which is simply alternative truth," she retorted robotically. "As you should know from the special relationship with our friend in the White House. And, in your position, it is not a question of reasoning why. Yours just to do or die, eh? One assumes you have signed the Official Secrets Act and pledged allegiance to the Crown."

Despite his inbuilt loathing of said crown, Maurice couldn't deny he had. It had been a humiliating experience, but without such nauseating oblation he would never have been given the job he'd most wanted since leaving Oxford.

"Indeed so, ma'am,"

"Well then, get to it, man," said "Phoebe," who was starting to feel a tad cross at having to boss someone around like this. Why couldn't people just do the jobs they were paid for and stop being so pernickety about everything?

"Please," she added after a moment's silence.

At which backslide into unexpected decency, Maurice again felt a pang of sympathy. Just the wrong woman in the wrong job, he reckoned. How long would it take her to realise?

"Okay," he said, running a hand along Terpsichore/Tiddles' fur, which caused her to roll on her back and dangle her four legs in the air. "I'll do my best."

"Thank you, Casanova. Thank you sooo much," said "Phoebe," cutting the call as her foreign secretary barged into the office with disturbing news concerning the president of Iran's reaction to a "misspeak" the FS—some read the acronym as "Fat Slob"—might or "might not" have made in response to the "Muzzie" president's claim his country had every right to nuclear weapons given the hostility to everything Muslim emanating on daily tweets from the madman in White House.

"I mean, for fuck's *sake*, what was so *wrong* with my telling him he'd be better off building a yellow submarine?" huffed and puffed Fat Slob, pulling at his blond-going-on-whitish toupée.

"Nothing, dear boy. A jolly good thing to say, I'm sure. Now, why don't you pop off and get yourself a cup of tea and a bun? Then you'll feel a lot better," said Clarissa. "And close the door behind you."

~ * ~

Maurice Moffat pondered long and hard on the new task he'd been set, employing all the super-neurons he'd been born with and therefore examining the problem from every conceivable angle. First the entirely pragmatic matter of where to start looking for this Jeremy Crawford fellow. Whether to stay at home and employ only the top-of-the-range computer bank in his third bedroom, *or* whether to use the old-fashioned gumshoe methodology and skulk about in his three-piece tweed suit asking obscure questions of Jeremy's ex-coworkers and family in the hope of picking up the scent of a trail. A tricky choice. Additionally, however, he had at his disposal a tool of his very own invention he had not yet shared with MI5, MI6 or GCHQ because it was still in its experimental stages. The GRNAV (Genetic Response Navigator) he called it, a machine that combined the wonders of satellite imagery with advances in microbial genetics and could, in principle, detect any person at any distance when fed only a smidgeon of that person's DNA. All he would need for this course of action would be such a dab of the bonkers banker's genetic coding smeared onto a converted Satnav app and Bob would be Maurice's uncle. He'd never so far tried it out, but might this be an appropriate moment for a test run? After considerable reflection, Maurice thought so. What, after all, was the point of months of painstaking invention if it were to be mothballed and never to see the light of day? No point at all, he concluded.

From this example you will begin to understand the genius level at which Maurice Moffat's mind operated. An intellectual he was, but not one merely at the pedestrian level of disputing and revamping the work of others. A loner with both the rational *and* creative capacities to imagine the unimaginable, think the unthinkable, take the risk and maybe, just maybe, make something new. In other words, someone whose left and right brain hemispheres didn't just bicker with each other—"I'm the clever one, you're daft; no I'm not, *you're* the daft one, *I'm* the clever one" and so on—but worked together in constructive harmony.

"Oo*kay* then, cat, this shall be our path," he told Terpsichore/Tiddles, now "Cat."

"Miaow," said Terpsichore/Tiddles/Cat.

Maurice took that as a yes, laid back on the sofa with his hands laced behind his head, nodded off, and took to dreaming.

~ * ~

In Maurice's dream, Jeremy Crawford is located in no time at all by GRNAV and turns out to a thoroughly decent chap in some mysterious way connected to Maurice's old pal Prof Broadbent, who hovers about out of focus on the irritatingly ungraspable oneiric fringes of perception like some spirit. You know how it is with dreams, how they work vertically rather than horizontally. Like stacks of tarot cards that won't reveal their narrative meaning until laid out and interpreted, which they never allow in dreams. Just jumbled upside-down and back-to-front metaphors of all the dross on your mind they remain until you awaken perplexed.

So it was in Maurice's dream, although it wasn't puzzling him. In fact he was quite enjoying it. Apart from the elusively hovering Prof Broadbent, there were other folk around Jeremy too, all of them chuckling and having fun. And there were several animals. No cats as far as Maurice could make out. More like dogs, although there may even have been a wild boar in there in the mix. Anyway, not the sort of party Maurice wished to gate crash with threats to Jeremy of him being scapegoated for all the mistakes of Capricious Clarissa and her hapless government. Especially not after he was invited into the company, introduced to everyone and, after initial reserve, licked by the animals and accepted by the people. Even asked if he he'd care for a glass of the local brew. Not the Cockburn's Special Reserve port wine Prof Broadbent kept in his Oxford rooms, but tasty nonetheless.

It was at this juncture that the laced hands behind Maurice's head went numb and he was obliged to re-position himself further down the sofa on one side, thereby squashing Terpsichore/Tiddles/Cat, who said miaow in protest, waited till Maurice was off in cloud cuckoo land again, then sat on his head.

Immediate shift in dream scene possibly occasioned by having a confused tabby sitting on his head. Suddenly and inexplicably Maurice is in Moscow, where he has been many times before as a spy during the Igor Ripurpantzov regime. But this isn't the new Moscow he's dreaming of; this is the old one in the days of Mikhail Gorbachev's Soviet Union. Glasnost and perestroika are in the air and

Beatles' songs are being allowed on the radio for the first time ever. Pretty girls in short skirts and longhaired lads in blue jeans are dancing in the streets to John Lennon's "Revolution." And in "Back in the USSR," Paul McCartney is screaming about the Ukraine girls who really knock him out, the Moscow girls who make him sing and shout, and how Georgia is always on his mind. Also, and for no connected reason (right brain was having a ball), Maurice hears lines from Lennon's much later "Working Class Hero." How you were hated if you were clever but despised if you were a fool.

That's when Maurice awoke, took Terpsichore/Tiddles/Cat from his head, and sat bolt upright.

"That's *it*," he muttered as his limbic system shut down and Left Brain got in on the act, supplying Maurice with the memory of a TV programme he'd recently managed to stay awake for, which explained how much influence The Beatles had had on the revolution that led to the demise of the Soviet Union. Dimly he remembered the image of an old man in St Petersburg with lank hair who was building a shrine to John Lennon and peering out at the sea awaiting his return. Thinking even one of the seagulls might be John flying home.

"Never mind he is dead. He shall return. We need him now more than ever," the old man told the TV interviewer in Russian, before singing a croaky version of "Imagine" in English.

"Mmmm," mused Maurice, closing his eyes again and allowing Right Brain to do the thinking.

And some dream scheme it came up with. From *way* out in left field, so fantastical and audacious was it. Yet, given the common knowledge of Ripurpantzov's cyber finagling in Western elections, these days it was *not* beyond the bounds of practicality. But Maurice wouldn't mention any of this to Downing Street any time soon, if ever. First thing tomorrow he would prime his GRNAV, go in search of a smear of bonkers banker DNA, and with any luck find the fellow.

And if, as he had dreamt, Jeremy was *indeed* in the company of Prof Broadbent and some other decent types, well who knew what might follow? After all, in many parts of the world before Freud took to his meddling, dreams were regarded as prophesies.

Leaving Terpsicore/Tiddles/Cat to *her* dreams on the sofa, Maurice went downstairs, tucked his trouser cuffs into his socks, extracted his bike from the garden shed, and headed out into the midnight streets. Nothing he liked better for calm reflection than the dark winter streets of Tooting when the world had gone home, taking with it the fuss and the fights.

Sixteen

If you're as sceptical of the narrative potential of dream prophesies as I, you're not going to like what happened next, but the fact of the matter is that the part of Maurice's dream in which he finds Jeremy came true, so it's suspend-your-disbelief time for both of us, I'm afraid.

Anyway, what happened next *was* that Maurice Moffat found Jeremy Crawford the following day with his GRNAV, which to his delight worked with pinpoint precision. Leaving Terpsichore/Tiddles/Cat in the care of Hank and Butch, his neighbours at number eleven Oakshot Street, all he had to do was motor up to Fanbury in his Morris Minor Traveller at the dead of night, find the barn Jeremy had holed up in, according to all the newspaper and Internet stories, pick the lock and, with a special DNA detector device also of his own concoction, scrape from the palliasse the required smidgeon of the essence of Jeremy's being, feed it to GRNAV, and bingo! Within the half hour he was tapping at the front door of Barry's mobile Shepherd's Hut saying he was sorry for the disturbance, but...

It was Barry who opened the door.

"*Moffat*? Maurice Moffat?" he said. "What on earth are *you* doing here?"

It took a second for Maurice to recognise his old prof. He had to have aged since their Oxford days, but if anything, with his shoulder length hippy hair and the glint in his eyes, he looked sprightlier.

"Prof *Broad*bent?" he said.

"The same, old chap."

"But you look…"

"Different from when we first met?"

Maurice nodded.

Barry smiled. "I was older then, Moffat. I'm younger than that now. A small matter of what the Germans call *Weltanschauung*. May I repeat, however, what *are* you doing here? Not still some bally spook, one hopes. Speaking as someone who wrote you a rather flattering reference for MI6."

"I do not come in that *exact* capacity," said Maurice who, like Julie Mackintosh never told overt lies but had been groomed to obfuscate when it came to the whole truth. "Look, may I come in? I have a story in which you might be interested."

And so it was that, trusting his ex-student, Barry stood aside and ushered Maurice into the now somewhat crowded Shepherd's Hut where he was confronted by not only the elusive Jeremy Crawford, whom he recognised from his Internet exposure, but also two other people, of whose identity he had a fair idea. Plus there were the animals from his dreamscape. The latter sniffed traces of Terpsichore/Tiddles/Cat and were initially suspicious and standoffish, but once Maurice tickled them on their occipital bones, they were persuaded he was kosher and took to licking him.

By contrast, the humans, Jeremy in particular, remained mistrustful even after Barry had introduced Maurice, saying he was the most high-flying alumnus he'd ever had the pleasure of teaching and was a thoroughly decent chap. Even so they wondered what the hell the bloke was doing here of all places and at *this* time of night/early morning. And *how* had he tracked Barry down to the middle of nowhere when their host had assured them all connections with his past life had been severed years ago when he quit Oxford to become a gardener.

Even more pertinently, what if it weren't actually Barry he was looking for? What if he were a Sir Magnus Montague appointee who had somehow stumbled upon Jeremy's whereabouts and who, despite the dogs' thumbs-up and his harmless-looking demeanour in his brown three-piece tweed suit, should be treated with extreme caution?

Jeremy's face betrayed this suspicion and Maurice wasn't surprised. How likely was it, after all, that one of the most wanted men on the planet would just smile and say "hi" to some stranger breaking into his erstwhile top secret hidey hole? Not likely at all.

"Perhaps I could take a seat?" said Maurice.

At which Barry waved him to a ratty American rocker.

"Make yourself comfortable, old chap. It's in that chair I do my crosswords. Cup of tea? Or perhaps something stronger?"

Like Julie Mackintosh before him, Maurice went for the stronger.

Sipping at the Château Broadbent 2015 Premier Cru, he declared it, "Magnificent, better even than the Cockburn's Special Reserve of our Oxford days."

"Sorry for the intrusion, Prof, truly I am," he added. "But believe me, I come in peace and the hope I may be able clear some waters which have become muddied."

"Such as?" said Barry, topping up the glass of Premier Cru.

Maurice levered himself up in the American rocker and went for broke. "The matter of the megalomaniac bonkers banker, for example."

Jeremy's eyes widened and he shrank back on his sofa, as did Dennis and Julie on their seats.

Barry frowned meaningfully. "And may one ask at whose behest such waters are to be clarified, Mister Moffat? *Not* MI6's, one hopes."

Maurice pursed his lips, stroked his chin, and nodded. "Not directly," he said, which did little to calm nerves. Jeremy, for example, was all set to head for the door until Barry placed the calming hand on his shoulder that kept him on his sofa.

"Care to be a *tad* more precise, old fellow?" said Barry. "Mystification not exactly the order of the day in the circumstances."

Maurice sighed and nodded again.

"Let us just say I *am* officially here on government business," he admitted. "But not The Circus's. I come on behalf of the prime minister."

"Tuh-to fuh-find muh-*me*?" said Jeremy.

Maurice couldn't deny it. "She has plans for you, old fellow. But, you will be pleased to hear, such plans do not meet with my approval and under no circumstances shall I be releasing to her any details of your discovery, hence my first somewhat equivocal response to Prof Broadbent's question as to my role in this visit. And, in case either of your other guests—"Betty" and "Jackie Lamur" I presume—may be worried by my presence, I can equally assure them neither their Internet sobriquets nor their real names shall ever be mentioned outside these four walls.

"You know who we *are*?" Dennis spluttered. "How...?"

But this wasn't the moment for Maurice to reveal the workings of the reverse algorithmic code he'd invented to backtrace not only the ID behind the megalomaniac bonkers banker post but also, through a complex series of arcane bugging processes, the names of those with whom he or she had subsequently communicated on the same subject. Nor was it the time to tell of the GRNAV device that had traced Jeremy to the Shepherd's Hut.

"For the moment, just let us say I have ways and means, shall we?" he said. "Which I would be glad to explain further at some later date. But meanwhile, I repeat, you can be assured that nothing of what I have discovered shall be released to parties with ideas potentially detrimental to the wellbeing of any of you—Mister Crawford, Miss Mackintosh, or PC Dawkins. A fine piece of sleuthing it was to find Mister Crawford in the first place, by the way, Constable. Does you credit."

"Thanks," said Dennis.

"Well now, so it was Wibbly Wobbly who sent you," said Barry.

"Wibbly...?"

"The PM. The one who likes to present herself as strong and stable but is about as steadfast as a blancmange in a high wind."

Maurice laughed. "Haven't lost your touch with similes, I see, Professor. And yes it was she."

"And these 'plans' she has for me?" said Jeremy, finally finding his voice.

"In a nutshell, to blame you for practically every aspect of Britain's current decline into a tiny fifth-rate island nobody in his right mind will want anything to do with once the Brexit fiasco is finally done and dusted."

"Blame *me*? I know this damned megalomaniac bonkers banker story has got a bit out of hand, but..."

"Now it's reached the realms of the absurd?"

"Quite."

Maurice nodded. "A perfectly understandable reaction, old boy. But the PM is desperate for *any* story, however far-fetched, to divert public attention from her recent multiple *faux pas* and, with a little manipulation, yours must have appeared to fit the bill. Unfortunately for you, not even royal births or weddings were sufficient to distract Mister and Missus Joe Public's attention from the failings of her governance, so she needs a mega focus switcher to persuade them everything is still hunky dory in the sceptred isle and stop them believing it's her and her flimflam cabinet who've got us into the multiple messes we are currently in."

Jeremy frowned. "And how is she planning to...?"

"By concocting a fabric of lies around you, young man. How you had secret and subversive contacts with Igor Ripurpantzov and his Kremlin cronies in pursuance of the destruction of Western democracy as we know it. *Vide* the election of the fruitcake to The White House and the infiltration of the Brexit referendum campaign by bot farms all across Russia. How, singlehandedly once you decamped to Moscow, you diverted billions of tainted rubles from the City of London to illicit 'paradise' accounts all across the globe, thereby depriving the UK Treasury of the sorts of cash it needed to fund the army, the navy, the air force, the NHS, housing for poor people, and…so…on. How..."

"Don't go on. I get it," said Jeremy, holding up a palm.

"Bloody *hell*," said Julie.

"Bugger me," said Dennis.

Barry blew out his cheeks and stroked them.

"And you're here to...?" he asked Maurice, who hung his head and kneaded at it before replying.

"To deny Wibbly Wobbly her pleasure. I didn't sign up with the Secret Service with *this* sort of nonsense in mind. Was rather hoping to keep the world in some kind of order. For the general good, you might say. In pursuance of which objective I have a little ruse in mind for giving some of our leaders, Ripurpantzov in particular, a bit of a headache. For irony's sake, shall we say?"

Barry smiled. "Ah, *irony*. I remember it well, old fellow. Always something of a Socratic, were you not? Otherwise I would never have written you the glowing reference for the spooks. And what, may one ask, *is* this little ruse of yours? As it is to us you have come, one can only assume our participation might be required."

"Indeed," said Maurice, yawning. "But might I crave your patience until full daylight before I go into the details? It's been something of a hard day's night and..."

"No problem," said Barry. "I'm sure we could all benefit from a little shuteye."

So it was that Maurice, Barry, Dennis, Jeremy and Julie bedded down for what remained of the night although, with OO17's delayed explanation on their minds, sleep did not come easily. Even on the sofa bed they came to share either by accident or design, Jeremy and Julie were restless.

Shirley, Pete, Hans and Colin, by contrast, slept the sleep of the innocent. Such is the advantage of bestiality.

Seventeen

From his majestic chambers on the top floor of the Kremlin, Igor Ripurpantzov looked out over the nighttime Moskva River, rubbed his hands, sipped at a glass of Cobetckoe Ntpnctoe champagne and marvelled at his power. From his days as a small fry KGB officer, he really had done *rather* well. The old Soviet Union was dead and buried with all its oil and gas assets safely sequestered in his various beneath-the-radar banks and companies, and the new Russia was safely under his control for the better part of two decades, during which he'd either been president or prime minister with a puppet president speaking his words. *Such* a clever—and rich—chap he was. And...how...*good*...that felt. The tsars would have been proud of him, although of course he had done a lot better than any of them, and certainly better than their Soviet replacements. Whenever before had Russia ruled the world? Never, that was when. Until Igor took command, that was. And now the world was his oyster; he could do anything he liked and nobody had the cojones to stand against him. Invade Crimea and suck it back into the Russian union, easy peasy. Ensure Syria went on singing from his hymn sheet by pretending to rid the country of its "terrorists." No sweat. And so on, and so forth. It was even better now he had the dork in The White House in his pocket and a number of European governments were jittery and crumbling just the way he'd planned. And none of this with any effort or expense. No cold war missile stand-offs required. Just some little low-cost pieces of code fed by his IRA (Internet Research Agency) into the right places at the right time, and hey presto, *zhizn'prekrasna* ("life is wonderful" in Russian).

Igor sipped down a little more of his Cobetckoe Ntpnctoe and toasted his achievements. Yes, he'd had to have poisoned or shot a few dissidents who'd made their way from the homeland with anti-Igor messages, but, hey, casualties were an inevitable part of any bold strategy, weren't they? And no judge in Russia would have the temerity to raise an eyebrow, not when the entire judiciary was in his pocket. From where else would they get their fancy 4x4 Mercedes, and their dachas on the Black Sea, and the billions of rubles to flush through sad little old London? No, no, Igor Ripurpantzov had no worries on that front. Or any other.

He strolled away from his window, humming to himself a Western song called "If I Ruled The World." Only, in Igor's case, the hypothetical had become redundant. There had just been another presidential "election" which he had won hands down as expected. As things stood, he would be president for*ever*. Oh, what joy it was be alive in these wondrous times! After a quick workout in his gym to maintain the alpha-male-with-big-pecs image, Igor reckoned he deserved a long, hot, unguent-rich soak in his marble-tiled, Roman-type, sunken bath in the company of his currently favoured concubine, Ludmilla.

So that's what he did.

~ * ~

At much the same time—minus the three-hour difference, of course—PM Clarissa was in Brussels for a European heads of state summit, before the commencement of which she was getting an ear-bashing from the president of the European Commission, Bastien Duchamps, during a *sub rosa* meeting in a locked antechamber well away from the waiting TV cameras and microphones outside on the rue Wiertz.

"Now listen up, Clarissa. And listen up good," Bastien kicked off with while Clarissa smiled one of her gormless smiles. "No way can you keep on with the Bregshit bullshit you're peddling, okay?" he continued in the fluent American he had learnt during his exchange year between the Sorbonne and Harvard Law School.

"No *way*," he stressed.

"Um...erm..." said Clarissa, adopting what she thought of as a steely look. "Let me be clear. What ex*act*ly are you saying here, Sebastian?"

"Bastien."

"Pardon?"

"My name is *Bastien*."

"Ah," said Clarissa, twiddling, she hoped sexily, her left long-drop silver earring with the single diamond inset. "And your point is?"

"You want the trade deal you say you want, you gotta give us: Number one, a whole lot more dough than is currently on the table. Number two, a legally *binding* assurance on EU citizens' future rights after Bregshit. And number three, an equally legally binding solution to the Ireland border business agreed by all parties. No watertight answer to those little problems, no deal on trade or anything else."

"Oh," said Clarissa. "Look, Bastiano, let me be clear. Point taken. I'll get my top chap on it straight away."

"Not if it's the dingbat you *keep* sending, the Bregshit secretary dude you got along with you today for back-up." Bastien winced. "Guy's a banana skin waiting to be slipped on."

"Peter Peters?"

"That's the bozo."

"He tells me he's been making *splendid* progress in the talks over here."

"Splendid, my ass."

"No need for obscenities, Mister Ducheese."

"Du*champs*. And, for the record, it's Doctor."

"Golly. And you gave up a lucrative medical practice for..."

"I am a doctor of philosophy, Clarissa."

"Oh."

"And could we puh-*lease* get back to the point? You Brits mightn't have noticed, but it is the future of the European Union I am responsible for here. And I do not mean to let it flounder and sink in the wake of your dumbass Ruskie-rigged referendum."

"Good thinking," Clarissa was saying as a press aide called Maxine knocked on the door reminding them the media were outside on the street, eager for any hint of developments in the private talks before the summit meeting itself began.

"Any hopeful little whisper I might feed them?" asked Maxine.

"Ah, *l'espoir*," Bastien sighed, before taking Clarissa's hand and leading her like a lamb to the slaughter toward the parliament chamber in which, after a brief consultation with the egregious Peter Peters, she was hoping to present the cast-iron case for the best possible deal for the UK while making no mention of money, Euro citizens, or Ireland. On the way, over her shoulder, she whispered to Maxine trotting along behind that she and Sebastiano were making "excellent progress."

Once inside an antechamber, however, Bastien set Clarissa adrift and hurried off to discuss more urgent matters than Brexit with representatives from the twenty-seven other countries in the union. Smiling, in some cases laughing, pressing the flesh, kissing cheeks, back slapping, and in every instance speaking at least a modicum of his friends' languages. Unlike Clarissa, who, until the official agenda began, was left to wander about on her stork-like legs trying to meet and greet, but failing. Nobody seemed keen to talk to her. There was the occasional "hello there, how's it going?" from the German chancellor or the Dutch prime minister or the French president, but nothing to write home about. None of the crucial one-to-one insider deal-making hints and whispers she'd been hoping for. Partly because she was, in the Europeans' view, a petitioner claiming an outrageous alimony settlement from a dubious divorce. Partly also because, working on the principle that if a person spoke loudly enough in English, Johnny Foreigner would eventually understand, she hadn't even a *Bonjour* or a *Guten Tag* at her disposal, let alone a whole phrase or sentence. Thus ostracized, she searched the room for Peter Peters to have at least *some*one to chat to before her big speech.

"Excusey moy," she asked of a passing prime minister from some country or another. "Any idea where Peter Peters is? He's s'posed to be around here somewhere."

"Peter Peters?" The Danish PM Anders Frederiksen scratched his head and frowned while trying to put a face to the name. "Ah, Peter *Peters*. Your back-up guy?" he said in impeccable English.

"My Brexit secretary. I need to speak to him urgently on a top-level matter."

Anders smothered a chuckle. "Yes, okay, Peter Peters. So I *have* seen him."

"*Where*?"

"In the little boys' room, although he didn't see *me*."

"Why not?"

"Because he'd lost his spectacles. Last I saw of him he was walking backwards into a cubicle saying, "Where're my *specs*? Oh, shit."

"Dearie me," said Clarissa, gloomily recalling both Peter Peter's failing eyesight and his ongoing bowel issues.

"Now, if you'll excuse me, Clarissa? People to see, deals to do. Busy, busy, busy. Longing to hear your speech later, though. Sooo *great* Britain used to be. I loved it over there."

And with that Anders was off for a handshake and shoulder bump with emcee Bastien Duchamps, who knew how say "good day" in Danish.

"*God dag*, Anders," he said, before the two of them lapsed into English, neither referring to the Brexit dilemma except for a passing mention.

"Blast it all to blastiness!" whispered Clarissa to herself before snatching a vol au vent from the tray of a passing waitress and wolfing it down in one.

"Mmm," mused the waitress, an ex-concubine of Igor Ripurpantzov's called Katya, newly promoted to the role of international spy.

And within microseconds, Clarissa's discomfiture had been relayed in super-secret code to Moscow with the question: "How much longer can we allow this woman to survive?"

To which pinged back Ripurpantzov's instant reply: "Forever. She's fucking up the UK for us even better than *we* could. But nice work, keep the posts coming."

~ * ~

After a few hours of fitful sleep and a breakfast of poached eggs on toast with tea or coffee according to preference, Barry suggested he and his guests take a ramble in the bluebell woods behind his mobile Shepherd's Hut.

"Nothing better than a little nature to soothe the troubled breast into a magnitude of quiet, eh?" he said. "Bring the animals along too, shall we?"

Maurice was delighted at the proposal and, once persuaded they would be safe from prying eyes, so were Julie, Jeremy, and Dennis. Shirley, Hans and Colin were over the moon. The only one who wanted to stay at home was Pete the pig. As the others were ready to leave, he expressed this wish by lying down in Barry's front garden, grunting contentedly, and refusing to budge even when prodded or offered a parsnip.

"You're *sure* now, Pete?" said Jeremy, who during his recent adventures had never once been separated from his pig.

"Oink!"

"Okay then. So off we go. Sure you'll be okay?"

"Oink, *oink*," said Pete like a child reassuring an anxious parent he'll be just fine left home-alone for the first time.

"Oo*kay* then."

And once satisfied Pete's decision was final, Jeremy trotted off in the wake of Barry and company, who were waiting for him at the gate to a dense area of silver birches, old oaks, pines, and, by a rivulet, even two or three massive swamp cypresses. And yes bluebells. There were thousands of them stretching away along the borders of the single footpath, which would lead on a circular route through the woodland and back to the gate.

"Wow," he said, taking a deep breath and Julie's hand.

Shirley, Hans, and Colin were yipping and pawing at the gate, eager to be released from their leashes.

"So, young Jeremy, the world's most wanted man," said Barry. "Ready to ramble?"

Maurice and Dennis, who'd been getting better acquainted through spy/cop chat, smiled.

"Pete all right, is he?" Dennis asked.

"He's fine."

"So let's hit the woods," said Maurice. "Open the gate, Prof, and let us experience that magnitude of quiet of which you spoke."

And apart from the barking of Shirley, Colin and Hans at the squirrels thumbing their noses at them from the branches of trees, and the twittering of birds, including a squawky flock of newly immigrant parakeets, the quiet was indeed magnitudinous. As he ambled along,

Jeremy felt the pressures of recent days falling away. Julie's hand in his helped too.

"Great, eh?" she said, skipping along beside him. "Haven't felt this good since Dad took us up to the Lake District camping."

Then she broke into song. "I love to go a-wandering, along the mountain track. Val-deri, Val-dera, Val-deri, Val-dera-ha-ha-ha-ha-ha..."

Jeremy smiled. "Only we're in a forest," he said.

"Never mind, same effect."

Ahead of them, Barry, Maurice, and Dennis turned and smiled too.

"Young love?" said Maurice.

"*New* love maybe," said Dennis. "Mind you, you can't blame the bloke after Missus Sophie finicky fancy pants."

"That would be his wife to whom you're referring," said Maurice, stumbling over a swamp cypress breathing tube.

"Yeah, how did you...?"

"One does one's homework, old chap."

Which was when, after throwing three sticks in three different directions for Shirley, Hans, and Colin to chase instead of chasing the squirrels they'd never catch anyway, Barry left Dennis in charge of the dogs, and, checking that "new love" Jeremy and Julie were still otherwise distracted, took Maurice by the arm and guided him down a side path which would re-join the main one at the entrance gate.

"You have yet to tell us of your ironic plan for friend Ripurpantzov, old fellow," he said. "And possibly best for now were it to be shared only between the two of us, do you not think? For old times sake, before we pass it along to the troops. Give it a little scrutiny first."

"I thought you'd never ask." Maurice laughed. "Lost none of the old wiliness, gardening or no gardening, eh, Prof?"

"One does one's best as one ages, young man. Vital to keep the mind sharp, whatever the circumstances, I have found."

Maurice nodded. "Tell me about it."

"Soo...any beans you'd care to spill?"

Which was when Maurice recounted to Barry his dream-inspired memory of the TV programme in which the old man in St Petersburg with lank hair was building a shrine to John Lennon and peering out at the sea awaiting his return. Thinking even one of the seagulls might be John flying home to where so many people still worshipped him.

"Very popular he and The Beatles were over there," he said. "There are even those who claim it was *their* influence on youth culture that led to Gorbachev's new thinking and the end of the cold war."

Barry blinked. "And this has what to do with your ironic plans for Ripurpantzov, old chap?"

Maurice watched on with suggestively raised eyebrows as his old mentor struggled to compute the admittedly abstruse logic behind his plan. He didn't have to watch on for long however. As he had already noted, Barry had lost none of his old wiliness.

"Maurice, old fellow, you *don't* seriously mean...?"

"Well actually, Professor, yes I do. Only a little idea in its embryonic stages so far, of course, but it is hard to deny the manner in which the current occupant of the Kremlin is leading us back to days even more dangerous than those of the last cold war."

Barry nodded. "Indeed. A very nasty piece of work."

"Quite. And neither can one deny the continuing popularity of The Beatles as evinced by the TV programme I mentioned. John Lennon is a particular favourite."

"The one who said The Beatles were more popular than Jesus and upset the Yanks?"

"The same."

"Who you're now suggesting could become more popular than Ripurpantzov and upset some apple carts over there," said Barry as the tumblers fell in quick succession.

"I think he's got it! By George he's got it," trilled Maurice in a poor imitation of Henry Higgins in *My Fair Lady*.

Barry laughed. "A fine idea. But, correct me if I'm past my sell-by date, only The Beatles split up, did they not? And poor old George and John are dead. Bit of a snag, eh?"

"Indeed. However, just as old Igor has tampered with the Internet to further his own nefarious interests, so too could we in order to undercut those interests."

"Your irony.'

"My irony."

"And you would achieve this by?"

"Creating through computer generated imagery a tribute Beatles band nobody could distinguish from the real thing."

Barry's eyes widened. "Despite two of them no longer being with us?"

"Trust me, Internet users will believe *any*thing. Including revenants. And we start with the advantage of Jeremy Crawford looking more than a teensie bit like old John, would you not say? Same sort of nose. Similar eyes. Add a wig and a touch of makeup and…"

"Bob's your uncle."

"And Fanny's your aunt. And, from his post-Beatles career, my new John will take to the Russian people the very messages Igor will least want them to hear. He will speak to them of making love not war, of giving peace a chance, of working-class heroism, of people coming together and sharing all the world…and so on. And woven into each clip will be subliminal cuts showing the manner in which Ripurpantzov ripped off the ex-Soviets' oil, gas, and metal wealth before rigging elections and going for the record as the longest serving Russian leader since Stalin."

"And all done on the naughty Internet?"

"Every last bit. I have all the kit I need. And call it serendipity but, as I said, Mister Crawford has some of the very characteristics we shall need for the Lennon role," Maurice was saying as Shirley, Colin and Hans came bounding towards them.

"Shhhh, *shhhhh*, here he comes," said Barry as they reached the end of their side path and were re-joined at the woodland gate by Jeremy, Julie and Dennis, all of whom had had a thoroughly good time but were starting to feel peckish again.

Eighteen

Since biffing PC Jason Humphreys on the nose, suffering a (mercifully treatable) cardiac arrest, and, after an unexpectedly rapid recovery from his triple bypass being hauled up before the magistrates and handed down a six-week Community Service order sluicing out public lavatories, Sir Magnus Montague had become a new man. Not as the result of any single one of these events, of course. It was more of an accretional process.

Very grumpy he had been after his heart op. *So* grumpy with his nurses that Professor Doctor Hugo Printemps had threatened to discharge him early if he continued with such ungrateful behaviour as refusing his meds and yanking at the wires attaching him to his life support machine.

"Zree more strikings and you're *out*," said Hugo in Franglais. "Alzough it may soon not be me tellin' you zis. Maybe some uzzer professor doctor."

"Uh?" said Sir Magnus, with difficulty.

"Already I am receiving letter from ze 'Ome Office zaying I gotta register or I go back in France. Brexshit, *non*? Okai, *je m'en fous*. I go back in France an' fuck you Brits," he said before stalking out of Sir Magnus's private room, slamming the door behind him.

"Hugo...Hugo...come back here," Sir Magnus managed to squeak.

But his squeaks were silenced once nurse Angeles Rodriguez, who was also contemplating leaving the UK, told him to shut up and zapped him with a megadose of intravenous bisoprolol/hydrochlorothiazide spiked with Valium.

It was only upon regaining consciousness that Sir Magnus took the first baby step towards becoming the new man he now was. This he achieved by thanking Angeles and Hugo for saving his life. You know how it is when you've been spared a visit to the Pearly Gates, how grateful you feel.

"Sorry if I was a bit bitchy before," he said. "But I am very grateful, truly I am."

"It was nozzink," said Hugo, who had conducted the surgery. "Every day we do zese sings. Tomorrow you will be good to leave."

He was about to turn on his heels when Sir Magnus called him back.

"Look, if there's *any*thing I can do to help with your Home Office problem, you only need ask. Let us just say I have connections."

Hugo shrugged Gallically. "We shall see what we shall see. Only first you could help my friend Angeles. She too has had ze letter."

"Good God," said Sir Magnus, who had thus far been an ardent Brexiteer. "You mean...? There must have been some kind of a mistake."

More Gallic shrugging, this time accompanied by Angeles's Hispanic equivalent, during which Hugo explained that if Brexit meant repatriating any more European doctors and nurses, the UK wouldn't have a health service any more, let alone a "free-at-the-point-of-entry" national one. Then they were both gone, leaving Sir Magnus aghast.

It was PC Jason Humphreys who, bearing no grudges despite his broken nose and having visited Sir Magnus every day since his hospital admission, took the place of Hugo and Angeles at his bedside.

"Feeling better today, are we, sir?"

"Like a new man. They're letting me out tomorrow."

"Glad to hear it."

"And look, Jason, I'm *so* sorry about the busted beak."

"These things happen, sir."

"And I don't know if I can ever thank you enough for the on-the-spot resuscitation you gave me. I'd have been a dead man otherwise."

"All part of the job, sir."

"For which I hear you guys are not paid nearly enough. And no need for the 'sir,' you can call me Magnus."

"Okay…Magnus," said Jason, before giving the big city banker some of the facts of life for those dependent on public sector pay. How, as long as austerity continued to bite, nobody on the government payroll was looking at a wage hike anytime soon: police, firemen, doctors and nurses (e.g. Hugo and Angeles), teachers, and on and on. No wonder that morale in the NHS and so many other critical public services was at an all-time low. And all this while the I'm-all-right-Jack rich looked the other way.

Sir Magnus chewed at his lower lip and swallowed hard.

"Sorry," he said, holding out a hand to Jason. "So sorry. What more can I say?"

Clearly there was more the knight of the realm might have said, but these were waters in which he never before swum and so he remained wordless. There was also plenty more Jason might have said. Such as, "The next time your Bentley won't start, don't waste police and hospital time by hitting it and having a heart attack, call the AA. But he didn't. All he said was, "Sorry is fine, Magnus. Now, if you'd excuse me? Work to do?"

"Of course. Of course," said Sir Magnus, racking up baby step two.

Which leaves baby step three, namely the manner in which he hung his head and told presiding magistrate Dame Sally Swinburne at his magistrates court appearance how remorseful he felt at breaking PC Humphreys' nose, particularly when afterwards PC Humphreys had saved his life with CRP. So it was an unreserved guilty plea he was entering. At which Dame Sally told him he was a lucky man indeed to be facing no more than a Community Service order sluicing out public lavatories when, without the leniency plea from PC Jason Humphreys, the defendant might instead have been looking at six months of jail time.

"Thank you, ma'am. *Thank* you," said Sir Magnus, "I shall do my very best to leave the toilets spic and span. *And* to review my future role in British society."

Dame Sally raised her eyebrows. "With which project I wish you the very best of luck," she muttered before ordering a flunkey to remove Sir Magnus from her court.

"Next case, please," were the last words Sir Magnus heard echoing behind him before being released into the custody of his probation officer, Terry Wishbone, for an introduction to the latest lavatory-sluicing devices and a list of the conveniences, male and female, for which he would be responsible.

~ * ~

Sated after a lunch of sausages, mash and peas, Jeremy, Julie and Dennis said what a fine walk they had enjoyed, reiterated their thanks to Barry for his continued hospitality, and lay back with the dogs on the tatty sofas in the Shepherd's Hut parlour looking as though they might nod off. Meanwhile in the tiny kitchenette, dressed in pinnies as they washed the dishes, Barry asked Maurice if he were truly serious with this Ripurpantzov revenge idea.

"I mean, on mature reflection, it does seem a little, how shall I put it?" he said.

"Preposterous?" said Maurice, rinsing a plate.

"Quite. Not just in conception but also in practice. Are you *really* asking me to believe that dressing up Jeremy as a John Lennon lookalike and shooting his image all around Russia on the Internet will change *any*thing over there? Ripurpantzov is no Gorbachev, after all. And who are we, just the little people, to imagine we could make such a difference anyway?"

Drying the plate, Maurice nodded. "See where you're coming from, Prof. It does sound a tad outré, doesn't it?"

"Just a mite," said Barry, squirting more washing-up liquid into the green plastic bowl.

"But," Maurice said, "as you taught me back at Oxford, if a problem is to be addressed, first it needs to be broken down into its constituent parts. No chance of a workable principle being adduced otherwise. I believe it was Albert Einstein you used as an exemplar in those days."

Barry smiled while teasing sausage remnants from a frying pan. "Indeed so. Some memory you have, Mister Moffat. And how, may one ask, does this bear relevance to our current discussion?"

"Well, so far you have mentioned two elements: little people and practicality."

"Yes."

"Well, there are a couple points I would make."

"Just as when you were a student, old chap. Although sometimes back then it was three or even *four* points. All of them always relevant, of course."

Maurice held up his dried plate and asked where the plate cupboard was.

"Behind you, the red one. The blue one's for cups."

"Okay," said Maurice, stretching backwards. "So let us take the 'little people' first, shall we?"

"With pleasure."

"Well, it is my view they are no longer so little and they're now basking in their new power."

"Explain?"

"Because in America it was they who were directly responsible for electing the psychotic baby man to The White House, and here in Britain for severing our forty-year-old ties to the European Union. Far from being 'little,' these guys' power grew in proportion to the opportunities offered them."

"Um…I don't quite see…"

"Populism, old chap. The manipulation, largely through the social media's tribal mentality, of the disaffected underclasses which suffered most from the banking crash of two thousand and eight. There's nobody a disadvantaged person is more likely to vote for than a superhero promising to fight for his rights. Ripurpantzov's power works on much the same principle with Russians when he demonizes the West."

Barry nodded as the logic hit home. Since his gardening days he had paid little attention to politics.

"Which," Maurice continued, "left armies of white trash voters in the West easy prey to all manner of alt-right machinations. What were they told they should want? 'Change,' that was what. *Any* change which would put more money in their pockets and restore their national pride. And they fell for it hook, line and sinker. All that was then required were false enemies, normally 'outsiders,' for them to hate. Think Hitler here. So in the last two years, these 'little people' have changed Western politics out of all recognition while the liberal centre was caught napping and the extreme left and right took advantage by colluding in their fake news and post-truth versions of history."

"Good God," said Barry.

"And I cannot stand idly by and watch on while my world is turned on its head. Both personally and professionally, I take it as my duty to do whatever I can, if not totally to reverse these trends but at the very least to plant a few bombs in their path. As for the practicality of my plan, I have no idea if it will work. But then nothing ventured, nothing gained, eh? No E equals MC squared, no General Theory of Relativity, for example. And Einstein himself wasn't absolutely sure he was right even then."

Barry chuckled and scrubbed harder at his frying plan.

"So all I can suggest is that we trust our analysis and have a bash. If we make just the tiniest inroad, that would be a bonus. If we don't, we don't, but at least we will have tried. I say 'we.' Are *you* prepared to join in, despite the preposterousness? Need time to think it over perhaps?"

Barry shook his head. "No, no. I'm persuaded. But I'm no computer whizz, Maurice. Quite what skills I could offer, I…"

"You would leave all that to me, Prof. As I said, I have the equipment and I know how to use it. But a second pair of eyes to look over the final product would be invaluable. The way you once corrected my essays with those little pencilled comments in the margins?"

Barry nodded and smiled. "And such essays they were, a pleasure to read. Much like the argument you have just prosecuted."

"Thanks."

"Oh, and by the by, improbable though it may sound, I used rather to like John Lennon. My favourite of his songs was 'Imagine.'"

Maurice laughed. "Just like the old guy in St Petersburg. And who knows what the fallout might be once we dress Jeremy up as John returned from the dead and send the image virally with a suitable text? Russia would be the primary target, of course, but who knows what other spin-off effects there might be? We might even be able to resurrect in the US and the UK echoes of bygone better days and whip up a backlash against the unreason of *these* times. So you are with me?"

"Every step of the way," said Barry. "But there remains the problem of persuading Jeremy into his role in all of this."

"Don't worry. I'll talk to him," said Maurice. "But judging by the radical moves he's recently made to change his life around, I have the feeling he's the sort of chap ready for another adventure, albeit only a virtual one."

Nineteen

Following the "triumph" of her grovelling last ditch offer of billions of pounds to Bastien Duchamps in exchange for his moving on Brexit negotiations from the tortuous issues surrounding the initial divorce to "serious discussions on trade," PM Clarissa was pooped. Talking all the previous night on the phone to the Northern Irish and squabbling members of her own cabinet to "establish her authority" and then taking a pre-dawn flight back to Brussels to "lay her cards on the table" before Bastien were enough to poop anybody. But pooped though she was, she went on grinning gormlessly from the announcement podium the following morning even when, in front of the world's media, Bastien reminded her from his lectern that in all divorces the first part was always the easiest. What came afterwards was harder to thrash out, much more complicated, and would certainly take longer to achieve than Clarissa apparently had in mind. If anything were achieved at all.

"Nothing is agreed until everything is agreed," said Bastien in summary.

But on Clarissa went nonetheless, waving the flag for Britain. Not the *whole* of Britain, you understand. The 48% of EU Remainers from the 2016 referendum, for example, ridiculed her performance. As, paradoxically, did a large proportion of the 52% Leavers, who reckoned she was being conned by the very unelected European morons they wanted no more to do with, which was why they'd voted leave in the first place. A similar division was replicated within her cabinet back at 10 Downing Street, although to the media hacks with their cameras waiting outside, every minister struggling through the door produced toothy smirks and thumbs ups while muttering undying allegiance to their leader. The only one to produce any joined-up language was "Fat Slob," the foreign secretary who, over his shoulder, said, "Finally we've got HMS Britain off the rocks and set her sailing again," before waving perfunctorily at the cameras and hurrying off "On urgent business in Bongo Bongo Land." No wonder, on her return to the sceptred isle, pooped Clarissa had scuttled through the doors of No 10 and headed straight upstairs to her bedroom, upon whose door she plastered the warning DO NOT DISTURB UNDER ANY CIRCUMSTANCES WHATSOEVER.

Not that Clarissa slept easy. Normally she went out like a light once her head hit the pillow and, being a person devoid of imagination, never dreamed. But not so on this occasion. Toss and turn, turn and toss she went in her prime ministerial four poster, alongside which, on a bedside table, sat her hotline phone to the madman in the White House, which never rang because the madman in the White House was too busy tweeting and re-tweeting he was a "stable genius" against the charge he was an unbalanced baby too much in need of perpetual instant gratification to be bothered with the "special relationship." And, during this tossing and turning, in semi-sleep, Clarissa uncharacteristically experienced what she assumed to be a vision. Terrible it was too: Clarissa being stabbed in the back while breast-stroking across the ladies' swimming pond on Hampstead Heath by Fat Slob who was abetted by Lurch, aka the chancellor of the exchequer, Jiggle Jaws the home secretary, the rest of the cabinet, and a significant number of the Nazi/Tory members in the Houses of Commons and Lords, all of them in black wetsuits and goggles treading water beneath her. And then came the *coup de grâce* administered by the Bowie knife thrust up her thorax by Bastien Duchamps. His wetsuit was blue with twelve gold stars on it.

Unsurprisingly, Clarissa emerged from this novel experience gagging and clutching at her throat, but, as she'd been taught on the playing fields of Roedean and Cambridge after being hit in the face by a hockey stick, one did not cry. Unlike her Roedean and Cambridge days, however, now she kept two bottles of spirits—vodka and gin—in the cupboard beneath her bedside table, and from them she took hefty swigs before calling Sir Hubert Humphreys and Dame Muriel Eggleshaw on her hotline phone to demand progress on the search for Jeremy Crawford, the guy she now realised she needed more radically than ever to re-focus the narrative on the UK's—and her—fate.

~ * ~

The man in question was currently back in the bluebell woods abutting Barry's Shepherd's Hut, but this time accompanied by only Maurice Moffat, who had invited him out for "a little chat." The dying sun cast oblique shadows on the pair as they ambled along through the trees before deciding to take a rest on the trunk of a fallen oak, which offered convenient indentations for both their bottoms.

"You cannot be serious," said Jeremy in the manner of John McEnroe querying an umpire's line call decision.

"Such was more or less the view of your new friend Barry," Maurice said, taking from his coat pocket a well-chewed rosewood briar and a pouch of St Bruno. "I think in the end, however, even he was persuaded," he added, tamping the tobacco into the pipe.

"That *I* should dress up as John Lennon, and…"

"Only a lookalike, old chap," said Maurice, using one hand to fire up the briar with a Zippo Pipe Master and the other to ensure no lit embers fell to the forest floor.

"And then have it fed all around Russia to upset Ripurpantzov? C'*mon*…"

"Stranger things have happened in the USA, Jeremy. But, before we go any further, may I be sure as to the root of your disquiet? Personal or political, which is it?"

Jeremy took a deep breath of the forest air and stared off at the setting sun, its shadows now longer.

"It's just…" he eventually said.

"That?" Maurice said, puffing at his briar.

"Many things have happened to me in recent times, things I could never have foreseen, and…"

"Things you chose, Jeremy, however. As I understand it, at least. Rather in the manner in which Barry chose to be a gardener instead of continuing to be an Oxford professor."

"True." Jeremy smiled. "Choosing for once, rather than being chosen."

"Exactly. And, let us be clear that with choice comes responsibility. It's not just a question of freeloading like the hippies all those years ago. We cannot merely opt out of systems. Which was the great thing about Lennon. The way he laid bare his weaknesses then tried to encourage others to do the same, even though everybody in those days thought he was crazy. 'Come together over me,' right?"

Jeremy nodded. "The personal and the political equal parts of the same thing?"

"Quite. And by 'political,' we're not talking party politics. We're talking everyday life."

"Mmm. And what exactly is your part in that, Maurice? From the super-spook perspective. You must be risking your neck a bit with this Ripurpantzov plan. Tricky selling it to the top brass, I should have thought."

"There are times, Jeremy, such as now, when the balance of global affairs has shifted so drastically that one senses the imperative to do something about it without asking anyone's permission and let the devil take the hindmost. You chose to leave your past life behind in silence and without a clue of what was up ahead. Such a choice is also open to me."

Maurice shrugged and fiddled with his pipe.

"That word 'choice' yet again," said Jeremy.

"Indeed. But, as Jean-Paul Sartre remarked, 'Commitment is an act, not a word.' According to him, if we are truly to *be*, first we must use our freedom to choose, then we must act in accordance with that choice."

In Jeremy's mind distant bells rang, reminders of the philosophy bit of his PPE programme all those years ago. "So we don't just *exist* like the other animals."

"Quite. In Sartre's view, human essence is supposedly beyond mere existence." Maurice chuckled while sucking at his pipe. "Mind you, a proper cock-up we've made of our superior powers so far, have we not? By wrecking the very planet we live on, just for starters."

"Maybe that's why Barry became a gardener," said Jeremy. "To save the last patches he could. Like this bluebell wood."

"And more power to his elbow. I wish him well. Meanwhile, there remains this little favour I was asking of you. Any further thoughts?"

"I'll think it over. If I've come this far, I could go a little further, right?"

"Up to you, old chap," said Maurice, tapping out the ashes of his pipe on the heel of his shoe and making sure they didn't set fire to any undergrowth. "Your choice. Now should we make our way back home? People will be wondering where we've been for so long."

~ * ~

Back at the Shepherd's Hut, Dennis and Julie had asked Barry why Jeremy and Maurice had gone off on their own, to which Barry replied, "Oh, you know just a little ramble. Some project Maurice has in mind. You'll find out soon enough, I'm sure. Meanwhile cups of tea all round perhaps? I also have some rather good Hobnobs we could chew on.

"Sounds good to me," said Dennis, mussing Colin's ruff with one hand and Hans's with the other from his armchair while Shirley lay curled at Julie's feet. Pete had opted to sit outside awaiting his master's return.

"Want a hand with the tea and biccies?" said Julie.

"Many thanks," said Barry. "Tell you what, I'll brew and you can carry. How would that be?"

Julie grinned. "So it's the girl that gets to be the waitress?"

"Oops, sorry, no offence intended, I promise you. So, to remedy matters, how about *you* brew and *I'll* carry. How would that be?"

"Perfect. But no bags okay. When I make tea, I need leaves and a pot."

"Follow me, Julie. A pot you shall have and access to leaves of many varieties from builders' to lap sang su chong. I shall leave the blend to you while I prepare my tray."

So off the pair went into the kitchen, leaving ex-copper Dennis/Betty to wonder what all the fuss was about. Where Dennis was concerned, girls were just girls and tea was just tea.

Mind you, when Barry returned ten minutes later toting the tray from which Dennis took his mug and sipped, even he was obliged to hoist his eyebrows and declare it the brew the best he'd ever tasted.

"Mmm," he said, licking his lips. "Perfect."

"My old dad's recipe. Glad you like it," said Julie. "Goes nicely with Hobnobs."

Colin, Hans and Shirley agreed as they were given pre-dunked biscuits to try.

"Raaf, raaf," they chorused, each sitting dutifully on their bottoms in the hope of more.

It was once everybody was seated again, happily sipping and dunking while offering the dogs the odd snack that Julie asked Barry for further elucidation of the question which had been nagging at her ever since her arrival at the Shepherd's Hut, namely: what exactly *was* it, this choosing and being chosen business. Okay, she could see why Jeremy might have wanted to change his life around, as indeed Dennis/Betty had. But…

"How might that also apply to you?" said Barry.

"Mmm, yes."

Normally Julie Mackintosh refused all questions about herself but now was not a normal time and Barry was a bloke—one of the very few apart from her father—she was starting to trust.

"Well," said Barry, "Given my recent *faux pas* on the waitress issue, you would be forgiven for not believing me, but I am and always have been a feminist."

Julie raised both eyebrows, Dennis blinked, and Barry nodded.

"Yes, I am," he confirmed. "I was never much impressed by the bra-burning and such antics, and was even more underwhelmed by their latterday little sister postfeminism because both rendered women easy prey to male mockery. But I believed and still believe in the vital issue of consciousness-raising, which to my mind was always the nub of the matter. And, interestingly, where it coincides with the 'choosing and chosen business' you asked about, Julie."

Dennis excused himself saying this was all a bit above his head and anyway he needed a pee.

Julie was interested though. "How?" she said, all ears.

"Well, in both cases what we are concerned with is 'know thyself,' as both Socrates and Plato pointed out. How can we understand other people if we don't understand ourselves, they asked. Sadly for many people such a question is relegated to the very depths of their psyches because they are so preoccupied with erecting an impenetrable self-image that to ask it would be inviting disaster. They *are* what they *seem* and that image needs to be constantly reinforced. Am I making any sense?"

Julie nodded. “Lots of it.”

“This is true for both men and women,” Barry continued. “But it seems to me that it’s women whose façades are the hardest to maintain. Call it a glass ceiling, call it anything you want, but even in these supposedly liberated days, it is still they who are the most exposed to the unexamined, predominantly male, assumptions of family, social class, race, religion, etcetera. The age old myths die hard.”

“In other words, we are always already chosen,” said Julie, reflecting ruefully on Sir Magnus’s view of what he still referred to as the gentle sex. “Still moving to the rhythms of others.”

“I couldn’t have put it more neatly myself. It seems you have just answered your own question.”

“Well, that kind of a life is not for *this* girl. Not anymore.”

Barry laughed. “I’m glad to hear it. Mind you, not *all* of us men are the blighters I describe. Some of us *have* done a little of the necessary thinking,” he was saying as Pete took to oinking and there came the knock on the door announcing the return of Jeremy and Maurice.

Julie ran to open it and took Jeremy by the hand.

Twenty

Sir Magnus Montague had taken even more steps towards becoming a new man and to honouring his promise before magistrate Dame Sally Swinburne to become more socially aware. He had, for example, written to PM Clarissa saying he didn't want to be a knight of the realm anymore and she could give his gong to anyone else she fancied, although his recommendation would be a deserving overworked person in the National Health Service. Nurse Angeles Rodriguez and Professor Doctor Hugo Printemps would be excellent candidates, in his view.

He had also radically reviewed his position at the bank. The initial temptation had been, like Jeremy, to quit altogether and run away. But on reflection he had opted to stay, albeit in the newly created role of the "facilitator" of an operation in which all employees, male and female, were equals, paid the same wages for the same work, and all of whom were granted both free shares in the business and votes at all board meetings. Amazed at this *volte face* were the employees, but also enthusiastic, grateful, and according to all indices, more productive than ever before. Ex-colleagues in the shrinking City of London were astonished, some of its luminaries even themselves considering similar moves in order to counter the threat of extinction as the Brexit negotiations continued to flounder.

Magnus, now known as "Maggie," was pleased. He hadn't transgendered or anything, you understand, just changed his name. But he had grown what was left of his hair into something vaguely resembling Elvis's—sideburns and a quiff—lost weight, and taken to wearing skinny black leather jeans, black T-shirts with logos such as PEACE AT ANY PRICE, and black brothel creepers specially crafted by a retro outfit called Old Shoes in Balham, South London. He had also sold his midnight blue Bentley—with a new battery—and donated the proceeds to charities for the homeless. These days, permanently sober and nicotine-free on doctor's orders, he travelled by Lambretta motor scooter wearing a white crash hat from which sprouted a little flag bearing in red letters the message FREEDOM. A new man indeed was (Sir) Magnus Montague but, as noted, a near-death experience can have that sort of effect on a person.

His desire to discover the whereabouts of Jeremy Crawford, however, remained un-diminished, although now for quite different reasons. No longer did he wish to punish the "little blighter" for having gone bonkers and deserted his post at the bank, no siree. Instead he wanted to shake him by the hand and congratulate him on the wisdom of his decision to get out of the game while he was still young enough to make a new start, unlike (Sir) Magnus/Maggie who, despite his recent lucky escape, was nonetheless in what he thought of a life's departure lounge. No spring chicken was he, despite his Elvis makeover. But he'd had no luck so far. Julie Mackintosh/Jackie Lamur was *still* as lost to the world as Jeremy himself, so hopes of finding him were fading fast on that front.

There had to be *some* other way, but what?

~ * ~

Even keener than Maggie to locate Jeremy was Clarissa the PM, "Post Mortem" as some of the more scurrilous organs in both the left- and right-wing press had taken to dubbing her. *So* keen she was unable to sleep at night without repeats of those damned dreams in which she is slaughtered by unnameable foes in terrible ways, including suspension by her heels over toilet bowls before being flushed down the S-bend with echoes of "Goodbye Cruel World" ringing in her waterlogged ears. Not great for a person in her position. Not great *at all*. Ergo the absolute need to find Jeremy Crawford fastest and brand *him* not her as the demon behind the nation's woes, in pursuance of which objective she again called her Casanova.

"Answer the bally phone, will you. It's *me*. Phoebe," she hissed as the super-triple-encrypted number rang and rang before going to message.

"Pah! Some bloody secret *agent*," she spluttered, pacing up and down her private Downing Street bedroom tugging at her hair while Maurice made his excuses to the company over supper at the Shepherd's Hut, saying this was a call he'd have to take.

"Bit of a clichéd line, old boy," said Barry through a mouthful of cheese and pickle. "Thought only B-list American movie PIs said that sort of thing. Still, if you must, you must."

"It's the PM," said Maurice, laying aside a newly forked radish. "Probably wanting updates. I'll get a better signal outside."

Jeremy paled with a half-chewed frankfurter in his mouth. "You're not going to tell her about…?" he managed to gurgle.

"Certainly not," said Maurice, as Julie leaned over and took Jeremy's hand.

"What *are* you going to tell her then?" she said.

"To get lost," was Dennis's advice, at which Maurice laughed.

"Not in so many words," he said over his shoulder as he made his way to the door with the phone in his hand. "Although you can rest assured legerdemain shall play an important role in my shtick. Think Iago here."

Barry smiled, amused to hear his protégé employing the sort of reference 007 could never have dreamt of.

"Sock it to her, old fellow," he said, but Maurice had already closed the door behind him.

"Phoebe, what a pleasure," he said after dialling the super-triple-encrypted number and holding the phone away from his ear until the torrent of staccato language blasting through it stopped. "And what can I do for *you* this evening?"

More torrential staccato language, much of it blurred by what Maurice took to be tears or fury or a combination of both. He was reminded of eyewitness reports from the West Wing of the White House when the baby man president was upset.

"Hello there Phoebe?" he said, in an attempt to stem the flow.

Which was when the prime minister of Great Britain, currently lying on the floor of her private Downing Street bedroom kicking her spindly legs in the air, gathered together what was left of her wits, remembered her Roedean training, and whispered, "That *is* you, Casanova?"

"The very same, ma'am. At your disposal."

"Thank God for that. Getting a tad confused. I need help."

"Too right you do," thought Maurice, although he was too well bred to say so. Instead he said, "Anything *I* can do to be of assistance?"

"Tell me where the megalomaniac bonkers banker is," was the reply, all the words run together so they sounded more like tell-me-where-the-megalomaniac-bonkers-banker-zzzz.

"I need him on *board*," Phoebe added in a more or less coherent utterance.

"Ah, so *that's* it,"

"Yesssss."

"I'm close to him. Very close," Maurice reassured her, not entirely untruthfully.

"Good. Good. Call me when you've got him. There's work for him to do," said Phoebe, reaching into the secret bedside table which contained not only high-percentage bottles of vodka and gin but also secretly prescribed packets of high dosage Valium pills, six of which she crammed into her mouth and swallowed before dropping her phone and crawling back into her bed. After all, she faced Prime Minister's Questions in the House the next day and needed to be on top form.

Maurice sighed, pocketed his phone, and returned to his Shepherd's Hut supper.

"Well, what did you *tell* her?" was the question on everybody's lips.

"As much as she needed to know and no more," said Maurice. "Don't worry, I gave nothing away," he added before outlining his worries over the PM's mental health, for which everybody expressed (limited) sympathy.

"So she still doesn't know where I am?" said Jeremy.

"No," said Maurice.

"Well, that's a relief, Iago. Jolly well your legerdemain must have gone down," said Barry. "Anybody fancy a top-up of the burdock brandy as a digestive?"

And everybody did. Julie even sang them a ditty of her own creation she'd never before admitted to anyone, not even her father. It was called "Let the Leaves Fall" and was autumnally sad to begin with but then, in verses two and onwards, came the new growths of the following spring. "Things can only get better," was the refrain.

Barry loved it. "Just hold on a mo," he said, rummaging in a cupboard until he found the battered old Gibson guitar he hadn't touched in years. "Bear with me," he added, "while I play you that old Chinese folk song called 'Tunin'.'

"Didn't know you were a guitarist, Prof," said Maurice. "One lives and learns."

"Indeed one does. Nothing fancy though, old chap, just a few basic chords," Barry said, holding an ear to the soundboard as he twiddled the pegs until satisfied with the tuning.

"Ah, that should do it. Now then, young Julie, sing us your song again and let's see if I can keep up with the melody."

So, giggling, Julie performed a reprise and, after only two more run-throughs she and Barry had a workable song, bluesy to begin with but then lightening up.

"How about we all join in on one last version?" Maurice proposed.

"Then we could be a group and go on X Factor." Dennis stood and wiggled his bottom.

"Yeah, yeah, yeah, all we need is love," chorused Jeremy Beatle-ishly.

And, you know what, the final result didn't sound half bad, decent harmonies and everything. When it was over, Julie did a little dance to thank everybody.

"WOW-EEEEE," she whooped as she pirouetted.

Jeremy shook his head and smiled in wonder.

~ * ~

Heartened by this musical coming together, when everybody was back on their chairs and sofas while Barry strummed through a serviceable rendering of Eric Clapton's "Layla," even including some of the twiddly riffs, Maurice leaned over and whispered in his ear, "Igor time?"

"Huh?" said Barry, his mind and fingers elsewhere.

"Ripurpantzov? Our little project? A good moment to spread the news?"

Barry carefully laid aside the ancient Gibson and nodded. "If you judge the auguries to be in our favour, Double O Seven."

"Seven*teen* actually."

"Ah, the new and improved model."

Maurice laughed.

"Jeremy on board, is he?" Barry asked.

"I judge so. Seems prepared for the next step."

"Well then, let us go for it. I believe that's the current parlance."

Twenty-one

For the psycho in the White House, things were going from poor to appalling, at least by rational standards, none of which, being psychotic, he shared. As if facing impeachment over allegations of Ripurpantzov's role in his election (which he denied as fake news) weren't bad enough, he was now facing a string of further allegations (also denied as fake news) of a plethora of sexual harassments and assignations with porn stars, as well as bestowing sinecures on members of his family, one of whom was claimed to be illegitimate, which he categorically denied as "the fakest of fake news. FAKE!!!"

Additionally there were continuing investigations into conflicts of interest between his business affairs and those of his presidential office, his refusal to declare tax returns, and nefarious money laundering deals done with the Russians by his son-in-law and his daughter. And matters weren't helped by the insider reports of backbiting, fury and intimidation in the White House, which the baby man commander-in-chief had dismissed in an outraged tweet as "a *fucking* fake fantasy" dreamt up by all his enemies: the Democratic Party, women, some "freaks" in the Republican Party, the media, immigrant communities, women, the UN, and "strangers" in general—basically anyone who wasn't male, mega-rich and white like him. In short, the guy was a mentally deranged bigot with a short fuse and, judging by his hands, some said, an even shorter dick.

Still he was the one who'd been chosen president, so he could do what he liked: declare Jerusalem to be Israel's capital even if it pissed off the Palestinians, play macho games with the "rocket man" in Pyongyang over who had the bigger nuclear button (dick) even if it pissed off the Chinese, dub as "shitholes" the countries from which he intended banning the intake to the US of any more brown or black people never mind how pissed off the UN got, "reform" tax laws so the poor imagined themselves less poor and the rich (him) got even richer, threaten to start World War Three any time he felt like it, fire or otherwise punish underlings who disagreed with these "policies" or, as in one case, called him "a fucking moron"...*any*thing he wanted he could do. And just like any baby craving affection, he threw out of his pram all the toys he didn't like, supporting the rationale for such actions by re-tweeting *his* view of himself as a genius who'd gone to all the best schools. Such wonderful tools the social media! Without ever leaving his lavatory, he could offload on the world all his darkest thoughts, albeit they lacked syntax, logic, or lexical accuracy. But that was just one more way he imagined of endearing himself to those who wrote their tweets just the same way he did. From the heart, he liked to think.

It was not only psychoanalysts around the globe who tut-tutted and shook their heads in concern at this behaviour. Practically everybody everywhere reckoned the bloke was off his trolley. You have to wonder how such a screwball could have been elected in the first place with or without Ripurpantzov's assistance, let alone remain in office for even six weeks.

Well, the answer is sadly simple. Because his hillbilly and redneck supporters from the outbacks of Tennessee and all points south all the way up north to the Rust Belt were as paranoid as he was, that was why. Folk who had been ignored by the "pinko liberals" in Washington DC "swamp" for far too long were over the moon suddenly to see their values reflected in the White House. John Wayne-type National Rifle Association bible-thumpers who shot first and asked questions later. Whose wives cooked them apple pie and looked sideways if they strayed a little into whorehouses. Guys with good ole American family values who shot moose, collected roadkill, and froze them for winter. Guys whose ancestors had driven the covered wagons west killing Injuns along the way, then given the Spanish invaders a good kicking when they arrived. Guys who didn't see why they shouldn't *still* be slave owners. In other words guys—and gals—stuck in a time warp falsely called the American Dream. And they were damned if any foreigner, especially Muslims or Mexicans, were going to take *that* away from them.

Hardly surprising the madman in the White House should be their hero. Every time he hollered "America First" at the only rallies he ever agreed to attend, i.e. those packed with his adoring hillbillies, rednecks and the "left behinds," they whooped and cheered. Which played nicely with the Republican Party establishment currently running both houses of Congress. *Far* too difficult it would have been for them to ditch the very working-class (albeit billionaire) hero who was keeping them in power even though he was clearly crazy as a coon under a red wagon.

And *this* was the president with whom PM Clarissa hoped to maintain the "special relationship" nurtured by Roosevelt and Churchill and later aped by Reagan, Thatcher, Bush and Blair when the Brexit negotiations came crashing down around her ears and there was no more Europe left to trade with. The president who, in a recent poll, had been deemed by 72% of British citizens to be a threat to world peace and thus never to be invited to their shores. How embarrassing would *that* be for the elderly Missus Queen and her gaga husband? Still Clarissa went on renewing the invitation, as did Fat Slob the foreign secretary, who had recently been seen practically genuflecting at the White House. Not that the baby madman seemed likely to accept when so many Brits loathed him. Might make him cry.

In Moscow, Igor Ripurpantzov looked on and smiled at the ensuing chaos. Everything coming nicely together just as planned, he thought, toasting himself with another glass of Cobetckoe Ntpnctoe.

~ * ~

Nowadays, even "Maggie" Montague had become aware of these potentially catastrophic shifts in the world order. As Sir Magnus, he hadn't given much of a toss, had actually quite liked the new president, thinking him a man after his own heart—a businessman who, unlike your regular politician, could tell shit from Shinola and didn't mind saying so. And if lily-livered liberals in the US had been taken by surprise by his improbable victory, the more fool them. Ditto the UK bunch of wet nellies currently bemoaning Brexit. More power to the elbows of the brave Brexiteers who had campaigned so valiantly to salvage British sovereignty from the clutches of the woolly-minded Europeans, was what Sir Magnus had reckoned. Which was why he had covertly funnelled funds from the bank's already in-the-red accounts to the Leave campaign in the belief he was helping preserve the power of the glorious nation which had for centuries defeated Europeans of all hues—on land, at sea, in the air, everywhere—to ensure it was Brits who colonised the world, not them.

So it was, just like the American hillbillies, rednecks and left-behinds, that Sir Magnus had unquestioningly accepted an always already mythic version of national identity, which on scrutiny bore no resemblance to current or even past reality. But neither he nor his fellow delusionists in the US had bothered with such parlous introspection…they had just swallowed history's stories/lies whole. Proud to be American, proud to be British, and happy to be chosen rather than take the time and effort to contemplate choice.

But that was the old Sir Magnus for you. The re-formed "Maggie" had rearranged his brain to see the world in a different context. Not cynical but resolutely sceptical such that nothing passed beneath his radar without critical examination. And how that had changed not just his external appearance, but also his mind! Even to the extent of wishing to repair some of the damage he had done in his old persona. His bank he had already fixed as best he was able, now he wanted to change the world. But first he needed to find Jeremy Crawford, congratulate him on his escape from mindless conventions, and offer any support he might need. But where the bloody hell *was* he?

It was for the wont of any better idea that he'd girded his loins in their skinny black leather jeans, donned the rest of his Lambretta-riding outfit—the crash hat with the FREEDOM flag and a Hells Angel-type black leather jacket—and burnt (okay "singed") rubber to Fanbury to see if the family had any news. He could have phoned but reckoned it better to go in person.

It was a bleary-eyed Sophie who opened the door, gawped for a second, and said, "If it's money you want, you can piss off," before slamming the door in his face.

Unsurprised but equally undeterred, Maggie pulled the bell-chime rope again and though the letterbox whispered, "It's me. Sir Magnus."

The door re-opened, just a crack.

"What…the…fuck?" said Sophie, recognition registering dimly. It was the eyes that were the giveaway. Less gimlet, mistier, but still the same old eyes.

"My name's Maggie now. Long story," explained the ex-Sir Magnus. "Mind if I come in?" he was saying as, behind Sophie loomed a burly polished-headed figure with a Zapata moustache.

"Bleedin' right we do," said Burly. "Don't we, Soph?"

Sophie girned rictally. "Um, erm, this is…" she was saying until Burly provided the answer on her behalf.

"Mitch," he said. "As in 'don't mess with Mitch.' Got it? An' if Soph says you should piss awff, you *should* piss awff. Narmean? Uvverwise you is looking at hospital time."

"Mitch, *Mitch*," said Sophie while Maggie examined his boots and flicked road dirt from his Hells Angels jacket.

"Things have changed around here I see," he said.

"Got that right, bruvver. Now, like I said, piss *awff*," said Mitch, taking a step forward so Maggie could inspect at closer quarters the knuckle duster embracing his muscly fingers.

"Sorry about this. Mitch is my new…" said Sophie.

"Live-in lover," said Mitch. Threateningly.

"Okay. Fair enough," said Maggie, turning to leave. "I was just wondering if you'd had any news from Jeremy, that was all. But never mind, I'll just…"

"Fuck *AWFF*," said Mitch, stroking his polished pate with the hand that wasn't dusting his knuckles.

"Quite. So…have a nice life, you two," Maggie called over his shoulder as he made his way back to the waiting Lambretta in which, during its owner's absence, a pig had taken an unnatural interest.

"Oink, *oink*," said Pete, when Maggie tried to shoo him away.

"Bally pigs," he was on the cusp of saying until peculiar tumblers fell in his brain.

Had not Jeremy *lived* with a pig during his time in the barn? Of course he had. And thought of it as his best friend according to the "bonkers" diagnosis provided by both the family and the shrinks. No reason to assume this was the *same* pig of course, but if it were…"

"Oink, oink," repeated Pete, who'd ambled off from the Shepherd's Hut while the humans were busy inside to check out his old stamping ground and make sure everything was in order. Which, he was glad to see, it was. But then the peculiar stranger had arrived and, employing his normally underrated porcine intelligence quotients, Pete sensed he needed guidance. Possibly a friend of Master Jeremy's, he surmised, hence the semiotic curly-tail-waggling he now offered as a lure. A sign Sir Magnus would never had read, but one new man Maggie—bamboozled but nonetheless—took as a gesture of friendship.

"You would like me to follow you?" he asked Pete, who waggled his tail some more.

"OINK OINK," he said, beginning to trundle off towards Fanbury's main drag. And for reasons he would forever question, Maggie, pushing the Lambretta, followed, although progress was slow.

"Look, piggy," he said after only twenty or thirty metres, "why don't you climb aboard? It'd be faster that way."

"Oink," Pete agreed, clambering onto the footplate and settling his trotters on the mid-section of the handlebars while Maggie slid back on his seat then leaned forwards around Pete to control the throttle and handbrake.

"Just point me in the right direction, okay? I tell you what, you can wear my crash hat too."

"*OINK OINK*!"

It was unsurprising given all the pressure he'd been under as the Internet's most sought-after person that when Maggie beeped his horn to announce their arrival and Jeremy peered through the window and saw Pete—over whose unexplained absence he'd been fretting—now driving a motor scooter with a passenger on the pillion, he should have fainted and needed to be revived with a shot of Barry's Special Reserve 80% beetroot brandy and a head massage from Julie.

It was OO17 Maurice Moffat who stepped into the breach to greet the new arrivals.

Twenty-two

Maurice had been encouraged by the responses he'd received from Julie and Dennis to his proposal of a Jeremy/John Lennon lookalike video clip to compete with Ripurpantzov's troll farm shenanigans. Like Barry and Jeremy before them, they had initially been incredulous, but with pleasing alacrity thereafter, both warmed to the idea.

"Sounds too wacky to make much of a difference to anything," Dennis said. "Could be fun, though. You up for it Jeremy, are you?"

Jeremy laughed. "Couldn't get myself into much more trouble, could I?"

Julie was even more enthusiastic. "I wasn't born when John got shot but my dad told me all about him. Drove my mam nuts singing his songs in the bath all the time. That's how I learned the words," she said, dabbing at the tear dribbling down her cheek. "Dad also told me about the fuss he caused with god freaks over in the US by saying The Beatles were more popular than Jesus. Took some guts that did, but the way Dad told it, John was just speaking the truth like he always did. Maybe that's what got him shot."

Barry hoisted both eyebrows. "Mmm," he said after a moment's thought. "One wonders, doesn't one, whether our little game might not have an equally affective impact on the mood of our cousins across the pond as in Ruskieland? Nothing like a reminder of times past to re-open some eyes, is there? I gather Mister Spielberg's Watergate film has been rather well received. With luck pigs *still* might fly," he was saying at the very moment Maggie beeped his horn and, before fainting, Jeremy peered through the window to see Pete apparently driving a motor scooter.

As noted, it was OO17 Maurice Moffat who took charge of the situation.

"May I be of assistance?" he said, watching on as Maggie and Pete got in each other's way while struggling to disembark from the Lambretta, which, unaccustomed to such ineptitude, keeled over, tossing both passengers onto the mulchy ground.

"OINK," Pete protested, rolling about with all four legs pointing in different directions as Maggie climbed to his feet and did his best to appear in control of the situation.

"Ah, um, hello there," he said, dusting himself down.

"And you might be?" said Maurice, fingering the little .22 Glock he kept in a secret pocket in case of emergencies.

In his other life, Maggie would have said, "Sir Magnus Montague, who are *you*?" But this was new man Maggie, who apologised for the disturbance of his unusual arrival before requesting the chance to explain.

"You have two minutes," said Maurice, OO17-ishly. The bloke didn't look like he intended mischief, but in these dark days one could never be too sure. In all his years on the spook circuit, Maurice was yet to confront a counter-agent riding pillion on a pig-driven motor scooter, but who knew what new sorts of camouflage they might have adopted. Maurice kept his finger on the mini-Glock's trigger just in case.

"Two minutes, eh," said Maggie. "A tall order."

"Go for it."

So Maggie did, clocking one minute and forty-eight seconds by Maurice's watch.

“Blimey,” he said, relaxing his trigger finger. In Maurice’s world, concision was a rare virtue and a key tell. Liars waffled endlessly off the point.

“So it’s Jeremy Crawford you seek?” he added as Pete clambered to his feet and peered accusingly at the fallen Lambretta.

“As I said, in light of my conversion to his view of things, I should be honoured to meet him again,” said Maggie. “Always assuming the pig brought me to the right place, of course. To be honest, I had no way of knowing. Simply trusted to blind instinct.”

Maurice liked that too. Real life spooks never admitted to blind instinct unless they were triple bluffing. Which remained a possibility but, looking into Maggie’s eyes, Maurice discounted the likelihood. Call it intuition. Call it anything you want, but the bloke’s highly compacted explanation for his visit had rung true, so…”

“Okay,” he said. “Anything in your pockets I should see before we step inside? A smartphone? Any little wires leading to…?”

Maggie took off his Hells Angels jacket and tossed it over.

“Help yourself. You’ll find no bombs, though. And there’s not much else of me that could hide anything. Unless you’re going to frisk me, of course.”

“Sorry, but actually I am,” said Maurice, checking the biker’s jacket pockets and linings before asking Maggie to spreadeagle himself against the Shepherd’s Hut garden railings. “I just need to be sure, that’s all. As you will be aware, Jeremy is a much sought after person these days.”

“Understandable,” said Maggie over his shoulder while Maurice patted him down. “And may I be allowed to know exactly *your* connection to him?”

In one minute and forty-*six* seconds, beating his previous personal explanation record by a whole second, Maurice introduced himself.

"So *that's* how important Jeremy has become?" said Maggie.

"Indeed," said Maurice, satisfied the stranger was clean. "Now if you would care to step this way. Sir Magnus, is it?"

"Maggie."

"Apologies. *Maggie*."

"Oink," said Pete.

~ * ~

Despite his born again hippy/Hells Angel appearance, Jeremy and Julie recognised Sir Magnus aka Maggie straight away and exchanged disturbed glances. Barry and Dennis just stared and raised eyebrows at Maurice, who palmed air and nodded reassurance.

"A friend," he said, while Shirley, Hans and Colin checked out their new visitor with leg and bum sniffs before wagging their tails in approval.

"Jeremy and Julie over there I'm sure you already know," he added. "The other two gentlemen are: Barry, the owner of this fine establishment…"

Barry smiled unreadably.

"And Dennis, who used to be a Fanbury policeman until he saw the light."

"Hi," said Maggie with a little wave. "As Barry indicated," he added, acknowledging Jeremy's and Julie's suspicious eyeballing, "some of you will know well enough who I am. As for you other chaps, explanations are clearly in order. May I sit?"

"Feel free," said Barry, wafting an arm at a battered old piano stool. "Looking a tad wobbly on your pins. A stiffener help at all?"

"I'd be obliged," said Maggie. "Non-alcoholic if you have it. On the wagon, these days, but a caffeine hit would be appreciated. No milk and just the one sugar,"

Jeremy and Julie exchanged frowns and puzzled glances while Barry fixed the coffee. The Sir Magnus they'd known had always been at least half cut and chewing on one of his absurd cigars.

"This time you have more than two minutes," said Maurice with a grin.

And so it was, sipping at Barry's fine brew, that Maggie offloaded his recent change of heart to perfect strangers, with the exception of Jeremy and Julie that was. But, along with Dennis and Barry, they listened in amazement and even chuckled along with Maggie when he told of the cardiac arrest, which had threatened an *actual* change of heart.

"Managed with just a bit of a bypass and a couple of stents as it happened," he explained, "as things turned out it wasn't the ticker that needed the transplant so much as the bally brain. Clearly needed a good clean out and some new nuts and bolts *that* little fella did."

"Is he for *real*?" Julie whispered behind her hand to Jeremy, who looked as perplexed as his new inamorata.

It was Pete, sitting with Hilary, Hans, and Colin who answered her question.

"Oink!" he said. Appropriately because this was the point in Maggie's narrative at which he was moving on from his epiphanic comprehension of Jeremy's motives in "leaving his life" to the need he felt to seek out his ex-HAA and compliment him on his decision. And how helpful Jeremy's pig pal had been in this quest.

"Couldn't have done without him," he said, leaning over to stroke Pete's head. "Much maligned chaps, pigs. Sorry about the arrival, of course. Must have looked a tad bizarre."

"Oink," Pete agreed.

"Sir Magnus," said Jeremy. "Are we *really* to understand…?"

"Maggie. The name's Maggie now."

"Sorry, *Maggie*. But are you telling us…?"

"That I'm a new man? Yes, and not ashamed to say so. And for all my past misdeeds I full-heartedly apologise. To both of you, but especially to Miss Mackintosh, the best PA I ever had and the most maltreated."

Julie blinked.

"And to you, Jeremy, I offer not only my most humble apologies but also my thanks for having presented me with the model upon which to reassess my own paltry existence and do something about it before it was too late. Which, of course, it almost was, what with the ticker problem and everything."

"And you *really* had to sluice out lavatories?" said Jeremy.

"As I said, the beak required it for biffing the copper on his schnoz, poor chap. Got rather good at it, even if I say so myself. Cleanest lavs in town, they are. And the stint's not finished yet. Still a few weeks to go. Just took a little break on the off chance of finding you, then I'll be back at it."

Barry smiled. "More coffee, Maggie?" he said. "Unless you're sure you wouldn't fancy a drop of something stronger? I do a rather nifty raspberry champagne. Can't imagine a drop or two would see you back in the A&E."

"Well put that way, I don't see why not. A&E more likely to kill me than raspberry champers these days, eh, so I'll take my chances."

"Tell you what," said Barry, who admired anyone who could clean toilets and be proud of the results, "why don't we *all* share a glass and perhaps indulge in a small toast to our new friend? Be up for that, would you, Jeremy?"

Maggie waited with some apprehension, but was glad to see his ex-HAA first nod then rise from his seat and then amble over with a hand outthrust.

"It would be a pleasure," he said, dropping the hand at the last moment and instead taking Maggie in a man hug. Which surprised and confused Maggie who, new man though he was, had no prior experience of man hugging, which he had always assumed to be only for the gay boys.

"Oooofff," he said, as Jeremy enveloped him. But he was smiling.

He smiled a lot more when Julie crossed the room to join the hug fest, although he was very careful not to touch her bottom.

Dennis, Barry and Maurice watched on and clapped.

"I like it when stuff comes together," said Dennis.

"Me too," Maurice was saying only moments before his phone took to trilling in his pocket and he headed to the door apologising for the call "he just had to take."

"That corny old line *again*?" Barry called after him, but Maurice ignored it and headed for the door.

Twenty-three

Maurice's caller on her super-unbuggable line from her MI6 office was Milly/Dame Muriel Eggleshaw, who was being plagued by calls from Phoebe/Clarissa over Casanova's progress, or the lack of it, and getting fed up with them.

"That bally woman calls me just one more time," she had told Sir Hubert "Hubby" Humphreys during their lunchtime schmooze at her Park Lane hinterland club, "and I'm going round to number ten and whack her over the head with my old lackers stick."

At Girton, Muriel had been captain of the most successful women's lacrosse team in college history and been given a blue for her troubles.

"Possibly not *the* most appropriate move, old thing," said Sir Hubert over vol au vents and Prosecco. "Not for one in your position. 'MI6 head bashes PM unconscious with hockey stick' not exactly the sort of media headline one would wish for."

"*Lackers* stick."

"Lackers, hockey, what's the difference?"

Pedantically, Dame Muriel was about to explain the pre*cise* difference between lacrosse and hockey sticks, but Sir Hubert placed the forefinger of one hand across his lips and, with the other hand, topped up her Prosecco glass.

"Not the kind of news tidbit one would wish to reach old Ripurpantzov's ears, either," he continued. "Brit Secret Services at daggers drawn with their mistress and so on. Would send pre*cis*ely the wrong message."

"Hrrummphh," said Dame Muriel, sipping her wine and reaching for another vol au vent.

"Bloody man," she added in mid-munch. "One does *so* wish he would go away. Be toppled in an internal conspiracy or something."

"Fat chance," said Sir Hubert. "Blighter looks nicely set to beat Stalin's record, and by employing more or less the same methods."

"All very disappointing, Hubby."

"Indeed, my dear. In*deed*. One only wishes there were something one could do about it. And, what's more, about the maniac in the White House. A double-edged, covert, intelligence led coup is what we need, but our hands are tied. Diplomacy the name of the game and so on, which I doubt would be helped by leaving Clarissa even more braindead than she already is through being whacked over the head with a…"

"La*crosse* stick," said Dame Muriel.

"Or hockey stick, or any other kind of a stick."

"You're probably right. Sooo, what *are* we to do?"

Sir Hubert shook his head. "Not the foggiest, my dear. But just think of the fillip for our reputations should something spring to mind as a means of upsetting apple carts in both Moscow *and* Washington simultaneously. Some really cunning ruse is what we need. Then we'd be talking feathers in caps, would we not?"

"But *how*?" Dame Muriel was saying as Sir Hubert took a long swig at his Prosecco, selected another vol au vent, shrugged, and said, "Look, why don't you just call Double O Seventeen and see if he's got any ideas? Never mind whether he's found Crawford or not. Always been pretty good at cunning ruses, Double O Seventeen."

"True enough," mused Dame Muriel.

"So let's touch base with him, shall we? Can't do any harm, can it? Clarissa or no Clarissa. Jeremy Crawford or no Jeremy Crawford."

"S'pose not. I'll give him a ring when I get back to the office."

"And *bonne chance, ma chère*. Now if you would excuse me, I need to debrief Foreign Secretary Fat Slob. The prat's just back from the UN where reports have him speaking pig Latin during a Syria debate leading to calls from all sides for his summary exclusion and—this the French suggestion—emasculation."

"About bally time too. Good old Frogsters," Dame Muriel muttered as Sir Humphrey levered himself from his chair and headed for the door.

Then she scoffed the remaining vol au vents, polished off the Prosecco, called Clarence her driver on another super-encrypted number, and marched off downstairs to where the limo would be waiting.

"Office, ma'am?" said Clarence, holding the door open with one hand and doffing his peaked driver's cap with the other.

"And don't spare the horses," said Dame Muriel, sinking into the leather seat, leaning her neck back against the super-padded headrest and, embarrassingly for Clarence when they arrived at MI6 HQ, although he'd known this happen to The Mistress on previous occasions, nodded off.

"Oops," she said as Clarence re-opened her door, coughed meaningfully, and said, "Sorry to wake you, ma'am, but we're here."

"Just a little cat nap, Clarry. Helps clear the brain."

"Quite so, ma'am. And have a nice rest of the day," said Clarry/Clarence before climbing back into the driver's seat and heading off for another Secret Service duty trip with maximum obsequiousness.

Once back in her 24/7 bug-swept office on the twelfth floor of MI6 HQ however, Dame Muriel got on the horn to OO17 straight away.

"Casanova?" she said.

~ * ~

"Milly, my dear. How nice to hear from you. What can I do for *you* today?"

"Tell me what you're up to, that's what. I'm getting bloody Phoebe on the blower every five minutes wanting progress reports and all she's heard so far is you're 'close' to the Crawford creature. Otherwise her calls all go to message. So bean-spilling time, Double O Seventeen."

"Ah..."

"Thick as a brick the woman may be, but she *is* the bally PM after all."

"At least *this* week. Rumour has it there could be a night of the long knives any time soon. Fat Slob and Lurch at each other's throats and hers, and so on."

"*Lurch*?"

"The chancellor. Both vying for the top job, from what one hears, eh? Cabinet in disarray as usual, all warbling from different hymn sheets over Brexit. Plotting rife. Insurrection on the rise around the Nazi back benches. And all the while the Brussels eurocrats watching on, laughing their socks off. Along with the madman in the White House *and* Ripurpantzov in the Kremlin, no doubt..."

"Double O Seventeen?"

"Yes, Milly."

"Enough of the flimflam. I asked you a question."

"Which was? Remind me."

"What 'close' to Jeremy Crawford *means*. To which I require an answer. Now!"

"Ah."

"Otherwise you may soon be finding yourself an *ex*-Double O Seventeen."

"I see."

"So no more muddying of waters."

"Point taken, Milly," said Maurice, "rest assured I'm working on the problem twenty-four-seven."

"With…what…*out*comes?"

Maurice took a deep breath and stroked the head of Pete the pig, who had nosed his way through the door Maurice had left ajar and wandered over to see what was going on.

"Oink," he said. Encouragingly.

"What was that noise?" said Dame Muriel, furrowing her brow.

"Wind," said Maurice. "In the willows. There're a lot of willows around here."

"*Where*?"

"Where I am."

"My patience is running *very* thin, Double O Seventeen."

"Understandably, ma'am."

"Quite. What, where you are concerned, one might term a career-defining moment. So get to the point or be damned."

Maurice opted for bean spillage and let devils take their hindmosts.

"Well, ma'am, I do have up my sleeve this rather cunning ruse, even if I say so myself. Like to hear it?"

Hiatus while Dame Muriel digested this resonant remark, reminding her as it did of Sir Hubert's hope for precisely the same thing and his belief if anyone could come up with such a plan, Double O Seventeen could. What she really wanted to know was whether Maurice had found Jeremy Crawford yet, but if…

"Milly? You still there?" said Maurice, as the hiatus persisted.

"I'm here."

"So cunning ruse time?"

"Okay, but it better be good. And make it brief," said Dame Muriel. "I'm not one for beating around bushes, as you well know."

"Indeed, ma'am," said Maurice, before outlining his plot to destabilize the positions of both the Russian and American dictators by flooding the Internet with images of John Lennon lookalike.

Another hiatus this time, an even longer one.

"Still there, Milly?" said Maurice. "*Milly*?"

"Have you com*plete*ly lost your marbles, Double O Seventeen?" Dame Muriel eventually spluttered. "A John *Lennon* lookalike, for God's sake! If memory serves, was he not LSD-addicted, long-haired, Liverpudlian oaf who sent his MBE back to the queen?"

"Indeed so, ma'am. In protest at our involvement in the Vietnam war. *And* who, along with his fellow Beatles, played a major part in Gorbachev's glasnost."

"*What*? The bally Beatles weren't poli*ti*cians."

"No, ma'am. At least not overtly. But you have no idea of the power of popular music when it comes to consciousness-raising. You may recall the effect of Bob Dylan's 'The Times They Are a-Changin' on American society. And he's a Nobel Laureate now," said Maurice, adding for good measure his tale of the ancient St Petersburg guy still praying daily for Lennon's spirit to return to Russia.

"Cloud bloody cuckoo land," spat Dame Muriel. "And even *if* it were to work on Ripurpantzov, which…I…very…much…doubt, are you also telling me it could work on the cretin in the White House?"

"Point taken. It's a long shot, Milly," Maurice agreed. "But given the power of not only music but the social media in these bizarre days, in my view it's one worth taking. What we're looking at here is an iconic reminder of a less jingoistic, less me-me-mine age and, given the psychosis emanating from the White House and encouraged from the Kremlin, you just wonder how many folk might welcome that."

Yet another hiatus as Dame Muriel reflected on Sir Hubert's comment on the fillip for MI6's and MI5's reputations should the cunning ruse he hoped for manage to upset apple carts in both Moscow *and* Washington simultaneously, feathers in caps and so on.

"*Milly*?"

"I'm here, Double O Seventeen. And your assessment of the potential impact of all this on fatuous Phoebe and her Brexiteers is? She is our current client, remember."

"Only too well."

"So?"

"In a word?"

"If you please."

"Wipeout," said Maurice.

Dame Muriel liked the sound of *that.*

"A reversal of the knee jerk alt-right, and indeed alt-left, populisms currently wreaking havoc on British democracy as we once knew it, to be replaced by a resurgence of wiser, dare one say it, more reflective arguments."

"Like 'make love not war'?" said Dame Muriel, vaguely recalling the line both she and Clarissa had scorned back in their distant Girton days.

"Not *such* a foolish idea after all. A case of 'coming together,' as Lennon had it in his usual double-entendre-ish manner. A shame he had to be shot."

"Which leaves you with something of an impasse, even if I *do* agree to this nonsense, doesn't it, Double O Seventeen?" said Dame Muriel. "What with the fellow being dead and everything. No good swamping the cyber waves with a *dead* person's image, is there? Hardly likely to arouse much of your consciousness-raising, given people will have seen the images a million times already. Might as well put up pictures of Mozart."

"Quite so, Milly. Hence the part of my cunning ruse which posits John as a walking, talking returnee to planet earth, an avatar if you wish."

"A *ghost*?" whispered Dame Muriel, whose childhood had been spent in a haunted house in Hertfordshire.

"Well, if you want to think of it that way, Milly. Mind you, Jesus Christ pretty much fits the same bill, would you not say? Another chap back from the dead, even though nobody's ever actually *seen* him. But even so, just look at the clout *he*'s had. And indeed continues to have, whether in his Catholic or Anglican version."

An*other* hiatus while Dame Muriel struggled with her demons, namely the enduring paradox of the ghost of her recently deceased father whispering to her nightly, "There is no heaven, sweetie," and the happy clappy religion she quotidianly had shoved down her throat by her governesses, all of whom assured her heaven was where the good girls went. And this while her mother danced the nights (and days) away with fancy boys in Soho.

"Milly? Or should I call you M?"

"Muh-muh-Milly's fine," said Dame Muriel, remembering her lacrosse days and pulling herself together sharpish. "Whatever you wish to call me, and always assuming I agree to your plan, we are *still* left with the problem of Lennon being dead, whether or not people believe in afterlives."

"You will, however, recall my suggestion of a lookalike, Milly, an entirely *live* person who, through computer generated imagery, could easily be confused with the *real*, albeit supposedly deceased, John Lennon. Same Scouse accent, same hair, same guitar style, same everything. I have all the means to achieve that."

"And you have a candidate in mind for this role?"

"Milly, *Milly*? Sorry, you're fading on me. Battery low, reception masts on the blink perhaps, don't know what's happening," said Maurice, tapping at the Get Lost button on his phone. "But before you vanish into the ether altogether, may I assume you will at least consider my little plan?"

"A pre-launch run-through in my office before I make any final decision, but in principle..." Dame Muriel was saying as Maurice fully depressed the Get Lost button.

"Yessss," he then said, punching air.

"Oink, *oink*," said Pete, dancing a little pig dance called the Pig Trot.

Twenty-four

"PM on the line again?" Barry said when a gleeful Maurice re-joined the company accompanied by a still Pig-Trotting Pete.

"Not this time. The circus. Perhaps you would care to step outside with me while I explain?" whispered Maurice, casting a meaningful eye over at Maggie, who was busy exchanging choosing/chosen experiences with Jeremy, Julie and Dennis.

Intuiting this concern, Barry refreshed guests' glasses with raspberry champagne and said he'd be just outside with Maurice for a moment and if anybody wanted anything they only need call. But nobody seemed to notice, all of them engrossed in sharing tales of their previously unexamined lives in a combined effort to make the current ones worth living. "Yeah, exactly the same thing happened to *me*," was the comment featuring most regularly. It was all very therapeutic.

"So, circus?" said Barry, when he and Maurice were through the door and out of earshot. "Which one assumes to be one of the MIs."

Maurice nodded.

"Five or Six?"

"Six," Maurice confirmed. "Dame Muriel, my boss."

"The Girton gal?"

"That's her. How did you…?"

Barry shrugged. “Oxbridge gossip from the old days. Pal of Clarissa’, if I’m not mistaken. Could’ve ended up PM herself if she’d played her cards differently.”

“Pity she didn’t. At least Muriel has the power of thought.”

“Not what *I* heard on the ancient grapevine. But never mind that, what did the dame have to say?”

Maurice recounted the conversation.

“And you took her response as a thumbs up?” said Barry.

“Well, she didn’t say no. And my policy with a door that’s ajar has always been to put my foot in the opening and push a little harder before it gets slammed in my face.”

Barry nodded. “Very wise, my boy. Reticence never got anybody anywhere. Unless of course they didn’t want to get anywhere in the first place.”

“Quite.”

“So, your plan of campaign?”

“Is what I wanted to discuss with you. Who better than my old mentor?”

“Even if he is now a tatty old gardener.”

“Cultivating his garden just as well as he once cultivated minds.”

Barry smiled. “Okay, enough of the flattery, let’s get to the point, shall we?”

And so it was that, in the heart of rural England, Maurice repeated the plan he hoped would shake up and re-balance the corrupt conceits currently dominating world political institutions, both East and West.

Barry nodded and shrugged.

“I know, I know, it all sounds a bit like William Morris’s ‘News From Nowhere’ or some of Ivan Illich’s more bizarre proposals,” Maurice concluded. “But, if we ever lose sight of utopia, we might as well kiss our humanity goodbye and accept we are no more than the instruments of global greed. How are future generations of SATs-driven and smartphone-brainwashed kids ever to grow into thinking adults if they can't dream? Look how long it took Jeremy to achieve his freedom, and against what odds. One assumes the same may be the case for Dennis, Julie, and even this Maggie fellow."

Barry couldn't deny it. He'd walked the same road.

"You may remember Lennon's lines in 'Working Class Hero.' About children getting tortured and scared by parents and teachers for twenty-odd years until they can't think straight because they're too full of fear. And these days there are Twitter, Facebook et al to add to the mix, channels through which all sorts of unregulated bullying and indoctrination can be transmitted, which is why the madmen in the White House and the Kremlin are addicted to them. So, ironically using the very same weapons, it is in my humble opinion time to fight back."

Barry held up his hands in submission. "Say no more," he said. "To stick with pop music, you're talking to a man who's still crazy after all these years. Just need to be reminded from time to time, that's all. Which you have achieved with the same starred first you won from Oxford. So…to the actual strategy."

Maurice smiled and clapped his old tutor on the back.

"Just one more little doubt, though," said Barry. "You're quite, *quite* sure it is within your Secret Service remit to undertake such a mission?"

"What else but saving the world from megalomaniacs were James Bond's missions ever about? And let us be clear, Barry, Fleming's stories were only marginally embellished. Then, of course, there are John le Carré's. I'm not comparing myself to Double 0 Seven or George Smiley, you understand, I would never make so bold. Also I'm clearly not fictional. But…"

"Cometh the hour, cometh the man," said Barry.

"You might put it that way, although the sources of that epigram remain obscure. *Now*, you asked about the actual strategy."

"So I did."

Which was when Maurice explained how he intended to fashion the Jeremy Crawford character through make-up, lip-syncing, an intensive course in method acting and computer generated imagery to sing an album of Lennon songs, including "Revolution" as if they had only newly been recorded.

"As *if*?" said Barry who, since opting for a career in gardening, had spent no time wondering about distortions of reality.

Maurice nodded. "It's admittedly a leap of the imagination, but sadly I have to say it is also the hallmark of the make-believe world we currently live in. How many films are made these days with*out* recourse to digitalized suspensions of disbelief?"

"Don't know. Don't go to the pictures much these days. *Ever* actually," said Barry. "The last film I liked was *Brief Encounter* with Celia Johnson and Trevor Howard. After that, everything seemed to go downhill a bit."

"You're right. *So* far downhill that what attracts and persuades the twenty-first century consumer of instantly streamed movies and the dross swirling around the Internet is precisely 'as *if*.' We are currently living in a simulated world, Barry, and a very dangerous place it is."

"And you know the tricks of this new trade?"

"I've learnt. I had to or there was no longer a way to do my job. In some ways it's a cop-out, I agree. But to beat your enemy, first you have to join him. Then, when he's not looking, you whack him with his very own tools."

"You've come a long way from your Oxford days, my boy. And more power to your elbow," said Barry. "I'm proud of you."

"Thank you. What I was also wondering, however, was what sorts of contribution Julie, Dennis, and now Maggie, might make to this scenario. It would be a pity to waste *their* new-found resources, would it not?"

"Well," said Barry after a moment's thought, "how about we dress *them* up as Paul, George and Ringo? Then we'd have the *whole* crew back from the dead."

Maurice laughed long and hard at that.

"Silly idea?" said Barry.

"No, no, not at all. *Brill*iant idea," Maurice spluttered when he'd finished laughing long and hard. "Possibly a little tricky where Julie's concerned…she is a girl after all. Mind you," he added, "she does have a certain look of Paul about her. And Maggie *has* lost a lot of weight, so I can see him as George. And Dennis for Ringo, well why not? We'll need to obtain the consent of the real Paul and Ringo, of course, but my sense is they would be onside happily enough."

"Okay, so meanwhile shall we pop back inside and explain to the guys how the good news, in its twenty-first century version of course, has been brought from Ghent to Aix?"

"Might take another stretch of the imagination, but we can try," said Maurice, turning back to the Shepherd's Hut.

On the way he reminded Barry of Browning's omission in his poem to divulge either what the good news from Ghent *was* or why it was important to Aixians. A lot of the time, the poet was apparently unsure, or had forgotten, *what* his poems were about. As evinced on the occasion when asked by one of his female admirers for the meaning of one of them, only to receive the reply: "When I wrote it, only God and Robert Browning knew the meaning; now God alone knows."

"Let us just hope *our* good news can be explained a little better," he was saying as Barry pushed open the already reopened door.

"Oink," agreed Pete, who had yet again nosed his way outside to see what the humans were up to.

Twenty-five

Having secured the agreement of Jeremy, Julie, Dennis, and Maggie to take part in his little project, Maurice motored back to number thirteen Oakshot Street Tooting in his dad's old Morris Minor Traveller to prepare the computer mock-ups he would need for his meeting with Dame Muriel. Along the way he mused on the gratifying speed with which Jeremy and company had accepted the challenge of becoming The Reconstructed Beatles, or TRB, as they had finally agreed to be known. Ignorant of the Liverpool music scene, Maurice had proposed The Bootleg Beatles, but Julie/Paul had scotched that idea.

"We've already got them back home and they're great," she'd said. "Be wrong to go stealing *their* name, wouldn't it?"

"Quite wrong," Maggie/George had agreed. "Wouldn't want accusations of plagiarism stalling our plans at their very inception."

And so it was that Jeremy had come up with the "reconstructed" idea. Against some opposition from Dennis/Ringo, who had proposed "new and improved" until reminded by Julie of Billy Connolly's mockery of the phrase, noting a product was either new *or* improved but couldn't be both.

It was on the word "reconstructed" that Maurice dwelt as the old Morris Minor trundled along A and B roads at its top speed of 45 mph. No use taking the poor old thing on motorways where it would get flashed and honked at even in the slow lane. Maurice had once tried the hard shoulder as an alternative, only to be stopped by a wailing police siren and threatened with a lifetime driving ban until he showed the coppers his MI6 ID. And even then, albeit huffily, they'd escorted him off the main drag onto a D road occupied by sheep and cattle and told him to get lost. Not the sort of treatment James Bond would have tolerated, but then, unlike Maurice, OO7 would have been driving an Aston Martin DB7 in the fast lane. And outrun the coppers anyway. But, on balance, Maurice was glad he was only OO17 rolling along quietly on uncongested roads. More time for thought. And it was to reconstructed that such thoughts kept returning.

Because, from the tales they'd told him, that's exactly what Jeremy, Julie, Dennis, and now Maggie were—re-made, re-*born* almost. As indeed was his erstwhile professor, Barry. And not through the intercession of outside agencies, but from their own initiative, Maurice mused while slipping Dvořák's cello concerto in B minor into his CD player and humming along—dee dum dee dee dee do dah, dee dum dee dee dee dee dah. How peculiar yet how courageous such fight back was *that*, against a culture devoted to the myth of belonging? A very special one, he concluded, mindful of the dread with which so many twenty-first-century people would regard the prospect of standing outside the flock, the original Latin meaning of the now pejorative term "egregious," if he remembered rightly. Where would Twitter and Facebook and company be were more to follow the example of Barry, Jeremy & Co. and become loners? Out of business, that was where. And so much the better for it, Maurice was reckoning as he drew up outside his house and the Morris Minor gasped its relief.

"Hi there, Tiddles," he said, opening the door and nearly tripping over Terpsichore who was catnapping on the inside mat. "Hank and Butch been looking after you nicely, have they?"

"Miaow," said Tiddles (/Terpsichore/Cat) non-committally.

"Glad to see Daddy home?"

"Miaow," Tiddles repeated, also abstractedly.

You know how it is with cats. How dogs come bounding up to lick you when you come home but cats don't. As an admirer of their insouciant nature, Maurice just nodded and smiled.

"Thought so. How about we open a nice tin of Pussy Chunks?"

Tiddles semi-shrugged but nonetheless wandered off into the kitchen where Maurice's landline phone was ringing fit to bust until, as usual, it went dead just as he picked up.

"Bugger," he said, dropping his overnighting travel bag and dialling 1471.

"You were called today at sixteen thirty-two hours," said the British Telecom lady accusingly. "The caller withheld their number."

"Thank Christ for that," said Maurice, slamming down the phone.

His patience with telephone scam artists was running on empty. How dumb did the dorks have to be to think that he of all people would believe they were the International Fraud Crime Squad—IFCS—operating out of Manhattan (more likely Mumbai to judge by the Bollywood accents) and unless he gave them the details of all his credit cards and pin numbers immediately, he would be opening himself to "total financial wipeout and potential accusations of terrorist sympathies" seeing as they had evidence of his cards having been stolen by a gang of ISIS thieves intent on branding him as one it its members and thus rendering him in mortal danger of retribution from the lunatic in the White House and his alt-right redneck and hillbilly backers.

"Good riddance to bad rubbish," he was saying as the phone took to warbling all over again.

Sighing but nonetheless hoisting the receiver off its cradle, Maurice rehearsed the line he'd long ago invented for IFCS and their like, namely: “This telephone contains a special voice-activated recognition device which is currently recording your name, address, eye colour, underpants size, and the condition of your vital organs—heart, liver, kidneys, and so on—all of such details to be fed into a special computer program which will pinpoint your location and allow me to press the button that will zap you into outer space without a parachute.” Which, given Maurice’s computer wizardry, was no idle threat. Not that he ever intended to use it, of course, but the Mumbai hackers weren’t to know that.

This time it wasn’t IFCS or one of their copycats on the line, however. It was Dame Muriel.

“Casa*no*va? What the bloody *hell*’s going on?” her voice boomed down the line. “Tried your bally mobile a thousand times, but it kept going to message. What kind of an OO17 *are* you?”

“One who switches *off* his mobile when he’s driving in case he causes a fatal accident, ma’am.”

“You don’t have hands-free?”

“Never saw the need. Now, how may I be of assistance?”

~ * ~

Dame Muriel wasn’t the only one suffering practically terminal impatience at the absence of news from OO17. Clearly PM Clarissa knew nothing of The Reconstructed Beatles plan, but she remained obsessed with the need to find Jeremy Crawford, brand him the hidden architect of all her tribulations, switch focus, and for once and for all to *stop* the media dubbing her as dithering, incompetent, mealy-mouthed, and, in the words of the *Daily Snitch*’s latest editorial: “So feeble she couldn’t knock a hole in a damp Kleenex.” It was all too much, *truly* it was! Half her time these days she spent on aeroplanes trying to stitch up jazzy trade deals with thriving economies out*side* the blasted EU: Kuala Lumpur, Uzbekistan, and Timor, to name but three. And all the while playing what she thought of as hardball with the squabbling Tory factions in not only her own cabinet, but also in parliament and increasingly amongst the very grassroots membership, as well as playing even harder ball with the sanctimonious Europeans who still wouldn't agree to a bespoke trade deal for Britain after Brexit. What the hell was *wrong* with them, she wondered, pacing up and down her Downing Street bedroom. Had *they* ever had empires upon which the sun never set? Had *they* invented the language now spoken, albeit often distortedly, by practically everybody on the planet? Did *they* have a Shakespeare? Did *they* have monarchies dating back a thousand years? Of course they bloody didn't. So they were just jealous, that was all. It was enough to make a PM cry, which on occasions Clarissa did. On and *on* she struggled to do her job, and *still* it was only sneers all around she received in return. If only Miserable (probably also Jealous) Muriel and her fancy boy Casanova could do their bally jobs properly and find the megalomaniac bonkers banker, everything would be sooo…

It was during one these fits of pique that, keen to wring any last drop from the Special Relationship with what was after all one of her ex-colonies, Clarissa called the madman in The White House on her red-button hot-line to seek his advice on story-switching. After all, as a fellow sufferer from the slings and arrows of outrageous journalists, "enemies of the people" as he termed them, he should know. What if there were some new angle she could use as back-up to the awful possibility of Jeremy sodding Crawford *never* being found?

"Yup? Oh hi there, Clarrie. Only you gotta be quick, sweetheart," said the madman only seconds before the call went to super-encrypted message. "I got me a little fake photo problem here."

"Fake *photo* problem?"

"You ain't seen it? It's all over the freakin' Innernet? Two trillion hits an' countin'."

"No."

"Of me climbing up on board Air Force One and then there's fake wind blowin' at the back of my head and my hair comes awf. Fake, fake, *fake*."

"Your *hair*?"

"No honey, the damn *photo*. *My* hair's the most beautiful natural hair any president ever *had*. Everybody knows that and is jealous. The photo's fake. Worked up by some Democrat computer nerd, most likely. Or mebbe a Mexican. I ever catch the guy who dunnit he's gonna be waterboarding in Guantanamo till it's his *dick* that drops awf."

"Sorry," said Clarissa, keen to move the conversation along.

"So you should be. But I'm comin' back from this, like I always do. You better believe it, Clarrie. You know whut I'm gonna do?"

"Not off hand," said Clarissa, in her well-practised equivocation voice.

"I am gonna order me a parade of all my biggest, most nuclear, most long-distance miss'les and *thousands* of my soldiers, airmen, and marines to march past along Pennsylvania Avenue while I take the salute as Commander-in-Chief," said the president who'd dodged the draft claiming he had a sore foot and was in any case too busy avoiding sexually transmitted diseases to go off fighting yellow people. That was his *per*sonal Vietnam.

"Ain't no fake hair disser gonna argue with *that* kinda power," he added.

"Golly," said Clarissa, attracted to the notion of Britain's heavily armed bravest and best marching up Whitehall from Parliament Square past The Cenotaph to Trafalgar Square surrounded by tanks while she looked on and saluted commandingly. Possibly with a fly-past from the RAF and a few nukes on display, too. Not bad as a diversionary plan. Not bad at *all*.

"Sorry about your hair," she said, but mercifully for her, the follicularly challenged sex pest in the White House was already holding the phone from his ear.

"Gotta love ya an' leave ya, pussycat," he muttered. "A business—excuse me *country*—to run. Busy, busy, busy...like always."

As indeed he was, hanging up the phone and moving from behind the presidential- decree-signing desk to stand before a wall-length mirror and hold behind his head a smaller glass to inspect the extent of hair loss and seeing only the patch of blue-veined scalp now so (fakely) familiar to millions across the Twitterverse.

"Holy Christ on a fuckin' *bike*, sumptn gotta be *done* about this," he was saying as his new rug toupée director, Marianna Kolmover was ushered into the Oval Office all confidence and smiles.

"No problemo, Mister President. Just a brand new hairpiece and little more glue here and there," she said, taking from her EHL (Emergency Hair Loss) satchel a brand new, gleaming blond, man-wig and a tube of Super Stick.

"This better be good, babe," said the world's most powerful cretin. "I'm a guy on camera *all* the time an' I gotta look my best. An' *al*ways better than Ripurpantzov! Other hand, he's nearly bald, so I got the advantage over him right there, don't I?"

"Sure you do," said Kolmover. "You wanna turn around and sit down so I can take a closer look?"

"Okay, honey. Hey, nice tits you have. And some *ass*! Mebbe, when you're through with my hair, we could, ya know, spend a little cozy comfort time together?"

But ex-Miss Kansas Kolmover was no new kid on the block. She knew only too well of the president's peccadilloes and had been prepped for any of what, in the wake of recent Hollywood scandals, the media were now calling HLISBS (High Level Inappropriate Sexual Behaviour Syndrome). A shame from the president's perspective he had no idea she also currently headed up a national cross-party women's campaign called "Gropers Go Fuck Your*selves*" and had been weaselled into the White House in the undercover guise of a rug toupée expert to collect any dirt she could on the asshole currently running the White House. In her bra lay secreted a micro-recorder, which hadn't been found by the goons at the door when they tried to frisk her because she had threatened them—and their boss—with instant international HLISBS media exposure if they laid so much as a finger on her.

"Whoa there, buddy," she said, when The Leader of the Free World made a grab for her backside, "Touch this gal and you're toast," she added, clicking a hidden switch which replayed his lubricious language back to him and caused him to flinch. "Now d'you want me to fix your goddam hair or dontcha? Elsewise I'm outta here right now."

This left the prez in a no-man's land between lust, rage and narcissism. To demand one more freebie fuck with an ornery babe even if it meant yet another infuriating sex slur, or to get his rug fixed, that was the question. After a fleeting hiatus during which he scowled threateningly and stumped about promising to "stiff" Kolmover if she ever released a single word he'd said, he backed down and went for getting his rug fixed. A case of looks *über alles*.

~ * ~

Back in Downing Street, PM Clarissa was already on the phone to the head of the armed forces, Sir Stanley "Six Gun" Michaelson, requesting a full military march-past (and flyover) up Whitehall while she saluted from the steps of The Cenotaph.

"And make bloody sure all the papers, and the telly people, and the Internet, and the whole nation, know about it," barked Clarissa.

"Noted, ma'am," said Sir Stanley. "Only it's going to cost you."

"*Cost* me?"

Which was when Sir Stanley reminded the PM of how much government expenditure on the armed forces had been slashed in recent years on the repeated excuses of austerity and the costs of Brexit.

"We have only half the manpower we need to rule the world as we used to, nuclear submarine building is in tatters, the RAF has no nice new planes, chaps and chapesses on the ground are eating from food banks to survive. Need I go on? And *now* you want a godforsaken march-and-fly past?" said Sir Stanley, slamming down the phone and posing yet another challenge to Clarissa's supreme authority.

"Oh, for God's *sake*, where's the blasted megalomaniac bonkers banker when I need him *most*?" she wailed into the echoing silence.

~ * ~

In the Kremlin, Igor Ripurpantzov chuckled as he listened in to the latest results from his Sputnik bugs in both the White House and Downing Street. Okay, he was a little pissed at the allusion to his near baldness, but didn't the knobhead US prez know that bald guys had bigger dicks than guys with hair, even fake hair? Sometimes he wondered why he'd gotten the guy elected in the first place. And as for the *shlyukha* (whore) in London, she could have all the military parades she wanted—*if* she could rustle up the kopeks to pay for it—but none would ever match the ones he saluted. Still it was always good to know his enemies in the new cold/chilly war were such *priduroks* (morons). Made his job a whole lot easier. Which, now he remembered, was exactly why he'd had the madman elected to the White House in the first place.

Happy with himself, Igor wandered off for an ice bath followed by a hundred one-arm press-ups—fifty for each arm—all the while singing to himself, "I am the iron man, I am the iron man, I am the *iron* man, goo goo g'joob," blissfully unaware of the origins of the tune and Lennon's goo goo g'joob lyric. Such is the nature of hubris.

Twenty-six

As coincidence would have it, at roughly the same time Igor was fêting himself with goo goo g'joobs, Jeremy/John and the other Reconstructed Beatles were singing "I Am The Walrus" too. Not with guitars or drum kits—Maurice had said those, along with face recognition treatment, could be superimposed with CGI at a later stage—but at least they were wearing the Beatle wigs Barry had dug out from his ex-thespian store in his cellar. And it was not only "I Am The Walrus" they were practising. Before he left the Shepherd's Hut, Maurice had downloaded from Barry's ancient computer the whole Beatles' playlist as well as clips from their Cavern days, scenes from their movies, interviews on US TV (notably the Ed Sullivan Show), and the iconic events at Shea Stadium and the Hollywood Bowl.

"Look, listen and learn, guys," Maurice told them before he left at Dame Muriel's behest. "All the little gestures, winks, leg positions and mop top shakes, especially on 'Twist and Shout.' And never forget Paul's a leftie, guitar always the wrong way around. To make this work, you guys have got to be spot on. Think Stanislavski. You are not just going to be *playing* The Beatles you are going to *be* The Beatles. Especially you as John, Jeremy. He's going to be a hard act to follow, but it must be believable. Every little gesture, every little nuance, particularly on 'Revolution.' The lip-syncing *I* can handle, but the gestures, the knees, the sidelong glances at Paul, the head-bobbing, those you must get down to a T."

"I'm up for it," Jeremy said. "Best moment of my life so far."

A sentiment echoed by Julie/Paul, Maggie/George, and Dennis/Ringo. Every day since Maurice's departure for the city, with Barry's enthusiastic encouragement, they'd watched the tapes, listened to the songs, and rehearsed. Julie/Paul in particular was over the moon.

"My dad would *sooo* love this," she told Jeremy every night as they snuggled down together on their sofa bed.

"Only don't tell him," Jeremy would say. "Not yet. Not till it's over. If it's *ever* over."

"You think I'm daft, or d'you think I'm daft?"

"I think you're the nicest daft person I've ever known."

"So kiss me."

"Okay, Paul." That was the line that had Julie chuckling till her eyes closed on a whole new future.

~ * ~

"So Double O Seventeen, come to your senses on this Beatles nonsense yet?" Dame Muriel asked Maurice Moffat when he finally turned up for his appointment at MI6 HQ. "I've been talking the matter over with Sir Hubert at MI5 and he reckons you're off your trolley. He likes the idea of music-related Internet counter activity, but reckons Richard Wagner would be a better bet than the mindless tunes of some scruffy louts from Liverpool. He became somewhat exercised over the matter."

Maurice smiled. "He would."

"Explain yourself, Double O Seventeen."

"Sir Hubert is a high culture snob."

"Ex*cuse me*! Sir Hubert is a man of the greatest distinction, a man who…"

"Has conveniently forgotten Hitler's passion for Wagner. You may recall the Führer's hi-jacking of the *Übermensch* when calling for racial purity in Germany."

"Oh dear," said Dame Muriel.

"'Oh dear' is correct, ma'am. And to use such music when working to nobble Ripurpantzov and the madman in the White House would only play into their equally dirty hands. By the by, we are clear, are we not, that you have passed *none* of my plans along to the PM?"

"Not a dicky bird."

"Good, because one suspects she too may be susceptible to delusions of grandeur."

"Am I therefore to assume it is to *low* culture snobs you are hoping to appeal, Double O Seventeen? Because it seems to me they can be as nastily parochial as the *high* culture brigade."

"Indeed so, ma'am. When it comes to outsiders, there is an unholy alliance between the non-reflectives on both sides, with only the liberally democratic "art-farties' in the middle. Hence the disaster of Brexit."

"And you think your Beatles have a role to play in all of this?"

"Indeed I do, ma'am."

"Because?"

"They're class-neutral. Their words, especially Lennon's, strike chords in all of us."

"Play me one of his songs, could you?" said Dame Muriel.

"You've never heard one before?"

"Remind me."

"Okay. So how about this one?" said Maurice, taking out his laptop and calling up Our World, the first ever international satellite broadcast of June 25th 1967 featuring Maria Callas, Pablo Picasso...and the BBC's contribution to the show of The Beatles playing “All You Need Is Love,” a song Lennon had written especially for the occasion.

“I particularly like the line about us all being able to learn how to be ourselves in time. You didn’t see the programme, ma’am?”

“I was a mere girl at the time and school would never have allowed it anyway. No Beatlemania for *us* girls,” said Dame Muriel by way of explanation. “And you’re younger than me. So how did you…?”

“Through an indulgent and Beatlemanic father, ma’am.”

“Ah. Quite a nice little ditty, though, *and* with a whole bally *or*chestra to go with it,” said his boss as the screen faded. “I rather liked the Marseillaise bit with the French horns at the beginning. May we hear it again?”

Maurice smiled and hit replay, to which Dame Muriel clicked her fingers and giggled a bit.

“And the Lennon chappie is *which* one?” she said as the video re-ran.

Maurice pointed him out in his long silk jacket and Indian beads.

“Mmm, one has to admit one can see a certain attraction,” said the head of MI6. “And he’s dead, you say?”

“Shot to death outside The Dakota apartment building in New York. He said it was the only city on earth he’d ever felt free to walk the streets.”

“Dear, dear. And this was long ago?”

“December the eighth, nineteen eighty,” said Maurice who, like many people around the world, remembered precisely where he was when the news broke. In the case of a fledgling OO17, it was deep undercover in Moscow of all places.

“And it’s the revenant of this fellow you’re telling me who could, after all these years, so appeal to the global public imagination as to…?”

"As I have always said, it's a gamble, but I believe the odds could be in our favour. There are, after all, people who believe Elvis is still alive and living on Mars, so…"

"*El*vis?"

"Presley, ma'am."

"Was he a Beatle too?"

"No. He was an American singer known as the king of rock 'n' roll who…"

"Anyway, *any*way, Double O Seventeen," said Dame Muriel, "to return to topic, you mentioned a lookalike to play this revenant."

"I did, ma'am."

"And may one ask who? After all, your original mission was simply to find the bonkers banker, not to fiddle-faddle about with solutions to global neo-fascism."

"Quite so, ma'am," said Maurice, sufficiently encouraged by Dame Muriel's visceral attraction to Lennon to lay before her *all* his cards. Which was when he fessed up to having found Jeremy Crawford and his new albeit improbable friends, all of whom had found it easy to learn how to be themselves in time.

Dame Muriel paled, then flushed, then paled again, then flushed again.

"You…mean…to…*tell*…me…you…*found*…? she eventually spluttered.

"The bonkers banker? Yes. And he is very far from bonkers. Sorry I didn't tell you earlier."

More spluttering, ending with, "And you didn't tell Phoebe either?"

"No, ma'am. You're the only one to know."

"Well, *that's* a relief. And these friends of his?"

"One used to be a philosophy prof, *my* philosophy prof as it happens, at Oxford. He's a gardener now. Another is an ex-policeman. And the other two are Jeremy's ex-banking boss and his woman PA."

"A *very* odd bunch."

"Indeed, but they have come together through shared life experience."

"Explanation please, Double O Seventeen. All a tad esoteric for me."

So it was that Maurice outlined the difference between choosing and being chosen and the way such an insight could alter the course of a person's life, never mind their background or gender.

Hiatus while Dame Muriel digested this and Maurice took another happy look at The Beatles' offer to Our World in 1967.

Once the digestive hiatus was more or less over, she said, "And these people of yours are to play a part in this plan?"

"A critical one. They are to be The Reconstructed Beatles, although the focus of my attention will be on John, who will be played by Jeremy, the bonkers banker."

"And the rest of the *real* Beatles. Are they dead too? I mean, if they're still alive, how are *they* going to feel about having other people playing them? Can't have MI6 facing plagiarism and impersonation suits for huge sums."

"Don't worry, ma'am. I've already thought of that. Poor old George died some years ago too, but Paul and Ringo are still alive and very much kicking. To assuage your fears, I have already been in touch with them and they are happy for tribute bands to play their tunes without any royalty claims. All they ask is for any money raised to go to charities of their choice."

"Pretty decent chaps then," said Dame Muriel.

Maurice smiled, sensing a shift in his boss's position and, thus emboldened, threw into the conversation an adaptation to the plan for her to ponder, namely the new Lennon narrative he had dreamt up on the tube from Tooting to Vauxhall Cross, the one in which John *is* shot but doesn't die. He and Yoko have fabricated the whole murder scenario so they can escape forever the hassle of fame and live in peace on some desert island where nobody can find them. Only now, given the awfulness of world politics, he has decided to return and save the day.

"Yoko? Funny name. Who she?" asked Dame Muriel.

"His widow, ma'am. She's Japanese."

"Gosh. Will she come too?"

"No," said Maurice, making a mental note to check with Yoko Ono, although he was pretty sure as co-writer of 'Imagine' she would love the story."

"And you're floating this fantasy, although presumably the killing was recorded and somebody locked up for it…"

"Mark David Chapman, and he'll never leave prison."

"Even if his murderee suddenly turns up alive? Surely then he could claim a legally suspect verdict and damages galore."

Maurice nodded. "The thought has also crossed my mind, ma'am. But remember what we're tapping into here is the power of myth, in which verifiable facts play little part. Chapman can plead whatever he likes, it'll make no difference."

"You mean we would be lying? I have never known you to lie, Double O Seventeen."

"There are outright lies, ma'am, then there is massaging of the truth, as you will have observed in the clouds of obfuscation surrounding both the madman in the White House and his counterpart in the Kremlin. Hard to tell in such circumstances what 'truth' even *means* any longer, except that it's normally declared 'fake' in these post-truth days. One only needs think of the pearls of solipsism dripping from the lips of our current foreign secretary, let alone the loony in the White House."

Maurice shrugged meaningfully.

Dame Muriel nodded. She was no fan of either.

"And as you must well know, ma'am, there are moments when counter intelligence requires us get *our* hands dirty too. Whether we like it or not."

Dame Muriel nodded again. "Okay, I'm beginning to understand, Double O Seventeen. A case of means and ends we're talking here, am I right?"

"Yes, ma'am. And Machiavellian though it may be, if it's the only game in town what is the point of us standing on the side lines shouting boo at the ref when the ref has already been paid off by the opposition to go deaf?"

"Point taken, Double O Seventeen. So what we are about to toss onto the pitch here is the bombshell image of a dead/undead person and hope that will shake things up."

"Couldn't have put it better myself, ma'am."

"Just one last thing though. How *old* was Lennon when he was shot?"

"Forty."

"Which means he'd be in his late seventies by now. Bit *old* for a rock star, isn't it?"

"Some of them are still around and gigging, ma'am."

"And what age is Jeremy Crawford?"

"Mid-forties, perhaps."

"So you'll dress him up as a pensioner?"

Maurice laughed. "Jeremy will only be the subject of a computer generated image, an image I can manipulate to suit any taste. You'll just need to trust *my* eye to find the one that works best."

Dame Muriel sighed for a bit, then said, "Okay, Double O Seventeen. Keeping all my fingers and toes crossed, I shall sign off on this. But it better bloody well *work*."

"I can promise you nothing but my best, ma'am."

"Good enough for me. And remember, schtum is the name of the game where Phoebe is concerned."

"I wouldn't have it any other way. And thank you, ma'am," said Maurice, levering himself up from his chair and heading out of the MI6 HQ office, downstairs, and then out of the Vauxhall Cross building for a contemplative stroll along the banks of the Thames. Along the way he sang to himself extracts from "All You Need Is Love," getting stuck on the line about how there was nothing he could sing that couldn't be sung.

Twenty-seven

During the following three months Maurice, Barry, and The Reconstructed Beatles worked tirelessly at perfecting the precise image for the final launch across the Internet. The key rehearsal work on the songs—body language and so on—was done on weekdays at the Shepherd's Hut, after which at weekends Maurice would motor back to Tooting to upload the footage he'd taken into his computers, match them against recordings of the real Beatles, then fiddle into the wee small hours until his eyes failed and his brain hurt. It was a task he loved however. In some strange way he almost felt himself reincarnated as Brian Epstein, the original Beatles maker.

Barry, Jeremy/John, Julie/Paul, Maggie/George, and Dennis/Ringo were having the best time of their lives too. Okay, they'd all abandoned their pasts but none had any particular future in mind. Now they had one: to bring a little light into a darkening world. Not that they truly believed it would effect radical change, but still the idea was a lot more fun than working in a bank or a police station. Each Sunday evening when the Morris Minor Traveller sighed to a halt outside the Shepherd's Hut, they would be clustered on the doorstep hungry for the latest Beatle computer imagery Maurice had manipulated. Would it be the early tight-fitting smart suits and fresh-faced grins again or had they moved on to the Sergeant Pepper-type moustache stage yet? Or, in full denial of fresh-facedness and fancy dress, would they sport the shoulder-length hair and beards of the pre-split up period? It was all very tantalising.

Julie was still longing to tell her dad Steve what she was up to but Jeremy still wouldn't let her.

"Total top secret, luv," he told her in the Lennon-esque Scouse he'd been practising so hard it had become part of him. "Stanislavski eat your heart out," he was fond of saying.

"I wouldn't tell him *every*thing," Julie argued in the Paul tones she'd adopted, which wasn't hard seeing as she'd been born within a mile of the Liver Building. "Just the part about us making a new tribute band. Dad loves The Bootleg Beatles. Goes to all their gigs. He'd be sooo proud of me."

"But this is news he can't know. Top secret like Maurice told us. Last I heard you'd told your dad you were away on a all-expenses-paid bank business trip to Kathman-fuckin'-du."

"First time ever I lied to Dad. He was the one who told me lies would always catch up with me in the end. Have a fit if he knew, he would."

"Well, there're lies you tell for your own good, then there are those you tell for other people's, right?"

"True enough."

"And Steve must know the phone and Internet connections in Kathmandu aren't the greatest. Also what the *fuck* would you be doing joining a Beatles tribute band in Katmandu anyway?"

Just like the old John, Jeremy sprinkled his sentences liberally with "fuck" after watching a clip of "Working Class Hero," the first time he'd ever heard the expletive used in a song. Now it was across the media all the time, even on the BBC, but back in 1970 it must have been pretty revolutionary. Sometimes Julie used it too, just for fun. Mind you, as she remembered from the time before she left Liverpool, in that city it was used pretty much as punctuation, although more by the lads than the girls.

"Fair dos," she finally agreed. Then she told Jeremy/John to kiss her and he obliged with smackeroos on both cheeks.

The rest of the team had no trouble obeying Maurice's omertà injunction though, mainly because they had no loved ones to tell of their exploits. Maggie was too old to have parents any more, Dennis was a foundling, and neither of them had spouses let alone children, so no complications on that front. Jeremy of course *did* have family but the last thing he wanted was for any of them to know what he was up to. Overriding all of that, however, was the bliss of having ditched their previous existences to become anything else they might fancy, and what better, pro tem at least, than to become a computer-reconstructed Beatle with an ideological purpose? Nothing they could think of off hand. Plus they were intrigued by Maurice's insights into the nebulous world of counter espionage and thrilled to feel they could become a part of it.

That left Barry, who was also unmarried, childless, and too old to have parents. And *he* hadn't been given a Beatle role to lose himself in because there weren't five Beatles. But Barry didn't care. He'd stopped caring about himself more years ago than he could remember. Gardener was fine with him, by which term he meant anything he could help to grow. Until recently that had meant tending the plants of the earth but if, as had been his happy experience since rescuing Jeremy and Pete from their barn, it could also be interpreted to mean helping people flourish, that was fine with him. That's what he'd hoped to achieve at Oxford until he deconstructed the fissures in the dreaming spires.

It was Jeremy who asked him about such matters one late night/early morning Saturday when everybody else was in bed.

"I hope you don't regret bringing me here," he said. "And drawing all the other guys in my wake. There you were peacefully cultivating your garden, and now all *this*."

Barry smiled. "How's your French, Jeremy?"

"Poor going on minimal."

"But you may remember Édith Piaf?"

"Vaguely."

"Well, this is what she had to say about regret. I'm sure you'll catch the gist."

And then, in the best Piaf imitation he could muster, Barry sang: "'*Non, rien de rien, non, je ne regrette rien. Ni le bien qu'on m'a fait, ni le mal, tout ça m'est bien égal.*'"

"At my stage in life there's little point in looking back in regret," he explained. "What's done is done and cannot be undone. Some parts of it were tolerably good some were rubbish, but no good fretting over spilt milk, eh? As Édith says, it's all the same to me."

"Sounds a little fatalistic," said Jeremy.

"It does, but it is also wise because it allows the mind to stay open to whatever may befall us, and deal with it. To see clearly when the rain has gone and welcome a bright sunshiny day when one dawns."

"And this is one of your sunny days?"

"One of my sunniest. As they say, learning never ends. Just so long as we keep open our eyes to see. In answer to your original question, Jeremy, it has been a great pleasure for this old man to welcome you and your friends to my humble shack and, because of you, also to have attracted my most promising alumnus to it. And, as for the adventure we're all embarked on, how could I ever have foreseen *that*? No, no, I regret nothing. I am after all no more significant in the grand scheme of things than a butterfly or a wasp. Another drop of the dandelion brandy?"

Jeremy passed his glass.

"I'll have to remember the Piaf song," he said.

"Ah, the *petit moineau*—or little sparrow to the non-francophones," said Barry. "How about a toast to her?"

And so it was that Barry and Jeremy touched glasses and, clearing his head of Lennon-esque Scouse, Jeremy stood and launched into a barely recognisable reprise of "*Non, je ne regrette rien*'s" first verse.

Barry laughed and clapped. "Possibly not quite nasalised enough and a little light on the syntax, but nonetheless an excellent rendition. You're a fast learner, old chap. Now, do you not think we should turn in for the night? Tomorrow promises to be another busy day. One wonders what Beatle trickery Maurice will have up his sleeve *this* time."

~ * ~

Back at No. 10 Downing Street, Clarissa/Phoebe was feeling a whole lot less relaxed than the occupants of the Shepherd's Hut, her mind aflutter, aflurry and afizz with discrepant inputs to which it could find no coherent answer. After becoming prime minister she had expected all those beneath her—her cabinet, her MPs, Mister and Missus Pleb of the general population—to kowtow, bow, scrape and defer to her wishes. After all, apart from the queen, she was the top woman in the land. But had there *been* any kowtowing, bowing-and-scraping, let alone deference from *any* of those parties? Like hell there had. The opposite in fact as daily she faced carping from all sides, including aspersions she didn't even *have* what in human terms might have been thought of as a mind. "Robotic" was the description she was becoming increasingly infuriated by. Mind you, "wishy-washy U-turner who doesn't know her arse from her elbow" wasn't pleasing her much either. Such slights were endemic, *even* from the bally foreigners in Brussels who kept on and on and *on* wanting to know what exactly she meant by "Brexit" because none of the explanations she'd given them the previous week tallied with the one she was giving them *this* week. Worse still even her *own* people, the valiant Brits who had voted by the victorious margin of 4% to tell foreigners where they could go shove themselves, were champing at the bit, unhappy at her persistent doublespeak. As, even more worryingly, were the far right of her own cherished Tory party whom she knew she had to keep on board while she tried to steer a steady middle course through choppy, some said tsunami-ish, waters. Not even Sir Stanley Michaelson, Head of Armed Forces, was apparently onside. All he had offered by way of a march-past up Whitehall was a couple of battalions of Territorial Army recruits and one tank. No nukes, no squadrons of saluting full-time army, navy and RAF officers, just the TA guys and gals and the one (obsolete) tank.

"Take it or leave it, ducky," Sir "Six Gun" had texted.

"*Men*," Clarissa/Phoebe spat in response, wondering as she spat how good a plan it would be to implicate Sir "Six Gun" in an inappropriate behaviour towards female—and possibly male—officers scandal. It had worked with Hollywood producers and with the bosses of international aid organisations, so why shouldn't it work with the boss of the British armed forces?

But, as usual, Clarissa/Phoebe couldn't make up her mind on that.

"Oh, for the love of Christ on a *bike*," she screamed instead. "Where *is* the megalomaniac bonkers banker when I need him? He's got to be *some*where."

Which was a perfectly understandable assumption. As Spike Milligan replied when walking into a room and being asked what he was doing there, "Everyone has to be *some*where!" Clarissa/Phoebe's problem was she didn't know where Jeremy's somewhere was. Time and time again she had called Milly, only to be sent straight to a cryptic voicemail reply saying: "Due to unforeseen circumstances Milly is unavailable. Do not leave a message."

The head of MI6 una*vail*able for a conversation with the prime *min*ister, what in tarnation was *that* all about? Clarissa/Phoebe toyed with accusations of absence without leave, desertion of post, treachery and even treason but, as with her potential sex pest "Six

Gun" allegations, couldn't make up her mind on this case either. Instead she merely smashed a few smartphones by throwing them on her office floor and stamping on them. For a fleeting moment, she considered calling Hubby at MI5 to see if he had any idea of the whereabouts of either Milly or the bonkers banker or both. The Secret Services were meant to be in constant communication with each other, weren't they? Also she'd heard whispers on the Westminster rumour mill that Milly and Hubby were an "item." But Clarissa didn't call Sir Hubert because she had never liked him much. And liked him even less when he'd been quoted in a *Daily Grunt* article as referring to her Brexit performances to date as, "Much like a headless chicken ice-dancing in wellingtons."

So where *was* Dame Muriel when Clarissa/Phoebe placed her last despairing call, you will be asking.

At number thirteen Oakshot Street Tooting is the answer. Watching on with Terpsichore/Tiddles/Cat as Maurice OO17 Moffat sat before his bank of computers morphing The Reconstructed Beatles into an Internet weapon capable of competing with Igor Ripurpantzov's IRA cyber troll farmers in St Petersburg. And with any luck raising the American public's resistance to the tweeted delusions of the head case in the White House, the latest of which had proposed arming teachers as the best way to protect students from being shot to death by crazed gunmen, using the tired old wild west cliché, "The only thing that stops a bad guy with a gun is a good guy with a gun."

"And you honestly think we can make a difference here, Double O Seventeen? With just a dead-but-not-dead person and a few songs?"

"And the alternative is what, ma'am? We declare a *military* war against the Ruskies and the Americans? No, no, in my humble opinion cyber subterfuge is a much more cost effective strategy with the possibility of much higher returns. It has its risks, of course it does. What in human history doesn't? But an interesting way of puncturing the balloons of the crazies in both the White House and the Kremlin would be to turn their populations against them, do you not think?"

"Through electoral revolution you mean?"

"Who knows? That's how the trick was worked in the US election and indeed in the Brexit nonsense. You may also remember Florida's hanging chads during the George W. Bush election. But a better alternative would be direct action. After all where did the French revolution come from? Radical ideas generated by largely bourgeois thinkers to begin with and only then the trickle-down mass reaction from *les citoyens*. After that goodbye monarchs. Similar situation in the American revolt that robbed us Brits of our cherished slab of God's chosen country. What was the slogan again? 'No taxation without representation,' if memory serves."

"Mmm," said Dame Muriel.

"By the by, speaking of revolution, would you care to see my version of the bonkers banker singing Lennon's song of the same name. The voice and image syncing is pretty decent even if I say it myself. I'm particularly pleased with the way Jeremy handles the line about refusing to contribute money to people with minds that hate."

"With pleasure," said Dame Muriel, the echoes of "All You Need Is Love" still playing in her hippocampus.

And so impressed was she with what she saw and heard that, tentatively when The Reconstructed Beatles' version of "Revolution" was over, she asked OO17 if she might have the pleasure of finally meeting this bonkers banker chappie in person.

"His name is Jeremy, ma'am. Jeremy Crawford."

"Ah."

"But yes, I'm sure a visit could be arranged."

Twenty-eight

It was on the journey to Fanbury in the old Morris Minor Traveller that Maurice and Dame Muriel thrashed out a few of the key operational elements when it came to the release of the new Beatles material across the Internet. And now she was fully on board with the plan, Dame Muriel proved her worth. Not for nothing had she been promoted through the ranks to become head of MI6.

"A number of questions I have for you, Double O Seventeen," she said as they left behind them the mayhem of London traffic and took to pottering along country B roads.

"Fire away, ma'am," said Maurice, braking behind a flock of sheep herded by a rookie Collie called Ronnie who was being put through his paces to no great effect by a pipe-smoking shepherd called Albert, such that the sheep were confused and wandering about all over the place.

"Numero uno," said Dame Muriel. "And *do* let us drop the 'ma'am,' shall we? From here on in you can be Maurice and I can be Muriel."

"Okay…Muriel. And your numero uno?"

"What the narrative is that shall accompany your message, video or blog or post or tweet or whatever these things are called nowadays."

"Narrative ma'am...um, Muriel?" said Maurice, watching on in amusement as Ronnie failed to obey Albert's double-whistle command to coax a ram from a ditch and instead cocked his leg against a silver birch sapling.

"Yes. You see, in my understanding, what you have on offer in this band of yours is a bunch of well-rehearsed and very cleverly computer-manipulated nobodies purporting to be The Reconstructed Beatles. Correct?"

"Indeed so."

"And how are we going to cover our backs with the two that are still alive? Remind me."

Maurice nodded, one eye on how Albert might persuade Ronnie to stop pissing on trees and get on with his job.

"As I said, I've already talked to them and they're happy to lie low and let others impersonate them," he said. "I've shown them clips of my work and they just laughed and said 'good luck, pal,'"

"Okay, that all seems in order. And are we also safe as far as the dead ones' families are concerned? We must be super-careful not to give rise to either offense or legal repercussions in their case, particularly that of Lennon's, seeing as he's so critical to your story. In regard to which, have you consulted his widow yet?"

"Yoko. Yes, I called her in New York and she's on board big time. Loves the idea. Nothing she'd like better than a revolution and she is even prepared to make a cameo appearance herself if required, so no danger of law suits there," said Maurice.

"She lives in New York?"

"Yes," said Maurice, watching on as Ronnie the Collie, with Albert's assistance, finally managed to persuade the ram (called Desmond) back to his feet and join the rest of the flock.

"Problem there, Double O Seventeen?"

"No, ma'am. Not if what you're suggesting is fellow New

Yorkers and friends would know the truth of her whereabouts and it would not have been on some desert island with John."

"That is precisely my suggestion. Could blow our entire enterprise wide open."

"Indeed it could have, but as it happens, that was a problem Yoko herself foresaw and addressed."

"By?"

"Explaining her absences from New York were frequent and, to protect her valued privacy, she never told anyone where she was going so she might just as well have been on a desert island with John as anywhere else."

"Fine. So that just leaves the other dead fellow. George, if memory serves. You have spoken to his kin too?"

"Yes. And they have no more of a prejudice against tribute bands than Paul, Ringo or Yoko as long as a slice of any proceeds go to the support of Hare Krishna. George was a very spiritual person."

"And where is *he* supposed to have been since he 'died'?"

"In a Hindu monastery at a secret location in India. The death was feigned in order to escape the evils of the material world. Like John, however, he becomes so disturbed by the re-emergence of oligarchic and fascist tendencies across the globe that he agrees to break his purdah this one true time and play a few of his old band's songs to remind folk of the sort of world he still dreams of and the urgency of reawakening that vision."

"And you truly believe people will swallow all this?"

"In the alternative facts world we live in, ma'am, I suspect there is a distinct possibility. The power of Internet myth these days is such that people will believe practically anything," said Maurice as Ronnie managed to herd his sheep into an adjacent field and Albert tapped out the dottle from his pipe on a boot and waved cheerily at the Morris Minor Traveller to continue its journey.

"And Lennon's voice will be his own or…"

"It will be his, but coming from the mouth of Jeremy Crawford, his avatar. You seemed to like the way I had fitted those things together."

"I *did*, Double O Seventeen, pardon me 'Maurice.' I thought it a splendid piece of work."

"Well then, we finally seem to be singing from the same hymn sheet here ma'am…Muriel," said Maurice, tapping his foot on the accelerator, which responded with a tired grunt but at least they were underway again.

"And your other pertinent questions were?"

Dame Muriel had two more. Firstly, which songs Lennon and the faux Beatles would be performing, and secondly which channels he was thinking of using to maximize their distribution.

Maurice shrugged while yet again being obliged to halt the Morris Minor Traveller, this time behind a broken down tractor that had jack-knifed across the road the wagonload of dung it was towing.

"Well," he said, "my preferred compilation would be 'All You Need Is Love,' 'Working Class Hero,' 'Revolution' of course, and then after the Beatles' split up, 'Give Peace A Chance,' and 'Imagine,' although the latter would have to be a solo piano effort. Not too hard to work it up, though. If I can manipulate whole bands, solo piano jobs shouldn't be too hard."

"And the distribution?"

"The usual Internet channels. Unless of course you could…?"

Dame Muriel chuckled. "Use my influence with GCHQ to see what sources *they* might be able to open up for our little charade?"

"Well, that would be an *aw*fully good idea. Wish I'd thought of it myself," said Maurice, who had thought of it himself but didn't like to say so. "An excellent source. Just think of the contacts *they* must have," he added, winding up his window against the stench of dung seeping through it from the stricken wagon ahead of them.

"Well, I believe that about settles matters, Double O Seventeen. So it's all systems go and let us hope we hit our targets. *Now*, I'm so looking forward to meeting these new chums of yours," said Dame Muriel rubbing her hands. "Take us much longer to get there, will it?"

"At this rate, there's no telling, ma'am," said Maurice, nodding at the tractor up ahead, which was making farting noises and expelling clouds of smoke, causing the dung wagon to quiver and list dangerously towards a ditch. "But more haste, less speed, eh? Meanwhile I do have cups and a thermos of tea on the back seat should you wish to be mother."

Dame Muriel laughed, a rare occurrence for her. "Don't suppose you brought along any choccie biccies too, then we could have a picnic."

"In the glove compartment, ma'am."

"*Muriel.*"

"Muriel. By the way, just to keep you fully abreast of matters in the hoped-for expectation of your agreement, I have released a little teaser across the Internet to whet appetites of what might be to come."

"*Teaser*?" said Dame Muriel, ferreting in the glove compartment and, to her delight, finding a packet of Jaffa Cakes.

"You know, a mere hint at the as yet unverified but nonetheless distinct possibility of John and George not having died after all and perhaps—just maybe—being prepared to make a one-off and one-time only comeback."

"To tempt the cats amongst pigeons, eh? You naughty boy," said Dame Muriel, leaning backwards across her seat in search of the tea thermos.

"Quite. You'll also find sugar sachets in the box. Two for me, please," Maurice was saying as magically up ahead the tractor stopped farting and blowing and its driver, Sam Smyles, strolled back to the stopped Morris Minor Traveller to offer his apologies for any delay.

"Sorry, big end problem," he said as Maurice wound down his window. "Happens all the bleedin' time with the old darlin.' Just needs a bit of a rest and a good talking-to and she's right as rain before you know it. Anyway, sorry for holdin' you folks up."

"No problem," said Maurice, "Similar problems with *my* old darling."

Sam nodded sympathetically at Dame Muriel's backside as she struggled with the tea preparation until Maurice clarified matters by tapping at the Morris Minor Traveller's dashboard.

"Ah, yes, sorry, the *car*," said Sam. "Also an old lady."

"Indeed," said Maurice. "Care for a cup of tea yourself before you head back with your load of…"

"Shit for the fields," Sam explained. "But, yeah, a cuppa would be nice. Very generous of you, squire."

And so it was that the head of MI6 and her top trouble-shooter, agent OO17, spent the next half hour sipping tea and chewing Jaffa Cakes in the company of Sam Smyles, who outlined to them with some passion the disasters awaiting local farmers like him once Brexit ensured there would be no more subsidies from Brussels.

"Be without a living we will," said Sam. "But the bleedin' government here couldn't give a toss, could it? Let alone money. And still they expect us to provide the food for folks to eat. And the cow jumped over the moon," he added tapping at his right temple.

It was with those words ringing in their ears that, some hours later, Maurice and Dame Muriel finally pulled up outside the Shepherd's Hut.

~ * ~

Maurice couldn't even have guessed at the impact his John Lennon comeback teaser was to have in St Petersburg, where the old man who had inspired his project still looked out to sea daily in hopes of his hero's return. His neighbours all believed poor old Fyodor Frumkin to be bonkers, harmless, but nonetheless two sandwiches short of a picnic. So they humoured him. Brought him flasks of vodka and plates of pryaniki and stood alongside him as he tended his shrine and sang "Imagine" to himself and anyone else in the vicinity. He'd learnt most of the words in English and had had them translated for him by his clever son Yuri, who worked for some top-secret computer outfit in town. And Fyodor so loved those words. Just to imagine all the people sharing all the world, how good was that? What the hell was the point, he would argue with anyone prepared to listen, in Russia and America continuing to threaten each other with more and more missiles capable of obl*it*erating all the people in the world? No point, was Fyodor's view. As, of course, had been Lennon's in his and Yoko's campaign for peace. Soon Fyodor would die and in some ways that would be a relief. But before that day, even for an instant, could there be a glimmer of hope? And as fate would have it, that glimmer came on a Tuesday evening as Fyodor was giving Lennon's shrine a final polish and taking a last hopeful look at the sea before heading home to his shack.

"Papa, *Papa*, look at *this*," said Yuri, running up to thrust beneath his father's eyes a smartphone and click on Maurice Moffat's teaser with its mini clips of the newly emergent and not-dead recluse John Lennon singing some of his favourite songs with his old band. Then came "Give Peace A Chance," at which Fyodor wiped tears from his eyes before punching air and shouting "*alliluyya*" (hallelujah in Russian).

Yuri was delighted. The only child of a widower, he loved the father who had sacrificed so much to ensure his son had the best education in town. Okay, the old man was a bit doolally, but who wouldn't be after enduring the privations of the soviet time, then rejoicing in glasnost, then watching on as the criminal in the Kremlin stole back all the freedoms? So often as a teenager Yuri had listened as Fyodor told him tales of better times when the world had been more open. When he'd also listened on an old record player to a bootleg original of the *Sergeant Pepper's Lonely Hearts Club Band* LP with its exciting sleeve...and to the Rolling Stones, and to Elvis and Chuck Berry, and to many more. But it had always been to Lennon that Fyodor returned, saying: "Hear what this man is saying, son. He has truth in his heart and isn't afraid to tell it." Devastated Fyodor had been when news came through of the New York shooting in which he had never fully convinced himself to believe: hence the shrine, hence the hope. And now it was Yuri who brought his father the news he most wanted to hear, that Lennon was still alive. What better gift could a son give such a father?

The fly in the ointment was Yuri's job with the top-secret St Petersburg computer outfit, the Internet Research Agency, also known as Glavset, internationally recognised as having meddled in Western elections, including most spectacularly the wipeout of the only candidate capable of preventing the madman in the White House from be*com*ing the madman in the White House. In Glavset's bunker beneath St Petersburg, his colleagues were running about like headless chickens trying—and failing—to block the further spread of Maurice's teaser with their firewalls and volts. But however many nifty counter-hacker algorithms they hammered into their keyboards, nothing worked, because Maurice's counter-counter-hacker algorithms worked better. Back and back came the Lennon songs like an unstoppable refrain. The big boss in Moscow wasn't going to like this. Not *at all* he wasn't.

Ripurpantzov had permitted a number of Western rock concerts, including one by Paul McCartney, but these had been carefully Kremlin-choreographed events, which would include nothing that might be interpreted as critical of the regime. Igor had learnt *that* lesson from the performances of Pussy Riot, several of whose members he had thrown in jail for sedition. Since then, some of the

Beatles' silly love songs were still allowed across the media as a warped symbol of glitz and "modernity," but chatter on the wires suggested the president was as aware as OO17—to the point of paranoia some said—of his potential vulnerability to the "decadent" Beatles' tracks which had foreshadowed the death knell of the Soviet Union. Maybe he'd even seen a translated version of the same TV show as Maurice, the one in which The Beatles had "rocked the Kremlin." After all, he had spies everywhere, some of whom he'd been obliged to poison with sarin. One thing was for certain, though. Nothing similar did Ripurpantzov want happening to *his* iron grip on power, especially from the likes of John Lennon.

And here was Yuri Frumkin handing over to his partially crazed father evidence of the continuing existence of the very person his president most wished to stay dead and buried. In principle, Yuri should have been conflicted in his duty to father on the one hand and his country on the other. But Yuri had only recently returned from a trip to Moscow, there to protest against Ripurpantzov's imprisonment of his only viable opposition candidate in the upcoming presidential election and lucky he too hadn't been incarcerated, so duty to his country was out the window. Pissed off with his country and its oligarch leaders was how Yuri was feeling.

"Papa," he whispered. "I know how these songs can be passed on to friends all across this country and in many others. Just give me the word."

"You could *do* this?"

"*Da*," said Yuri. "I have the means. Very *very* hush-hush it would have to be, but I could do it."

"With your computer thingummy whatsit?"

"*Da*."

"And you *would* do it?"

"For you, Papa, and for your dream. Now our shared dream."

That was when the tears came to Fyodor's eyes. At first he swiped them away. But more came, then more until they were dripping down his cheeks and through his straggly beard.

"My *son*," said Fyodor, taking Yuri in the sort of bear hug for which Russians are famed and smothering him in kisses. "You are a good boy, the *best* boy. Of you I am proud."

"*Blagodayra* (thanks in Russian)," said Yuri. "Need a hand polishing that shrine of yours?

Had he known of such developments, Maurice Moffat would have been moved and encouraged, but even in our super-informed world some things remain private and this was one of them.

Twenty-nine

Dame Muriel sensed a certain *je ne sais quoi* in the air the moment she set foot in the Shepherd's Hut and met Barry, Jeremy, Julie, Maggie and Dennis. Maurice had introduced her as "my boss, the head of MI6," but nobody seemed much impressed by the prestigious title. They just smiled and said "hi."

"Do take a seat. Cup of tea?" said Barry, at which Muriel said, "Thank you," reflecting the fellow would likely have said precisely the same words had it been the queen who had stepped into his parlour. No sense of surprise, deference or hierarchy. It wasn't even as though her visit had been announced in advance. All very peculiar.

"Sugars?" Barry was further enquiring as Pete, Colin, Hans and Shirley joined the party to investigate their latest guest—sniff her legs and so on—at which, unused to animals, Muriel recoiled a bit.

"Don't worry, they won't hurt you," said Julie. "Checking you out, that's all."

"I see," said the head of MI6, extending a tentative hand to pat a couple of canine heads. The pig she would leave for the moment, thank you very much. "And, um, no sugar or milk."

"No sugar or *milk*?" said Barry.

"No, I take it straight," said Dame Muriel, looking to OO17 for assistance but receiving nothing bar but a shrug and a smile in return.

"Ooo-kay then," said Barry. "But could I at least tempt you to a Hobnob to go with it?"

"A Hobnob would be nice," Dame Muriel was saying, shortly before Pete poked his snout up her skirt and Jeremy ran over to drag him away.

"Sorry about that, he means no harm," he said. "Oh, and by the way, I'm the bonkers banker."

"Oink," Pete confirmed.

Never mind a *je ne sais quoi*, it was all getting something of an overload for Dame Muriel, but struggling with her credentials and thinking of England, she strove to maintain her composure.

"Otherwise known as Mister Jeremy Crawford, I presume," she said. "Britain's most wanted man."

"A title I never wished for," said Jeremy. "But yes."

"And the main chap in Maurice's Reconstructed Beatles, as I understand it. The Lennon lookalike."

"Indeed so," said Jeremy as Muriel took to worrying less about her credentials, thoughts of England or composure maintenance. The fellow had honest eyes, which couldn't easily be dismissed.

It was as Barry was returning with the Russian tea and a plate of Hobnobs that he and everybody else in the Shepherd's Hut became aware of the thwacka-thwacka-*thwack* in the skies just above them.

"What *the…*?" said Maggie, leaping from his seat and heading to the door for a better look.

And what he saw didn't please him as the helicopter landed and, escorted by two armed policepersons—one male, the other female—Prime Minister Phoebe/Clarissa came marching in his direction grinning ghoulishly.

"*Found* the bonkers banker at last!" she warbled triumphantly as she marched.

~ * ~

And how, you will be wondering, had the normally clueless Clarissa achieved this feat of detection? In a rare moment of acuity, by appointing her super supremo smartphone tracker, Simon "The Sniffer" Southgate to track the phones of both Casanova and Milly to their current whereabouts, that was how.

"Duh!" I hear you say. "Two top-of-the-range spies leaving themselves open to such an easy ploy. Duh!"

And nine times out of ten, your derision would be perfectly understandable. But this was the tenth time and, far from being the result of operational fecklessness, instead marked the culmination of the cunning ruse Maurice had floated to Muriel on the last lap of their journey to the Shepherd's Hut.

"You know, ma'am, thinking things over, it might be of benefit to us all, but in particular Jeremy, were we to take this opportunity to lure Clarissa into a little trap."

"*Trap*, Double O Seventeen?"

"Yes. As I understand it, she is keen to offload onto poor old Jeremy recrimination for all her government's howlers by painting him as a criminal mastermind and thus get the press pack off her back. Not so?"

"Agreed. And?"

"Well, it did occur to me we might be of assistance to both Jeremy and Clarissa through a slight manipulation of the narrative."

"You're a demon for narrative manipulation, Double O Seventeen…um, *Maurice*."

"Comes with the turf…Muriel."

"And this new story?"

"Is the one in which our little enterprise, starring the same Jeremy Crawford albeit in a slightly different light, stands a much better chance of letting Clarissa off all sorts of hooks than the blame game she is currently working on. Just imagine if, by promoting Jeremy's Lennon role, *she* were to be credited as the single world leader to have dented Ripurpantzov's armour, even without recourse to threats of nuclear weaponry."

Dame Muriel smiled. "Some skullduggery, Maurice, but as part of our current fictions, possibly worth a try. And how would you suggest we set this lure?"

Which was when OO17 proposed leaving both their smartphones turned on full blast for the remainder of their drive to meet Jeremy and his new friends.

"Should be easy peasy for one of her top smartphone sniffer chaps. So, just let's give it a whirl, shall we? And hope Clarissa takes the bait."

"I'm in this up to my neck already, Double O Seventeen." Dame Muriel shrugged blithely. "Can an inch further make a signal difference?"

"My feelings entirely. So let's go for it, shall we?"

Dame Muriel shrugged blithely again.

And so it was that "duh" was not the only explanation to the surprise arrival outside the Shepherd's Hut of the RAF Puma HC2 helicopter bearing Prime Minister Phoebe/Clarissa and her two armed policepersons. Sorry about that.

~ * ~

It was Maurice who took charge of the situation, calling Jeremy to join him as he sauntered to the garden gate and waved cheerily at the prime minister as she continued marching towards the Shepherd's Hut.

"You wave too. And point at your hat," he whispered to Jeremy, who was wearing a black felt tricorn from Barry's thespian store upon which, going for levity, Maurice had inscribed in red letters, HI THERE, I'M THE BONKERS BANKER.

Jeremy chuckled and did as instructed while Maurice continued to wave, and also to call words of welcome. Sadly to no avail however, since unable from birth to tell a joke from a jam sandwich, Clarissa sensed the piss being taken, continued marching, and instructed her armed policepersons to arrest "these treasonous buffoons" on the spot.

Which was silly of her, because rarely though he had been obliged to employ his martial arts skills, Maurice was left with no other option but to resuscitate them as the policepersons advanced towards him and Jeremy cocking their pistols and hissing: "Hands in the air and don't move." What was he supposed to do, stand there and wait to be arrested when all he'd been trying to do was play nice?

Sighing therefore, he dived headfirst over the garden gate to make himself a thinner target, scrambled back to his feet...and the rest was a foregone conclusion. All it took while the policepersons were preoccupied loosing off futile bullets into nearby trees was a flying double reverse taekwondo Dwi Huryeo Chagi (spinning hook kick) and both officers were flat on their backs mewling softly. All Maurice then needed to do was pick up their weapons, tuck them into his belt gunslinger-style and shrug apologetically at Clarissa, who was peering boss-eyed at her fallen defenders.

"Sorry for kicking the lady cop, Prime Minister. Not my normal practice to kick ladies," said Maurice, "but this one was pointing a pistol at me."

PC Sian O'Brady mewled slightly louder as if in corroboration.

"Don't worry about her…or her friend here," Maurice continued, prodding PC Joe "Charlie" Chaplin with the toe of his shoe. "They'll be fine in a minute, although they will, of course, need to be stripped of any other unpleasant equipment they may be carrying and tied up. But they'll be fed and watered."

"Ug," said Clarissa, for a fleeting second turning her head to the pilot of the Puma HC2 for assistance.

But Harry "The Whirlybird" Warburton, staring through his windscreen at the mayhem Maurice had just unleashed, shrank back in his seat. Far beyond *his* remit or pay grade was it to mess with trained killers the likes of which he'd just witnessed. Harry's job was to fly choppers and mightily relieved he was when the call came through from RAF HQ that his "bird" was needed pronto at a riot in Lewes East Sussex where groups of dangerous-looking, albeit elderly, ex-hippies were marching around town threatening civic disorder and screaming Lenn-*on*! Lenn-*on*, *right*-on! while burning effigies of both the madman in the White House and the one in the Kremlin, even though it wasn't Guy Fawkes Night when Lewesians normally burn effigies of people they loathe.

Yes, folks, Yuri's promised diffusion of Maurice's Beatlemania teaser, never mind its creator's own distribution, had already hit the first of its manifold future nerves. Strange it should have been in the sleepy town of Lewes that residents reacted so fast, but such are the facts of the matter. Who *knows* how the World Wide Web works?

*Any*way, off Harry flew. Elderly ex-hippies he reckoned he could frighten away with dive-bombing tactics any day of the week.

"Bugger," Clarissa was saying as Maurice, now with Dame Muriel at his side, strolled over, proffered a hand for shaking, and said, "There there, Prime Minister, don't worry. Every little thing is going to be *all* right."

"I'll see to it, ma'am," said Jeremy, doffing his HI THERE, I'M THE BONKERS BANKER tricorn and bowing from the waist.

At which Clarissa fainted and had to be helped back onto her spindly legs by her ex-Girton College rival, Dame Muriel, who, while hoisting her up in a full nelson, whispered in her ear, "*Plus ça change, ma chère, plus c'est la même chose, n'est ce pas*?"

But what with the supply of blood to her brain having been even further reduced than normal *and* not speaking any language other than English, for which she had been repeatedly ridiculed by European leaders, as usual Clarissa missed the point. Like levity, irony had never been one of her strong suits, particularly when it was in French.

It was Barry who came out to pick up the pieces and offer a little hospitality.

"Cup of tea, Prime Minister?" he said. "And a crumpet to go with it, perhaps?"

At which one of Clarissa's glazed eyes squeezed open a fraction.

"Mmm, yummy," she managed to mumble.

Thirty

Idly while Maggie and Dennis were out tying PCs O'Brady and Chaplin to trees and Julie was coaxing Clarissa back to something akin to consciousness with tea and crumpets, Maurice flicked about on Barry's elderly laptop for any early indications of responses to his Internet Lennon teaser. And his eyes widened at what he saw.

"Look at *this*," he said, finger-hooking Dame Muriel, Barry and Jeremy to look over his shoulder, then scrolling through the thousands of hits.

"Hey, hey, slow *down*, would you?" said Dame Muriel. You know how irritating super-scrolling can be. Or a person riffling papers before your eyes and expecting you to digest the contents through hyper osmosis.

"Sorry," said Maurice, going back to the top.

"Perhaps just a brief résumé?" said Barry.

So Maurice picked out the effigy-burning incident in Lewes, and then the jerky video from St Petersburg showing pro-Lennon marches outside the IRA's supposedly secret underground offices and police spraying protesters with tear gas.

"Who could have *thought* it?" he said. "But there are more."

The "more" included similar demonstrations from places as far flung geographically and ideologically as Novosibirsk and San Francisco, which would have taken Maurice the rest of the day to list, so he didn't. Just let us say hamlets, towns and cities from practically every continent were represented.

"Wow," said Jeremy.

"And all this even before we've released our final product, when one hopes to stir up yet further interest," Maurice was saying as Maggie and Dennis returned from tying policepersons to trees—a task Dennis had particularly enjoyed—and Clarissa finally began to respond to Julie's ministrations, albeit rudely.

"Where *am* I and who're *you*?" she said, knocking the teacup from Julie's hands, springing onto her pogo stick legs and peering about.

"Excuse me," said Dame Muriel to Maurice. "A certain lady looks as though she needs to be taught some manners," she added before marching over to Clarissa and telling her to sit down and shut up if she knew what was good for her.

"Don't worry, love," I can handle it," said Julie. "I've got an auntie just like her."

"Only your auntie isn't a prime minister."

"No. There is that to it."

"What kind of a madhouse *is* this?" squawked Clarissa. "And what are *you* doing here anyway, Muriel?"

"My job, Clarissa. Now sit *down*."

"Your *job*? Your *job* is to protect national security, which does not include sequestering a dangerous madman, who…"

"You need as a cover story to deflect attention from your fumbling attempts to govern a country?"

Julie smiled. She was starting to like this MI6 boss lady. "Do like the woman says and sit *down* or I'll kick you behind the knees," she said. It was a tactic that had worked wonders on Auntie Gertie.

"Flibbertigibbet! Northern strumpet!" said Clarissa, so Julie did kick her behind the knees and Clarissa was left with no choice but to sit down.

Maggie and Dennis raised appreciative eyebrows. Especially Maggie, who, as Sir Magnus Montague, had twice been fêted at Downing Street for his contributions to "The National Welfare," aka the Tory Party.

"How *nice* to meet you again, Prime Minister," he said, proffering an ironic hand for shaking.

Clarissa's eyes widened and she looked as though she might faint again.

"Who're *you*?" she said, gazing at the unkempt person who claimed to know her.

So, at considerable length before Barry intervened, Maggie took to explaining exactly who he was with particular emphasis on his transition from City banker to happy hippy, thereby causing Clarissa to wobble on her seat.

"Another cup of tea for the lady, perhaps?" said Barry with a knowing nod at Maurice who, reading the runes, linked an arm through one of Maggie's and led him gently away.

"Blurg? Phlut?" said Clarissa. Understandably. After all, nothing in her previous existence had prepared her for *this* sort of treatment. Yes, there had been the daily barrage of jibes from the media and fellow members of the House of Commons at every fumble she made, but never before had she been kicked behind the knees and then faced with an evident lunatic burbling about the joys of self-reinvention.

Jeremy smiled, sat down beside the prime minister and recounted *his* story. Well, not *all* of it, just from the part where he could stand his old life no more and went to live in a barn with a pig called Pete.

"That's him over there," he said, pointing at Pete who preened, winked at Clarissa, and said "oink."

"Then Barry here came and rescued me."

Barry bowed slightly.

"And the next thing I knew, I'd been branded the bonkers banker and the rest is history. Some of it of *your* making, ma'am."

Clarissa blinked and edged away from Jeremy, who edged closer to her saying, “But let bygones be bygones, eh? Turn the page and begin a new chapter?”

“Quite sure you wouldn’t fancy another cuppa?” said Barry. “On the house.”

“Wuh-where’s muh-my wuh-whirlybird?” Clarissa gurgled, casting her eyes this was and that.

“Migrated,” said Dame Muriel.

“You’re all alone, your bird has flown,” sang Julie to the tune of Lennon’s “Norwegian Wood,” one of her dad’s favourites.

“Pretty harsh treatment even for a prime minister as doolally as Clarissa,” I hear you object. But, you might reflect, how *else* were the Shepherd’s Hut gang of seven to reduce to a modicum of compliance the woman in whom nobody in the land had much faith when it came to flexibility? By saying, “There, there, we’ll sing to *your* song sheet, my dear? I don’t think so. Anyway, like it or not, that was the treatment Clarissa got. Pro tem she was a prisoner and, with a little kindness thrown in here and there, she might eventually listen to *their* reason.

It was Dame Muriel who explained this rationale.

“A shame it has had to come to this,” she said as Clarissa’s head lolled. “But what is, *is*. And your job now is to make the best of it. You may or may not recall Girton’s old motto ‘better is wisdom than weapons of war,’ but it is precisely in harmony with that philosophy that you needed to be reduced to your current impasse, for impasse I’m afraid it is. Unless of course you are prepared to have a little wise re-think.”

Clarissa raised her head with difficulty and peered at Dame Muriel.

“You see, my dear, these chaps, *all* of whom you believe to be bonkers, have an interesting strategy up their sleeves that might just help you and your suffering government to a better place.”

"Heaven?" said Clarissa.

"Not *heaven*, my dear. We're not planning to kill you."

"Good," said Clarissa, gazing around the Shepherd's Hut at Barry, Maurice, Jeremy, Julie, Maggie, Dennis and their animals.

"Just help you along the road to the better place. So, d'you want to hear our plan or don't you?"

"Do I have a choice?"

"Not really."

"Okay then, let's hear the bally thing."

Which was when Dame Muriel called Maurice over to outline to the prime minister the cunning plan he'd developed to improve her status her from zero to hero by taking the credit for making Igor Ripurpantzov's governance of Russia a tad less comfortable than it had been to date and possibly unseating the madman in the White House. Equally it would be bound to raise her clout with the beasts of Brussels.

"You don't *mean*?" said a newly alert Clarissa when Maurice's shtick was over.

"That is precisely what we mean," said Dame Muriel. "Should you lend your approval to the idea, you may well find yourself becoming a credible world leader *and*, doubtless to your immense satisfaction, get the media off your back for the foreseeable future. Would you care to observe some recent responses to Double O Seventeen's initial foray into the Internet?"

And, although at first aghast, Clarissa was soon gazing on in wonder as Maurice replayed the clips from Lewes, St Petersburg and so many other places.

~ * ~

As noted, amongst those other places was San Francisco, specifically the Santa Clara Valley area better known as Silicon Valley and home to such super-hi-tech giants as Apple, Google, Facebook, Yahoo et al. Yet never in their illustrious and/or infamous postmillennial histories had the bosses of such companies witnessed outpourings of glee and rage on such a scale as those experienced at the announcement of John Lennon's sudden reincarnation on the world stage. The glee came from elderly ex-hippies just like the ones in Lewes East Sussex, and the rage from the bible-bashers who'd never forgiven Lennon for his comments on the relative popularities of The Beatles and Jesus, but either way it was good for business, thought the gazillionaire bosses.

There was one exception to this rule, however, and that was Harvard Law School dropout Monty Gaspachio, twenty-two year-old founder, owner and CEO of the newly emergent BlabberMouth, estimated on Nasdaq to be worth upwards of $56B. For it was Monty who was the only one to spot not only the big bucks angle in this latest outburst of furious tribalism, but also its political ramifications. It was on the very evening Maurice's teaser hit the global sites that Monty, relaxing in a Lay-Z-Boy lounger beside his San Jose pool with his newest girlfriend Jennifer, experienced the sudden epiphany in which he sensed how these outpourings of glee and rage eerily mirrored the current radical division in American society between the left behind rednecks, hillbillies and Rust Belt workers who worshipped the psycho in the White House and the liberals on the West and East coasts who loathed him.

"You see where I'm goin' with this, Jenny?" he said, jerking bolt upright in his Lay-Z-Boy lounger and verbalised his flash of insight.

"Not rilly," said Jennifer when he'd finished. Hollywood movie star wannabe Jenny was busy drying in the sun from her latest dip in Monty's pool.

"Oo*kay*. So I'm gonna spell it out to you, hon'," said Monty, launching into an exegesis of how the White House had been hijacked by a psychotic megalomaniac grifter who, with the help of Russia's Igor Ripurpantzov, had secured the presidency through deceit, lies and appeals to the basest instincts in human nature.

"*This* is the guy," he continued while Jennifer applied unguents to her breasts and legs, "who has torn up the consensus that kept America more or less in one piece for the most part of a hundred and fifty years. The guy who stands a good chance of causing civil war two."

"And you're gonna *do* something about that, Mont, am I right?"

"Sure as hell is hot I am, babe," said Monty, leaping from his lounger and belly flopping into his pool.

"Ouch," remarked Jennifer but, rolling onto his back and kicking his legs in the California air, Monty was laughing.

"Hey, babe," he called. "You wanna do me a favour?"

"Sure I do, Mont."

"Go in the house and dig out my music compilation gizmo. You know where that is?"

"On the bedside table?"

"Right in one. Then you hook it into the outside loudspeakers and the songs I'll be wanting to hear are Dylan's 'The Times They Are A Changin'' and Lennon's 'Imagine.' You can do that small thing for me?"

"Honey, for you *any*thing," said Jenny, who knew Monty was owed serious money by the kinds of wannabe movie directors in LA he might just persuade to find her a walk-on part in their latest blockbuster.

"Great. Thanks," said Monty, climbing out of the water and hitting the button on his Lay-Z-Boy armrest that would enhance Maurice's teaser and blazon it all across BlabberMouth, along with undisguised editorial comment reminding folk of how much the madman in The White House would have disgusted John Lennon and urging them to hit the streets en masse in sympathy. If he lost his BlabberMouth empire and all his money as a result of a covert White House smear campaign, well so be it. Money wasn't the only thing in life. This was the time for Monty to make a stand. He punched air when out came the sounds of Dylan and Lennon singing their songs. Jennifer had done a good job. The neighbours would hate it, but Monty hated the neighbours, so that was okay. Maybe tomorrow would be a *very* new day. He sure hoped so.

Thirty-one

Things gathered pace at the Shepherd's Hut once Clarissa had agreed to Maurice's plan and hailed a fresh helicopter to take her and PCs O'Brady and Chaplin back to London. En route she phoned RAF Air Marshal Sir Roderick "Biggles" Ramsbottom, insisting that under no circumstances should her Fanbury destination be divulged to anyone, an agreement she'd already secured from O'Brady and Chaplin without much difficulty, given their embarrassment at having been tied to trees.

"Top secret, Biggles," she'd said. "*Any*one *ever* finds out where I've been, and your job's down the toilet along with your pension rights. Understood?"

"Loud and clear, ma'am. Roger that," said Biggles, not one to waste words.

"Roger?" said Clarissa, but Biggles had already disappeared into the ether.

However, Clarissa had more to worry about than the bizarre lingo of a mere Air Marshal. Prime amongst her concerns was the growing fear she'd been an idiot to accede to a la-la-land plan cooked up by people very possibly out of their minds even *if* they counted amongst their number Muriel "The Maggot" Eggleshaw and Mister Clever Pants OO17. But it was too late now. She'd signed on the dotted line. On the other hand, what if the bally plan worked and she *hadn't* signed on the dotted line? Where would that have left her? Out in the cold while others gloried, that was where. Oh, how con*fus*ing life was.

"Buggerkins," she mumbled as the Puma HC2 banked for a landing on her private helipad close to St James's Park.

The further question that arose in her scrambled mind, however, was, "who am I going to *tell* about this?" None of the ministers in the bally cabinet, that was for sure. They couldn't be trusted to keep a secret between them*selves,* never mind maintain corporate confidentiality in face of the press hordes. Bunch of loose-lips they were. And not a whisper to the commie leader of the opposition, who seemed to have a soft spot for Ripurpantzov…soo, as Muriel insisted, this was a secret Clarissa would just have to keep to herself.

"Mind you," she reflected as she climbed out of the Puma, teetered down the steps, met her personal policeman and marched back with him to Number 10, "I'm pretty damn good at keeping secrets. 'The submarine' is what they call me, isn't it? Which is probably why they never understand what I'm saying."

"Everything OK, ma'am?" said PC Tom (no second name), the PM's personal policeman.

"Fine, Tom, *fine*. Have a nice rest of the day," said Clarissa, stepping across the threshold where her butler Billy was waiting to take her coat.

"Good trip?" said Billy, rumoured by many to be the second major source of leaks from No 10 after the fractious cabinet.

"Trip, Billy?" said Clarissa. "Oh *that* trip. Just been off at Chequers overseeing the new sapling plantings…cedars, silver birches, Japanese cherry blossoms and so on."

"Ah. And I hope they grow nicely, ma'am" said Billy, an early and enthusiastic recipient of Maurice's Lennon teaser. "The Foreign Secretary is waiting in the antechamber."

"Jolly good. Splendid," Clarissa lied, thinking, "What does foot-in-his-mouth Fat Slob want *now*?"

"Show him through when I'm ready," she told Billy. "Which won't be for at least an hour. Meanwhile give him a cup of tea."

"Just the one, ma'am?"

"As per normal, Billy. And offer him no biscuits."

Billy smiled and said, "With pleasure, ma'am."

What Billy would have liked most was to kick Fat Slob in the goolies, but for all the pleasure it would have afforded, it would clearly also have signalled the end of his No 10 butlership.

*Any*way that was what was happening to PM Clarissa in Westminster.

As noted, back at the Shepherd's Hut things were gathering pace.

~ * ~

Having completed his final edits of the Reconstructed Beatles footage, each take focusing heavily on Jeremy/John, Maurice congratulated the whole band on their "fab" performances and thanked Barry for "hospitality well beyond the call of duty."

"Never have I encountered such a splendid set of chaps," he told them all at the farewell party Barry threw before Maurice and Dame Muriel returned to Tooting in the Morris Minor Traveller.

Julie/Paul raised an eyebrow and winked.

"*And* the chap*ess*, of course," said Maurice with a thespian bow before taking her in a warm hug. "The movies never came up with a Bond girl better than this one. You're a lucky man, Mister Crawford," he added across Julie's right shoulder.

Jeremy blushed, nodded, and said, "I know."

Barry, Maggie and Dennis hear-heared and raised their glasses of Geranium Cava à la Broadbent in a toast.

"To Julie and Jeremy," they chorused as Julie left Maurice's embrace and entered Jeremy's.

"And I am a lucky woman," she said. "When this is all over, I'm taking him back to Liverpool to show off to my dad."

Maurice smiled. "That may not be anytime soon however, my dear. For a little while longer it may be wise for him to lay somewhat low. As is the case with the rest of you fellows, *n'est-ce pas,* Dame Muriel?"

"Indeed, Double O Seventeen. Best advice I can give is you all remain under your present cover for the foreseeable future. I will personally ensure, however, that any expenses you may incur meanwhile shall be covered by my department."

Barry thanked her but said neither he nor his new friends would be looking for any "expenses."

"We have pretty much all we need. Not so, chaps…and chapess?"

Julie, Jeremy, Maggie and Dennis nodded their agreement.

"An exciting adventure this has indeed been," Barry continued, "and one looks forward with interest to its potential outcomes, but, as Kierkegaard had it: "repetition is the reality and the seriousness of life," and such is the project in which I and my new friends are currently engaged, not with politics but with the natural world that surrounds us…which costs nothing. What, somehow or another and from different perspectives, we have chosen. And none of this comes with a bill to M16 or anybody else."

It was around then that, checking his watch, Maurice expressed sympathy with such an aim but said, in his and Dame Muriel's world at least, tempus was fugiting a tad and it was really time they hit the road.

"I have the sense of an ending," he said. "But who can know when that may be?"

And so saying, he and Dame Muriel took their leave and headed back to number thirteen Oakshot Street Tooting for Maurice's final remix before the grand launch on the Internet.

"Miaow!" said Terpsichore/Tiddles/Cat when they arrived. Hank and Butch next door were okay with their tins of Pussy Cuts and everything, but she'd missed her proper owner. Plus the lady he had with him hadn't proved all that bad either, so she was pleased to see them both back home.

Within minutes, however, Maurice was upstairs with his computer bank sharpening, titillating and finalising the missive he hoped might re-balance a political world spinning more or less out of control—in his view anyhow.

That was how pace was gathering on the home front.

~ * ~

Elsewhere on the planet, things were moving fast too, largely as the result of the continuing reaction to Maurice's initial teaser sparked by the Internet-flooding techniques employed by both Yuri Krumkin in St Petersburg and Monty Gaspachio in Silicon Valley. Unbeknownst to either, however, their enthusiasm for the cause had spread contagiously, such that similar hi-tech deluges were exploding from places beyond Russia and America. The computers of, inter alia, Wolfgang Hesse in Berlin, Gianfranco Maglioni in Rome, Francine Daudet in Paris, Mateo Garcia in Barcelona, Maureen McAteer in London and a certain Steve Mackintosh in Liverpool were sizzling with support messages. And all of this even before taking account of the tweeters, likers, and befrienders in countries where the idea of the potential overthrow of populist dictators had not yet even dawned as a possibility. And what did all of these folk want? Further evidence of Lennon still being alive, coming out of hiding and singing to them, that was what.

Maurice was delighted, watching on in the interstices between fiddling with the final cut of the Reconstructed Beatles video.

"What an audience we're going to have, Tiddles," he told Terpsichore/Cat, who was watching on from her vantage point on Maurice's lap.

"Mia*OW*," she said.

And it was not just on computer and smartphone screens that such evidence of international disquiet was evinced. It also spilled over onto the streets of cities across Europe, including the UK, where PM Clarissa was thrown and gladly took the lifeline of finally ignoring the alt right Brexiteers in her party and siding with the voices of moderation and reason. Even in places as normally quiescent as Tokyo and Hong Kong there were demonstrations. There, in imitation of the American protests in which pro-Lennon kids joined hands with the March For Our Lives kids sickened at the gun deaths in their schools, brave Japanese and Chinese students had also marched in defiance of their leaders. "Protest," for so long since the nineteen sixties a dirty word, was being rekindled.

Monty Gaspachio and Jennifer hadn't witnessed the original outpourings of demands for peace, love and flower power on the streets of San Francisco because they hadn't been born yet. But boy were they ever enjoying it now as they and their friends, joined by local groups of septuagenarian ex-hippies, demonstrated all around Haight Ashbury and into the Golden Gate Park. Then there was the wider network of Internet friends they had all across America, but best of all in Chicago, where the 1968 siege was still remembered, and in New York City, where so many vigils were being observed at the Strawberry Fields memorial area of Central Park cops were on permanent stand-by and bleating for more resources.

Even in Moscow there was evidence of a reawakening. Not out in the open in case they got shot or poisoned by Ripurpantzov's goons, but young Muscovites were nonetheless following Yuri Krumkin's advice to make their voices heard. Singing and playing Beatles songs at the dead of night, then like spooks vanishing back into the shadows and cellars where the police couldn't find them. Night after night after *night* it went on, and not only in the capital. In

Minsk, home of the old KGB headquarters, and in other cities all across Russia, there were similar ghostly whisperings. Even in Sevastopol on the newly "liberated" Crimean peninsula.

And how, you will be asking, were the psychos in the White House and the Kremlin feeling about this? Twitchy is the answer. Even Ripurpantzov, the guy who'd been newly re-"elected" as president having jailed any credible opposition, the "strong man" who was keen on following the example of China's leader and making himself president for life, was hearing the worrisome echoes of a history he believed dead and buried. Good at judo and other forms of manipulation though he may have been, the very last thing he needed was any underground interference in his mind games with the West or *any* contradiction of his assertion of its pernicious influence on Mother Russia. Some nights he lay awake and wondered.

As did the madman in the White House, as he stuffed himself with cheeseburgers and fizzy drinks while fiddling with his Twitter feed and flicking around TV stations, on which even his beloved Fox News was showing signs of nervousness at the re-emergence of what it contemptuously described as "youth culture."

"Gonna hafta *do* sumptn about this," he muttered to himself as he chewed. "Like shoot some of these bozos and make out it was the Mexicans or the Muslims who dunnit. Who got the kids braindead on dope then gunned 'em down when they told tales out of school. Yeah, nice move. Change the story an' go with the flow."

Only how *many* stories had the madman already changed? Hundreds, thousands maybe, as he made his way to the zenith of American power. He was no longer sure how many. But what he *was* sure of—and increasingly irritated by—was how many of what the pinko media had taken to branding as his "lies" were coming back to bite him the ass. Outside of his own family, there was nobody in the White House he could trust any more, never mind how often he fired his top advisors, Secretaries of State, FBI and CIA cretins and their like. All *they* then did was go away and write bestselling books about him being a moron, psychopath and congenital liar. The madman wasn't entirely sure what congenital meant, but it didn't sound good. Had they just focused on his *genitals* and all the babes he'd bedded, he'd have been happy. But *con*genital?

And now, along with all the other pinko dorks who didn't believe him when he said he was the best president America had ever had and were lining up to impeach him for nepotism as well as electoral, sexual and financial misconduct, let alone hero worship of the madman in the Kremlin, *now* there were these freakin' kids on the streets wanting gun control, holding hands with hippies, singing Beatles songs, and saying the Lennon freak was still alive and kicking. Je-*sus* H. Christ, what was his world coming to? Hell in a handcart if he wasn't careful, that was what. Unless his big brain could figure out a way of dealing with the situation, he could be looking at an awful lot of shit hitting an awful lot of fans.

"Hey, big brain," he said. "You good to go on this?"

But Big Brain had gone AWOL.

"FUCK, FUCK," said the madman in the White House, the first time because Big Brain had gone AWOL and the second time because of the wah-wah-wahs and the flashing blue lights all along Pennsylvania Avenue, where yet again city cops and National Guardsmen were struggling to cope with a sea of demonstrators waving banners saying THE PRESIDENT'S A DICKHEAD and playing through improvised amplifiers John Lennon's "Revolution."

"Shoot 'em, *SHOOT* 'em all," yelled the madman from a top window in the White House through a half masticated cheeseburger, but to no avail.

Nobody was listening. Just like all those years ago in the sixties, some of the cops and National Guardsmen were laying aside their flower-bestrewn weapons to join the rally in echoes of the 1967 anti-Vietnam war march on the Pentagon.

"*FUCK*," said the madman in the White House for the third time. Could this be the end of the America he knew, loved, and of which he owned huge swathes?

Epilogue

At the time of writing, only weeks since the release of Maurice Moffat's final Beatles/Lennon video, it is far too early to make predictions as to its impact. You know how it is with history, how unpredictably it can shift. Whoever could have forecast Americans could have been so dumb as to elect a narcissist loon for their next president? That Russians would succumb to the wiles of a small-time KGB officer turned post-1989 state assets thief and then present himself as their leader for life? That the British could be hubristic enough to believe they were still the colonial world power they once were and vote to opt out of the very European Union that had maintained the peace on that continent since 1945? Nobody, that's who, or else we wouldn't be in the mess we're in today.

The problem with history is it's only ever perceived in retrospect and normally only written by the victors, which leaves all sorts of unexplained lacunae. It's not as though philosophers do any better. It was all very well for Hegel to propose thesis, antithesis and synthesis as a formula to explain the manner in which human societies have progressed over time, but that now looks like wishful thinking. Hegel postulated such stuff *well* before the invention of the World Wide Web and the malign influence it has had on global shifts. Ask Hegel what he thought about the manner in which Facebook's research into "likes" and "dislikes" had been hi-jacked by populists to influence power politics and he'd have gone goggle-eyed. The name of the game these days is chaos theory, which takes seriously the concept of a butterfly flapping its wings in China and thereby producing a hurricane in Texas. So much for history.

*Any*way, at the time of writing, the madmen in the White House and the Kremlin are still in their jobs, and there is little evidence of the British prime minister Phoebe/Clarissa being elevated to the status of heroine of the West. But then Maurice Moffat hadn't expected such celerity. Too wise was he by far. Nonetheless, John Lennon's words were continuing to echo across the sorts of cyber space Hegel could never have dreamt of, so at least out there were the seeds Maurice had sown for potentially tectonic shifts. He, Dame Muriel, and the crew back at the Shepherd's Hut would just have to wait and see how long those seeds took to bear fruit.

Maurice asked Terpsichore/Tiddles/Cat for her opinion on the matter, but you know how it is with cats, how hard they find it to draw conclusions. Mind you, much the same could be said of human animals, despite their supposedly bigger brains. So on we stagger from an uncertain beginning to an even less certain end. Possibly T.S. Eliot got it right when he said, "time present and time past are both perhaps present in time future." Who knows?

One thing remains clear however, when everything else becomes misty, and that is the obligation we humans have to make choices based in our own reason and not the whimsy of others. Otherwise *we* become the chosen, not the choosers. As Jeremy Crawford, Julie Mackintosh, "Maggie" Montague, Dennis "Shorty" Dawkins and, well before them, ex-professor Barry Broadbent, found out. It took them sooo long, but they found out, so no more day tripping for them. And more power to their elbows.

Author's Note and Acknowledgment

It may well be you found the Beatles/Lennon idea on which this book draws overly fantastical or even specious, in which case I would refer you to Leslie Woodhead's book *How The Beatles Rocked The Kremlin: The Untold Story of a Noisy Revolution* (Bloomsbury Publishing 25.04.2013 ISBN 9781408840436). And to the BBC programme it inspired—the one Maurice Moffat watched.

Thank you, Leslie.

Meet Paddy Bostock

Paddy Bostock was born in Liverpool and holds a B.A. in Modern Languages and History, a PGDip TESL, and a PhD in English Literature. Down the years he has been a barman, a road worker, a songwriter, an educational researcher, a translator, a book reviewer, a university lecturer and Chair of Department, and a high school mentor. He lives in London with his wife, writer Dani Cavallaro, and likes animals and bicycles.

Works From The Pen Of Paddy Bostock

Mole Smith and The Diamond Studded Pistol - Tricked into believing he is to be accused of a murder he hasn't committed, PI gofer Mole Smith is inveigled into the search for an ancient order and its famous diamond-studded pistol. What Mole doesn't know, as he undertakes the quest with his partner Oksana, is what powers lurk behind the scenes.

Two Down - Failed crime-fiction writer, professional plagiarist and part-time private eye Dr. Jake Flintlock and his sidekick Dr. Bum Park are within a whisker of catching the killer of the Vice-Chancellor of the university that sacked Jake...But this is no ordinary murderer, as they are about to discover.

La Joie de Vivre - To escape a floundering relationship and writer's block, Ambler leaves London for La Rochelle, where he stumbles into a tangle of corruption and revenge with a grisly murder at its centre: a crime which could cost Ambler his freedom — and his sanity.

For The Love Of a Woman - Ravaged by sun, mosquitoes and his partner Claudia's extended family while on a summer holiday to seaside Italy, PI Jake Flintlock is keen—despite having been asked to stay to solve a local murder—to return to London for good. But then, after a second murder, he and his PI associate Bum Park are made an offer they can't refuse and once in Rome, discover a whole new meaning to the words la famiglia

Foot Soldiers - Outraged at the market economic policies adopted by their university, the Podiatry department kidnap a senior academic in protest. The chance coincidence of the interests of the gutter press, Welsh Freedom Fighters, and a Prime Minister struggling for re-election ensures a minor campus story escalates into cataclysmic national proportions.

Hand In Glove - PI Dr Jake Flintlock and his sidekick Dr Bum Park are inveigled by American theater director Chuck Cinzano into the investigation of a severed hand in a baseball glove on Primrose Hill, London. The assignment morphs into a murder case as Chuck is "stabbed to death" in Jake's home. Having flown to Sausalito, CA, Jake and Bum begin to suspect they are being used as actors in a play. Yet, a real crime has been committed and somehow the culprit has to be found.

Noddy In Wonderland - In his wildest dreams, Afghanistan war veteran Noddy Stoddart fantasised about becoming king of Liverpool, even though his brother, Knobby, told him he was crazy. But shooting government minister St John Jaunston in the bottom with an air rifle on a visit to the city leads bizarrely to Noddy's dream coming true--as president of the newly created People's Republic of Liverpool.

Peace on Earth - Mankind profits from nothing more than war. Hence, rumours about the existence of a disk said to contain the formula to "peace on earth," obtained by a failed actor with a penchant for visions, pose a major threat to the planet. This unleashes a frantic hunt for the disk across continents, involving government agencies, master criminals, petty criminals, and would-be criminals, plus the local population of Pont-y-Pant: the tiny Welsh village on which disparate characters converge as the putative location of the errant disk.
However, nobody has taken into account the role that will be played by the three-year-old Newfoundland acting as the disk's self-appointed custodian.

The Basque Head Case - Following the accidental discovery of a "head" afloat on the Regent Canal, London, PI Dr Jake Flintlock is seduced into taking on a case which draws him to Northern Spain and its darker history. There, in the company of his sidekick Dr Bum Park, Jake faces a mystery wherein an ancient Basque legacy of vengeance and strife intersects with a private vendetta - one with Jake himself as its unwitting target.

The Bore - Since birth, Professor Thaddeus Proctor has lacked any attractive qualities, his only asset being a formidable yawn capable of precipitating anyone who comes into contact with it into a state of soporific compliance. The yawn's power remains untapped until Thaddeus is offered the chance of competing in a TV game show, and becomes its champion.

Not even then, however, is the yawn deployed to the utmost of its capacities. It takes Thaddeus's removal to Fairyland, and involvement in the protection of its precarious peace, to test the yawn's true might, and reveal the professor is no mere "bore."

The Hanging - As the troll Vilius Vilutis hunts Cumbria in search of the magical onyx capable of revolutinizing smartphones and defeat his business foe Zingy Splitz, the elves Mordecai and Hazchem strive to keep the onyx safe. But then two hangings disrupt the peace, and darker forces begin to surface

Visit Our Website

For The Full Inventory
Of Quality Books:

Wings ePress, Inc
http://wingsepress.com/

Quality trade paperbacks and downloads

in multiple formats,

in genres ranging from light romantic comedy to general fiction and horror.

Wings has something for every reader's taste.

Visit the website, then bookmark it.

We add new titles each month!

Wings ePress Inc.
3000 N. Rock Road
Newton, KS 67114